Understanding Death & Dying

An Interdisciplinary Approach

Second Edition

Sandra Galdieri Wilcox and Marilyn Sutton
California State University, Dominguez Hills

MAYFIELD PUBLISHING COMPANY

About the Cover: *The Sun and Eagle,* a sand painting by Ernest Hunt . . . "four winds, four ages, four seasons."

By permission of Jane Anderson.

Library of Congress Cataloging in Publication Data
Main entry under title:

Understanding death and dying.

   Bibliography
      1. Death—Social aspects—addresses, essays, lectures.
2. Death—Psychological aspects—Addresses, essays, lectures.
3. Children and death—Addresses, essays, lectures.
I. Wilcox, Sandra Galdieri, 1943-   . II. Sutton, Marilyn,
1944-
HQ1073.U53   1981   306   80-29163
ISBN 0-87484-652-8

for
Stephen, Paul, and Matthew

Contents

v

2

3

4

Death and the Child   225

5

Preface

A class in thanatology is likely to appeal to diverse interests. The student of death and dying might be a curious but slightly scared twenty-year-old; the mother of teenage children wanting to prepare herself and her family for future crises; the nurse or paramedic wanting to improve patient care; the social worker who regularly sees the impact of violent death on the family; the teacher whose small pupils are in the process of discovering death; the nursing home staff member who works among those at the close of life; the widow who is seeking answers for herself as well as skills for helping others; the clergyman who must console bereaved families; or the funeral director who wants to improve his or her services to the community. Several disciplines—particularly medicine and the social sciences—offer courses in death and dying. Often workshops sponsored by university extension divisions, churches, or hospitals stimulate an interest in further study. *Understanding Death and Dying* can be adapted to any of these interests and uses.

Since the first edition of this text was published, thanatology has matured as a distinct field, drawing heavily from several source disciplines. Concepts that were emerging only a few years ago are now being applied, the literature of the field reflects a concern with the evaluation of theories and with synthesis of early work. This second edition of *Understanding Death and Dying* incorporates new areas of interest such as the application of hospice concepts and the social implications of decisions arising out of the debate over the prolongation of life, and expands the treatment of ethnic differences, aging, ethics, and the history of ideas.

CHAPTER ORGANIZATION

The overall book leads the reader from self-study in the encounter in Chapter One to reappraisal and action in Chapter Five. The chapters proceed through an analogous pattern opening with an integrative essay followed by an encounter and several multi-disciplinary readings and closing with one or more structured exercises. In this edition, Chapter One has been reformulated to focus more sharply on the study of attitudes as an approach to the contemporary meaning of death. Chapters Two through Four lead the reader through an examination of the experience of dying, a study of grief and mourning, and an exploration of the theme of death and the child. In Chapter Five, the range of choices and decisions explored has been expanded to reflect implications of choices in dying for values in living.

Essays

The chapter introductory essays are designed to provide a thematic framework for concepts presented in the chapters. In establishing a context for discussion, they identify key questions. In the second edition, a chapter overview integrates the readings into topical subgroupings.

Encounter

The encounter, whether it is a brief set of questions as in Chapter One, short samples of children's writings as in Chapter Four or a news account as in Chapter Five, brings the dominant themes of the chapter into focus, to root theoretical concepts in actual experience, and to provoke interest that will, in turn, provoke questions.

Readings

The readings include experienced-based selections that ground the discussion of death and dying to life situations, theoretical statements that develop technical skills, and analyses that suggest guidelines for intervention. Each reading is introduced by a brief headnote which places the selection within the structure of the chapter. The readings present key concepts in the social sciences (psychology, sociology) and medicine (psychiatry and nursing), as well as in gerontology and social welfare. They outline the germinal concepts in a study of death and dying and embed these concepts in a context provided by the history of ideas.

Questions and Projects

The questions and projects placed at the end of each chapter help the student to assimilate the ideas in the readings and to integrate information from several readings. Where the questions ask students to synthesize ideas presented in the chapter, the projects lead the students beyond the readings to further research and independent study. They invite students to apply the tools of research and patterns of investigation accepted in the social sciences. The projects have been selected to allow for a number of levels of sophistication; some can be used to introduce students to the ways a professional in the discipline investigates a topic; others can be expanded to provide a serious research problem for more advanced students.

Structured Exercises

The structured exercises at the close of each chapter provide the instructor with a ready means to tie together the concepts introduced in the readings and the student with a means to apply those concepts to his or her own life through a structured personal growth experience.

For Further Reading

In a rapidly changing multidisciplinary field, both instructor and student will be assisted by a selected bibliography. The reading lists at the end of each chapter identify sources for in-depth coverage of topics introduced in the chapter. Taken as a whole, the five chapter bibliographies provide an introductory survey of the field of thanatology.

SUPPORTING MATERIAL

After approximately twenty years of formalized study of death a considerable array of teaching materials is available, though not always readily accessible. An epilogue and three appendices have been compiled to supplement college level classes. The instructor may also wish to consult Daniel Leviton's paper "Death Education."* for a critical evaluation of instruction and for suggested goals for death education.

Epilogue

The newspaper account "Portrait of Jen: Memories from a Children's Cancer Ward" offers a "real life" situation for the application of the knowledge acquired in the study of the text. It demonstrates the fact that all the elements in a study of death and dying are interrelated.

Appendices

The appendices in this second edition have been expanded and updated. Appendix A includes medical materials of use in the exercises. Appendix B presents materials related to the handling of death in contemporary American society: statistical tables, legal forms, and death-related documents. Appendix C offers a topical listing for individual projects and an up-dated mediography keyed to each chapter.

---

*D. Leviton, "Death Education," in *New Meanings of Death*, ed. H. Feifel (New York: McGraw-Hill, 1977).

Note to the Instructor

The Use of Structured Exercises
in the Classroom

The structured exercises have been arranged topically at the end of each chapter throughout the book. Most exercises can be adapted to fit topics in other chapters. The kidney machine exercise in Chapter One, for example, could be equally effective as a closing activity for Chapter Five if the instructor led the class to focus on a different aspect of the exercise or modified the discussion questions. The student could be asked, for instance, to role-play the patients rather than the hospital committee and the decision under study might be "Who will accept the treatment?" and "Why?" rather than "Who will be given the opportunity of the treatment?"

The instructor should note that some of the exercises are constructed to pull latent attitudes, and for that reason potentially volatile terms are included. The instructor who has had little experience in conducting such experiences might wish to schedule a separate "experience" group where a staff member of the campus counseling center or an interested and qualified colleague from the psychology department could assist. The "experience" group should be limited to students enrolled in the course. The relationship of the group to the regular class can be determined by the individual instructor: the group could be optional or required, or offer additional units of credit; it may meet during regularly scheduled class time, or at another time and location.

Some instructors prefer to limit the use of group experiences to an intense day-long or weekend session at the end of the course. An intense encounter of this kind should be conducted only with the participation of a qualified group leader and participation by students should be contingent upon appropriate screening methods. The American Psychological Association (1973) has provided "Guidelines for Conducting Growth Groups,"* which lists responsibilities of group leaders.

---

*"APA Guidelines for Psychologists Conducting Growth Groups," *American Psychologists* 38 (1973):933.

The use of group exercises in any classroom requires responsible planning and constant attention from the instructor. At the beginning of each exercise, students should be reminded that they may choose not to participate without penalty, and that they may, at any time, withdraw from parts of the exercise that they find uncomfortable or anxiety-evoking. Before the exercise begins, the class as a whole should discuss the obligation to respect each participant's needs. Even an exercise which appears emotionally innocuous may elicit anxiety in a psychologically vulnerable individual. Students often choose their courses for personal as well as for scholarly or professional reasons. In a "death and dying" class these personal reasons may involve unresolved grief, anticipatory grief, or occasionally, suicidal preoccupations. In addition, adolescents as a group tend to be "mourning at a distance" for developmental losses of their own childhood and former parental relationships as they struggle toward the independence of adulthood.

A difficult moment for one or all students may occur from time to time. In such cases the students themselves can usually be trusted to respond supportively and constructively. When tensions in the group seem to be running high, it may be helpful to stop and go around the room, allowing each student to express his opinions and feelings in turn. Other students should not interrupt or argue until everyone has had a chance to speak, though the instructor may want to sum up and reflect back to the group the thrust of a series of related comments.

Chapter One

The Study of Death: A New Vantage Point

As recently as 1955, the taboo on the discussion of death and dying was so pervasive that Geoffrey Gorer could refer to interest in death as "the new pornography." However, in the 1960s, when Elisabeth Kübler-Ross began interviewing dying patients, she triggered widespread interest in death and dying. By 1977, when the first edition of this text was published, an abundance of death-related literature was available, and such issues as refining the functional (i.e., medical, legal, etc.) definition of death were being widely debated.

Today, the literature on death and dying is so plentiful that what is needed is a systematizing of existing research and a consolidation of current conceptualizations of death. A single technological development can still throw us back to ancient dilemmas; for instance, the social custom of centuries may dictate that disposal of the body follows immediately upon death, but given the medical resources to transplant human organs, the dictates of social custom undergo reassessment. And as they do, we, as a society, are forced to examine our attitudes and to seek out the assumptions that underlie those attitudes: in short, to continually *redefine* the meaning of death.

1

HISTORICAL PERSPECTIVE

The scientific tradition has, in certain respects, bequeathed us an adversary relationship with death. Scientific research, often motivated by an effort to conquer death and prolong life, has encouraged us to see the relationship between life and death as one of polar opposition. Although science assumes that we have biological immortality, in the sense that every creature alive today represents an "unbroken line of life that stretches back to the first primitive organism," that immortality is a continuance of the germ plasm rather than of the body. The scientist today is more likely to think of life in the same terms as Xavier Bichat, an eighteenth-century physiologist who described life as the "totality of all those functions that resist death."

Where the scientific heritage weighs death against life, the tradition of mythopoeic thought (including art, literature, philosophy and folklore) denies the polarity by employing a third category, afterlife, and placing death within the continuum of life–death–afterlife. Death, for the philosopher, has most often suggested a transition to a different state of being: eternal sleep, a world of shades or heavenly reward—in any case, a continuance.

CONTEMPORARY SITUATION

The concept of immortality, once accepted quite literally, has come to be interpreted symbolically by many today. Consequently, a person may see his children as his biological immortality, his lifework as his social immortality, and his memorialization in the arts (whether architecture, literature, or painting) as a form of cultural immortality. Unlike the medieval, whose guiding concern was his preparation for afterlife, the contemporary has, in the words of Nathan A. Scott, "relocated the ultimate problem of human existence from the dimension of eternity to the dimension of time." The interest in death no longer centers on *what follows* but on the more immediate issues of *how* and *when*.

Given the technological ability to alter the time of death, within certain limitations, we are likely to expand that control in the near future. As the power to extend life increases, the question may arise as to whether we should ever accept death. But we must remember that together with the power to extend life, we have the equally potent capacity to dilute the quality of life beyond recognition. Clinical death is no longer synonymous with *death*: it is only the most extreme of many kinds of death including the social death of the forgotten widower living in isolation and the mental death of the mongoloid child. Now the issue has become, *What constitutes an appropriate death?*

Attitudinal research is always of interest to the social scientist, but it is of primary value in the study of death; death must always remain unknowable, at least, from personal experience. Thus, the understanding of death will depend on the interpretation a particular culture gives it and will be reflected in values and beliefs held by individuals, in social structures surrounding death, and in ethical debates occasioned by the end of life.

OVERVIEW OF THE CHAPTER

Chapter One opens with the study of individual attitudes toward death. In "Thinking About Death: Death Anxiety Research," Richard Schulz, an experimental psychologist, introduces the reader to the empirical study of death-related attitudes and presents an array of data on contemporary attitudes based on controlled studies. In "Death and Ethnicity: Encounter with the Death of Self," psychologists Richard A. Kalish and David K. Reynolds provide additional empirical data on attitudes. Recognizing the rich diversity within American society, they study responses from four ethnic subgroups—Black, Mexican-American, Japanese and Anglo-American—as they ask: to what degree is ethnicity a variable in the formation of attitudes toward death and dying? Expanding the discussion still further, Talcott Parsons and Victor Lidz present a sociological interpretation of death-related behavior in contemporary American society. The selection taken from their extended essay, *Death in American Society,* traces the emergence of a concept of "appropriate death." Though the term *appropriate death* has been introduced into the study of death quite recently, assumptions about it have long operated in our society, whether it be the biblical "threescore and ten," the expectation of a task completed, or a life expectancy taken from a statistical mortality table.

Similarly, much of what has been "recently discovered" about responses to death is firmly rooted in tradition, as Philippe Ariès, French historian of ideas, shows in "Death Inside Out." He weaves evidence from literature and philosophy together with observations on social customs to construct an historical overview of Western attitudes toward death; as he does so, he traces the changing relationships between ritual observances and personal experience.

Finally, Paul Ramsey, identifying himself as a Christian ethicist, reacts, in "The Indignity of 'Death with Dignity'" against emergent clichés. One consequence of the increased discussion of death in the last few years is that significant dilemmas occasionally become glossed over with unexamined resolutions, and verbal legerdemain replaces careful analysis. Ramsey forces the reader to confront the inexorable fact of death and raises the possibility that acceptance of death may pose logical contradictions.

Before the reader turns to the issues raised by these writers, however, responding to the brief set of questions in the following encounter will reveal the personal attitudes and assumptions he or she brings to the study.

Encounter

CONFRONTING YOUR DEATH

1. Who died in your first personal involvement with death?
   a. Grandparent or great-grandparent
   b. Parent
   c. Brother or sister
   d. Other family member
   e. Friend or acquaintance
   f. Stranger
   g. Public figure
   h. Animal

2. What aspect of your own death is the most distasteful to you?
   a. I could no longer have any experiences
   b. I am afraid of what might happen to my body after death
   c. I am uncertain as to what might happen to me if there is a life after death
   d. I could no longer provide for my dependents
   e. It would cause grief to my relatives and friends
   f. All my plans and projects would come to an end
   g. The process of dying might be painful
   h. Other (Specify) _____

3. What does death mean to you?
   a. The end, the final process of life
   b. The beginning of a life after death; a transition, a new beginning

4

    c.   A joining of the spirit with a universal cosmic consciousness

    d.   A kind of endless sleep; rest and peace

    e.   Termination of this life but with survival of the spirit

    f.   Don't know

    g.   Other (Specify) _____

4.   If you had a choice, what kind of death would you prefer?
   - a.   Tragic, violent death
   - b.   Sudden, but not violent death
   - c.   Quiet, dignified death
   - d.   Death in line of duty
   - e.   Death after a great achievement
   - f.   Suicide
   - g.   Homicidal victim
   - h.   There is no "appropriate" kind of death
   - i.   Other (Specify) _____

5.   If you could choose, when would you die?
   - a.   In youth
   - b.   In the middle prime of life
   - c.   Just after the prime of life
   - d.   In old age

6.   For whom or what might you be willing to sacrifice your life?
   - a.   For a loved one
   - b.   For an idea or a moral principle
   - c.   In combat or a grave emergency where a life could be saved
   - d.   Not for any reason

7.   If you were told that you had a terminal disease and a limited time to live, how would you want to spend your time until you died?
   - a.   I would make a marked change in my life style; satisfy hedonistic needs (travel, sex, drugs, other)
   - b.   I would become more withdrawn; reading, contemplating or praying
   - c.   I would shift from a concern for my own needs to a concern for others (family, friends)
   - d.   I would attempt to complete projects; tie up loose ends
   - e.   I would make little or no change in my life style
   - f.   I would try to do one very important thing
   - g.   I might consider committing suicide
   - h.   I would do none of these

8.   If or when you are married, would you prefer to outlive your spouse?
   - a.   Yes; I would prefer to die second and outlive my spouse
   - b.   No; I would rather die first and have my spouse outlive me
   - c.   Undecided or don't know

RICHARD SCHULZ

Thinking about Death:
Death Anxiety Research

Addressing the question "Does man really fear death and, if so, what exactly does he fear about death?" Schulz urges distinctions between death fear, death anxiety, and death avoidance. After acknowledging the limitations of empirical studies and noting that some conceptualizations respond more effectively to intuitive analysis, he provides a critical summary of attempts both to assess death anxiety and to relate it to demographic, personality, and environmental variables. He concludes by suggesting three directions for the next stages of research.

AN EMPIRICAL PERSPECTIVE: DEATH ANXIETY RESEARCH

Death anxiety has been measured in a variety of populations and settings with a wide assortment of assessment devices ranging from projective techniques (such as the Rorschach and Thematic Apperception Test) to the measurement of galvanic skin response, a physiological correlate of anxiety. It is the aim of this review to bring order to the existing death anxiety literature and direction to the field by critically evaluating the various methods used to assess death anxiety, deriving conclusions warranted by the available data, and suggesting the direction that future research should follow. Before this literature is examined, one qualifier is in order. The distinction between death fear and death anxiety described earlier has not been made by empirical researchers. As a result, the two terms are used interchangeably in the discussion that follows.

Methodological Issues

Both direct and indirect techniques have been used to assess death anxiety. Direct techniques include questionnaires, check lists, and rating scales, while indirect tech-

Source: Richard Schulz. "Death Anxiety: Intuitive and Empirical Perspectives." PP. 69-83, 84-87. *Death and Dying: Theory/Research/Practice*, by Larry A. Bugen. William C. Brown Publishing Co.: 1979.

niques include projective tests, the measurement of galvanic skin response, and reaction times during death-related word association tasks. Direct techniques are by far the more frequently used, and at present there are six widely used death anxiety questionnaires (Boyar 1964; Collett and Lester 1969; Lester 1967a; Sarnoff and Corwin 1959; Templer 1970; and Tolor and Reznikoff 1967). An example of one death anxiety scale is presented in Table 1. After reading each statement, the respondent decides whether a particular statement is true or false for himself. These responses are then coded according to a key, and a death anxiety score is derived.

Only Boyar's (1964) Fear of Death Scale (FODS) and Templer's (1970) Death Anxiety Scale (DAS) have been validated. Validation is a procedure for determining whether a scale measures what it was designed to measure—in this case death anxiety. Exactly how this should be done varies with the type of scale used. Boyar attempted to validate his scale by administering it to subjects before and after viewing a highway accident movie intended to increase their death anxiety. Fear of death scores rose significantly more in the experimental group than in the control group, which saw an innocuous movie. Templer validated his scale both with psychiatric patients in a state mental hospital and with college students. High death anxiety psychiatric patients independently assessed by a clinician were found to have significantly higher DAS scores than control patients. The remaining four scales (Collett and Lester 1969; Lester 1967a; Sarnoff and Corwin 1959; Tolor and Reznikoff 1967) have not been independently validated, although intercorrelations among the scales are high enough to lend each a degree of concurrent validity. Durlak (1972a) found positive intercorrelations ranging from .41 to .65 among five of the scales. He inexplicably omitted Templer's DAS from his study, although Templer (1970) reported a positive .74 correlation between his scale and Boyar's (1964) FODS.

Table 1   Templer's Death Anxiety Scale

Content
I am very much afraid to die.
The thought of death seldom enters my mind.
It doesn't make me nervous when people talk about death.
I dread to think about having to have an operation.
I am not at all afraid to die.
I am not particularly afraid of getting cancer.
The thought of death never bothers me.
I am often distressed by the way time flies so very rapidly.
I fear dying a painful death.
The subject of life after death troubles me greatly.
I am really scared of having a heart attack.
I often think about how short life really is.
I shudder when I hear people talking about a World War III.
The sight of a dead body is horrifying to me.
I feel that the future holds nothing for me to fear.

Source: From: D. Templer, The construction and validation of a death anxiety scale, *Journal of General Psychology* 82 (1970): 167.

Two remaining scales (Dickstein 1972, 1975; Krieger, Epsting, and Leitner 1974) have neither been validated nor compared to the six scales discussed above. Krieger, Epsting, and Leitner's (1974) "Threat Index" has the interesting feature of being theoretically based but has poor test-retest reliability ($r = .49$ with one of 13 subjects dropped). Test-retest reliability is a measure of the reliability of the scale over time. That is, if an individual completes the same scale at different times, his scores should be very similar even though several months may have passed between the first and second time the scale was administered. This is based on the assumption that the scale measures permanent dispositional characteristics of the individual, which should not vary greatly over time.

Most death anxiety scales treat death anxiety as a unitary concept. This is based on the probably erroneous assumption that death anxiety is a single type of fear or anxiety. The one exception is the Collett and Lester (1969) scale, which is divided into four subscales measuring anxiety over death of self, death of others, dying of self, and dying of others. These subscales are roughly equivalent to the fear of nonbeing and the fear of the process (the pain and suffering) of dying as they apply to oneself and those close to us. Collett and Lester found low intercorrelations among their subscales, especially between the two subscales dealing with self and the two dealing with others, suggesting that death anxiety is a multidimensional concept. An individual may, for example, fear the process of his own dying and not be fearful about the dying process of those close to him. Durlak's (1972a) intercorrelation study showed that other scales correlate best with the death-of-self subscale of Collett and Lester. Many of the inconsistencies in the death anxiety data will probably be clarified once researchers begin paying closer attention to the components of death anxiety instead of treating it as a unitary concept. One such attempt is made below in the section on sex differences, where it is argued that inconsistencies in the literature are resolved when the cognitive and affective components of death anxiety are isolated. The accurate assessment of death anxiety is further complicated by recent findings that the method of administering a death anxiety scale affects reported death anxiety. Schulz, Aderman, and Manko (1976) found significantly lower reported death anxiety among college students on the Templer (1970) and Sarnoff and Corwin (1959) scales when administered individually rather than in group sessions. Death anxiety as measured by a group-administered questionnaire was not significantly different from death anxiety as assessed by the "bogus pipeline method" (Jones and Sigall 1971), in which a fake "emotion monitoring device" is attached to subjects to keep them honest. The rationale underlying the bogus pipeline is that subjects do not want to be second-guessed by a machine, and when asked to predict what the machine says about their attitudes, they respond without many of the social biases that obscure straight paper and pencil measures on sensitive topics. The findings of Schulz, Aderman, and Manko (1976) suggest that there may be a private and public component to death anxiety and that the private attitudes are more likely to be expressed when the respondent is anonymous.

In addition to the problems of the "unitary concept" assumption, death anxiety scales have been criticized by some researchers for their inability to discriminate between private and "unconscious" death anxiety. For example, Fulton (1961) has argued that even with a valid and reliable measuring instrument, a researcher can still only tap the "epiphenomenal" or surface-level attitudes of subjects, while Rheingold (1967) has stated that even the most elegant instrument can measure only public attitudes "passively acquired from culture or religion" (p. 33) and completely miss those attitudes and feelings existing at the unconscious level. In order to delve into the unconscious, according to Rheingold, it is necessary to turn to projective techniques and the intuitive insights of the psychotherapist. It is difficult to argue against such an approach except by pointing out its subjective nature. More objective measurements of unconscious death anxiety are possible by comparing reaction time, recall reaction time, galvanic skin response for death-related and neutral word associations, or through use of the Color-Word Interference Test (Stroop, 1938). Presumably, these indirect techniques assess death anxiety on a level beneath that accessible by questionnaires, although results from such studies must be interpreted with care.

Researchers have assumed that high galvanic skin response or slow reaction time during death-related word association tasks indicate "perceptual defense" and hence death anxiety (Alexander and Adlerstein 1958; Feifel and Branscomb 1973). Using a different indirect technique, Lester and Lester (1970) found that recognition of blurred death-related words was faster than recognition of blurred neutral words. They explained that "perceptual facilitation" makes evolutionary sense since survival requires hasty recognition of threatening stimuli. Since most investigators of unconscious death anxiety use word association rather than recognition tasks, the focus of this research has been on processes of perceptual defense rather than perceptual facilitation.

Another indirect technique is analysis of dream content. Handal and Rychlak (1971) had several judges (inter-rater reliability = .89) classify dreams reported in subjects' morning-after journals as positive, negative, or neutral and as death-related or non-death-related. They considered a high frequency of negative and/or death-related dreams to be evidence of unconscious death anxiety.

Taken together, these studies indicate that the measurement of death anxiety is indeed a more complex task than early researchers had anticipated. At present, it appears that death anxiety is not a unitary concept and may be comprised of four or more subcomponents. To complicate matters even further, it appears that death anxiety can be tapped at any one of three levels: public, private, and unconscious. Table 2 shows the three levels crossed by possible subcomponents. Although it is unlikely that each of fifty-seven possible cells can be clearly differentiated operationally, death anxiety researchers should nevertheless be sensitive to the complexity of their task, if confusion is to be avoided in the future.

Demographic and Personality Correlates of Death Anxiety

Although many variables have been found to relate to death anxiety, few clear and consistent patterns have emerged. The search for such patterns in the data is reviewed below.

Table 2   Specific death fears by different assessment methods

Specific Fears Relating to Death of Self*	Level of Assessment		
	Public	Private	Unconscious
Pain			
Body misfunction			
Humiliation			
Rejection			
Nonbeing			
Punishment			
Interruption of goals			
Negative impact on survivors			
a psychological suffering of survivors			
b economic hardship			

*All these fears can be experienced vicariously in relation to the death of someone close to us. In addition, the fear of abandonment can be experienced directly.

Sex   Although several early studies yielded no systematic sex-related differences in death anxiety (Christ 1961; Rhudick and Dibner 1961; Swenson 1961; Jeffers, Nichols, and Eisdorfer 1961), it now appears fairly certain that, on the level assessed by questionnaires, females fear death more than males. Templer's (1970) DAS has been administered to samples of apartment residents, hospital aides, psychiatric patients, ninth graders, and high school students and their parents (Templer, Ruff, and Franks 1971; Iammarino 1975), and in all cases females scored higher than males. This finding was replicated by several other researchers.

Only when death anxiety is broken up into its components do researchers find any evidence of a greater fear of death among males. According to Thematic Apperception Test (TAT) responses, males have more fear of the effects of their death on dependents (Diggory and Rothman 1961) and more fear of the violence of death (Lowry 1965). In contrast, women show more fear of the dissolution of the body and the physical pain associated with death (Diggory and Rothman 1961).

Degner (1974) identified two clusters of responses to the concept of death by having subjects fill out 36 semantic differential scales. Among males she found an "evaluative" dimension to be strongest and an "emotional" dimension to be weakest. In an earlier study, Folta (in Degner 1974) found the reverse to be true for women. These studies suggest that there may be a cognitive and emotional component to death anxiety, with women viewing death in more emotional terms and men viewing death in more cognitive terms.

Consistent with these findings is the preliminary work of Krieger, Epsting, and Leitner (1974) with their Threat Index, a scale that measures death anxiety by measuring the "cognitive distance" subjects place between the concepts "death" and "self." Males tend to have higher death anxiety scores than females—a finding directly contrary to that obtained when Lester's Death Anxiety Scale is used. Since the Threat Index is a cognitive measure and Lester's Death Anxiety Scale is a more affective one, these results, and those of Degner and Folta, can be understood if it is accepted that male death anxiety tends to be cognitive and female death anxiety more emotional. Further support for the existence of these two components of death anxiety is the lack of correlation between Lester's affective Death Anxiety Scale and the more cognitive Threat Index (Kreiger, Epsting, and Leitner 1974) and also the lack of correlation between Lester's Death Anxiety Scale and Boyar's FODS, which is also supposedly a more "cognitive" scale (Kreiger, Epsting, and Leitner 1974; Berman & Hays 1973). Finally, Kreiger et al. reported a very high positive (+.73) correlation ($p<.01$) between the two cognitive scales: the Threat Index and Boyar's FODS. In summary, these findings suggest that researchers who use affectively oriented death anxiety scales will find higher death anxiety among females than males while the reverse is likely to be true when cognitively oriented death anxiety scales are used.

Age Although most of the death anxiety data have been collected from college students and the aged, there are some pertinent data available for every age group, from infants to the very old. Hall and Scott (in Hall 1922) attempted to assess death concern in children by asking adults to recall their earliest experiences with death. Using this retrospective technique, they concluded that the young child's view of death is characterized by specific objects and feelings associated with a specific death. A more informative study on children's views of death was conducted by Nagy (1959), who directly interviewed 378 boys and girls three to ten years old. Nagy's results yielded three relatively discrete developmental phases: for ages three to five, death is seen as a temporary departure or sleep; for ages five to nine, death is seen as final and is personified as either a separate person or the dead person himself; beyond nine years of age, children recognize death as not only final, but also inevitable. Nagy's data suggest that the association between death and anxiety is established as early as three years of age, when death is viewed as separation.

According to Rothstein (in Kastenbaum and Aisenberg 1972), death anxiety is relatively low throughout young adulthood until the middle adult years. Relying on extensive interview data, he found that death anxiety peaks in the middle years. This is especially true for men, perhaps because this is the first time men become aware of their own vulnerability as a result of deaths among friends and acquaintances their age. Contrary to Rothstein's findings, Feifel and Branscomb (1973) found that subjects over the age of fifty tended to answer "no" to the question, "Are you afraid of your own death?" more frequently than younger subjects. On the other hand, a study by Templer, Ruff, and Franks (1971) yielded results contrary to both Rothstein and Feifel and Branscomb. Testing over 2,000 subjects of various ages, they found no significant correlation between age and death anxiety scores.

This discrepancy in findings remains unresolved and is further complicated by a study of death anxiety at the unconscious level. Feifel and Branscomb (1973) found that the same elderly subjects who reported below-average overt death anxiety exhibited unconscious death anxiety that was just as high as that of younger subjects. Corey (1961) similarly found that older adults tend to show avoidance of death in projective tests. While no explanation can account for all these data, they can perhaps in part be understood if it is assumed that people are more likely to deny their fears as death becomes a more immediate threat. Researchers frequently invoke the concept of denial to explain low death anxiety scores in populations such as the aged, who because of their nearness to death are expected to have high death anxiety. Unless other corroborating data are available, such interpretations of low scores are unjustified. Individuals who score low in death anxiety just may not be very concerned with death, regardless of their temporal nearness to death. The study by Feifel and Branscomb (1973) is one example of a study where a denial interpretation can be entertained. The relative discrepancy between overt death anxiety and unconscious death anxiety in the same population of elderly subjects could be the result of denial influencing the expression of overt death fears.

Physical Health   Evidence on the relationship between health and death anxiety follows a pattern similar to that of death anxiety and age. There is conflicting evidence on overt death anxiety and a possibility of denial among subjects most threatened by impending death. Lucas (1974) studied 60 hemodialysis and surgery patients and did not find their DAS scores to be significantly different from the normal mean scores reported by Templer (1970). Templer, however, found a significant negative correlation between scores on the DAS and a measure of physical health, indicating that the higher an individual's death anxiety, the lower his physical health status. Swenson (1961) suggested that people who are unhealthy might look forward to ending it all and so fear death less than the healthy. His finding that individuals in poor health tended to look forward to death more than fear it supports this view, although his sample included only aged individuals. Feifel and his colleagues (Feifel 1974; Feifel, Freilich, and Hermann 1973) found that terminally ill patients reported fearing death no more frequently than other subjects but demonstrated higher death anxiety on an unconscious level. Kübler-Ross (1969) reports some impressionistic data based on interviews with 200 terminal patients. She found that although patients experience a great deal of shock and anxiety when first informed of their terminality, most patients eventually come to accept their impending deaths. In a review of the literature on the feelings and attitudes of dying patients, Schulz and Aderman (1974) concluded that the predominant response of most terminal patients is depression rather than anxiety shortly before death. In sum, there is little evidence that persons closer to death, because of their health status, exhibit greater overt death anxiety than their healthy counterparts, and there is no evidence to suggest that extraordinary denial processes are operating in these populations.

Religiosity   While Lester's review (1967a) reported considerable confusion on the relationship between religious beliefs and death anxiety, recent findings have been refreshingly clear. It is possible that the disparate results from earlier studies (e.g., Faunce and Fulton 1958; Kalish 1963) are attributable to different conceptualizations of religiosity. Indicators of extrinsic religiosity (frequency of church attendance) might result in a positive relationship between religiosity and death anxiety, but religiosity measured in terms of fundamental values might produce the reverse relationship. Recent studies show that degree of religiosity (measured by self-report of beliefs and churchgoing) is unrelated to death anxiety for the general population (Feifel 1974; Kalish 1963; Templer 1970) but is negatively related when subjects are religiously involved (Templer 1972a; Shearer 1973). That is, for Templer's sample, which included many ministers, religiosity was correlated with low levels of death anxiety.

Belief in afterlife has been suggested as an intervening variable reducing death anxiety for highly religious people. Jeffers, Nichols, and Eisdorfer (1961) found that individuals with strong religious commitments were more likely to believe in afterlife and also showed less fear of death than less religiously committed persons. Osarchuck and Tatz (1973) found that for subjects scoring high in a Belief in Afterlife Scale, a death-threatening slide show induced still greater belief in an afterlife. In general, the link between belief in afterlife and religiosity has been amply demonstrated. Osarchuck and Tatz (1973) and Kalish (1963) reported that active Protestants and Catholics had higher belief in afterlife when compared to religiously inactive persons of any faith. The other link—the relationship between belief in afterlife and death anxiety, independent of degree of religiosity—is in need of further study.

Emotional Disorders   Research on the death anxiety of psychiatric patients is inconsistent. Broadman, Erdman, and Wolff (1956) and Templer (1971a) found psychiatric illness positively associated with high death anxiety. Similarly, Templer and Ruff (1971) reported above average DAS means for samples of psychiatric patients. However, contradictory findings are reported by Feifel and Hermann (1973). Using a wide range of death anxiety measurements devices, they found no differences between the death anxiety of mentally ill and normal subjects. They also found degree of mental illness to be unrelated to death anxiety.

Working with samples of "normals" from the general public, Templer (1970, 1972a) reported small positive correlations between Templer's DAS and the neuroticism scales of the Eysenck Personality Inventory and the Welsh Anxiety Scale, respectively. Other scales of general anxiety correlate similarly with the DAS (Templer 1970; Lucas 1974), as does the Minnesota Multiphasic Personality Inventory (MMPI) depression scale (Templer 1971a). Using projective measures, Rhudick and Dibner (1961) found significant positive correlations between death concern and four MMPI scales of neurotic preoccupation. These findings indicate that death anxiety shares features with more general forms of anxiety, neurosis, and depression. While it is important not to ignore this aspect of death anxiety, it is also important to note that Templer (1970) reports data suggesting that death anxiety is a concept distinct from general anxiety. The intercorrelations among various death anxiety scales are consistently and significantly higher than their correlations with general anxiety.

It might be expected that people who attempt suicide would fear death less than the general population. Lester (1967a) found this to be the case when he administered his and Boyar's (1964) FODS to attempters and threateners of suicide and compared their scores to those of subjects who never considered suicide. Similarly, Tarter, Templer, and Perley (1974) found a significant correlation between the DAS and the judged "potential for rescue" following the act of attempted suicide. One possible interpretation of these data is that those who fear death less are more serious about acting on their suicidal desires. The only evidence contrary to these findings comes from an unpublished study carried out by Lester and reported in his review (1967a). He found that suicide-threateners fear death more than suicide-contemplaters, who in turn fear death more than those who have never considered taking their lives; Lester admits this evidence is weak because of the small sample studied. The best conclusion is that suicidal individuals have lower death anxiety than comparable nonsuicidal populations.

Need for Achievement, Sense of Competence, and Purpose   At least three hypotheses have been generated relating need for achievement, sense of competence, and sense of purpose in life to death anxiety: (1) individuals with high need for achievement (nAch) will fear death more because it ends their chance for further achievement (Diggory and Rothman 1961); (2) individuals with a high sense of competence will fear death less because they are satisfied with their lives (Goodman 1975); and (3) persons with low fear of death will have a greater purpose in life because a crucial step in developing the latter is confronting death without fear (Frankl 1965).

Two studies (Nogas, Schweitzer, and Grumet 1974; Ray and Najman 1974) investigated the first hypothesis and failed to find a relationship between nAch and death anxiety, although Ray and Najman pointed out that the undergraduate samples used were too high in need for achievement to provide a sufficiently wide range of scores. The second hypothesis was partially supported by Nogas, Schweitzer, and Grumet (1974), who found a significant negative correlation between death anxiety and sense of competence. The data may indicate, however, that sense of competence includes competence in confronting death. The third hypothesis is supported by convincingly high negative correlations (ranging from -.54 to -.82) between overt death anxiety and Crumbaugh and Maholick's (1964) Purpose in Life Test (Blazer 1973; Durlak 1972b, 1973). Ignoring the fact that correlations say little about causality or about direction of causality, Blazer and Durlak suggest that children taught to accept death will become adults with more meaning in their lives.

Cognitive Style   A provocative study by Mishara, Baker, and Kostin (1972) indicated that college students differing in cognitive style hold different attitudes toward death. Cognitive style was determined by the Kinesthetic Figural After-effects task, which classifies subjects as "augmenters" if they overestimate the width of a wooden block held between their fingers after holding a wider "intervening stimulus" block. Subjects who underestimate the block's width after the intervening stimulus are classified as "reducers." Augmenters tend to magnify stimulus intensity; they tend to be more comfortable with stimulus deprivation and less comfortable with aversive stimuli. When asked to imagine the final year of their lives, augmenters avoided mentioning death (presumably an aversive stimulus) significantly more than reducers. While no death anxiety scale was administered in this study, these data suggest that augmenters have higher death anxiety than reducers.

This attempt to link death anxiety to cognitive functioning is a refreshing change from the usual pattern of relating death anxiety to other questionnaire measures.

Other Variables A host of other variables have been researched as possible correlates of death anxiety. No significant correlations were found for the following variables: projective measures of fear of failure (Cohen and Parker 1974); a dependency scale (Selvey 1973); guilt about hostility (Selvey 1973); race (Pandey 1974; Pandey and Templer 1972); and Eysenck's Extraversion Scale (Templer 1972b). Three of four studies relating death anxiety to Rotter's I-E locus of control scale reported no relationship (Selvey 1973; Dickstein 1972; Berman 1973); only Tolor and Reznikoff (1967) found a significant relationship between Rotter's I-E scale and death anxiety. Externally oriented subjects had significantly greater death anxiety than subjects with internal orientations.

Denial of Death Anxiety The idea that death anxiety can exist at both the conscious and unconscious level has been a theme throughout this chapter. While researchers have occasionally found consistencies between self-reported and unconscious death anxiety, more often than not the two are discrepant. When such discrepancies occur, researchers typically invoke the concept of repression, or denial, of death anxiety to explain these findings.

Handal and Rychlak (1971) found a much higher proportion of negative and death-related dreams among subjects scoring high or low on self-report death anxiety scales than among those with moderate scores. They concluded that many of those with low conscious death anxiety were denying their deeper fears. Feifel and his colleagues (Feifel and Branscomb 1973; Feifel and Hermann 1973) concluded that death anxiety is greater at unconscious than at conscious levels, especially for aged and unhealthy subjects. For this reason, the concept of denial has been invoked to explain the lack of increased death anxiety scores among dying subjects. Similarly, the failure to find a relationship between death anxiety and contact with death may be attributed to the exclusive use of conscious death anxiety measures in these studies.

Other evidence of denial of death anxiety makes use of Byrne's (1964) Repression-Sensitization scale. Subjects who tend to repress threats (according to the Repression-Sensitization scale) also tend to be low in conscious death anxiety as measured by the DAS (Templer 1971b). Templer found no evidence for the relationship between Repression-Sensitization score and unconscious death anxiety. Apparently repressors, while low in conscious death anxiety, are not high in unconscious death anxiety either.

Templer (1971b) also found a .30 correlation between DAS and unconscious death anxiety as measured by a galvanic skin response to death-related stimulus material. This moderately positive correlation suggests that the two levels of death anxiety are not totally independent.

Donaldson (1972) argues that operational and theoretical definitions of denial must be determined before conclusions are drawn about its existence. The discrepancies between conscious and unconscious death anxiety found in the research reviewed above represent a step in this direction. Research employing discrepancy between conscious and unconscious death anxiety as a variable and searching for its correlates appears promising. The internal dynamics resulting from disharmony between different levels of a person's attitudes toward death may prove to be more important than death anxiety itself.

Environmental Influences on Death Anxiety

Three classes of environmental variables are found in the literature. Researchers have examined the effects of educational intervention, contact with death, and the impact of the family on death anxiety. Lucas (1974) and Templer, Ruff, and Franks (1971) reported high correlations ($r = .59$) between spouses' DAS scores; child-parent correlations were less ($r = .40$) but tended to be somewhat higher when the two are of the same sex. Although these data say nothing about the relative importance of environment and genetics as determinants of death anxiety, they do support the notion that the environment, through parents' influence, affects death anxiety (Templer, Ruff, and Franks 1971).

Lester and Templer (1972) found a striking developmental trend in child-parent correlations. During adolescence, daughter-parent DAS correlations decreased steadily and were statistically insignificant by age eighteen or nineteen. No explanation is offered for the apparent tendency for adolescent boys to continue to be influenced by their parents while their sisters are cutting the death anxiety apron strings. Another finding of family influence was reported by Iammarino (1975). Ninth-graders living with only one parent feared death more than their two-parent peers. This could be interpreted as evidence that separation anxiety can be an antecedent of death anxiety. More generally, this serves to demonstrate the effect of family environment on death anxiety.

Since death anxiety has been shown to be a socially influenced phenomenon, one might expect it to respond to direct intervention. However, attempts to verify the success of intervention, in the form of nursing curricula and college courses, have met with mixed success. Nurses nearing graduation accept death more than students earlier in their training (Yeaworth, Kapp, and Winget 1974). Their death anxiety is lower (Lester, Getty, and Kneisl 1974), and thoughts of death are less frequent (Snyder, Gertler, and Ferneau 1973). With the exception of Lester and his colleagues, most researchers attribute the changes in death anxiety to the nursing curriculum, ignoring alternative explanations such as contact with patients. All that can be concluded with certainty is that something in a nursing student's experience reduces death anxiety.

Several specific "death education" programs have been evaluated, but only one caused a significant reduction in death anxiety. Murray (1974) found nurses' DAS scores significantly reduced after a six-week course. It is possible that the practical work of the students interacted with the program to lessen death anxiety, since courses for college students have not been found to change death anxiety significantly (Bell 1975; Leviton 1973; Wittmaier 1975).

While death education courses will certainly continue in colleges and nursing schools, an indirect approach to lessening death anxiety was shown to be effective by Templer, Ruff, and Simpson (1974). They evaluated the death anxiety of subjects before and after therapy dealing exclusively with reduction of depression. DAS scores declined significantly along with depression, demonstrating that depression and death anxiety covary to some extent.

In spite of many attempts, no study has shown that contact with death or with high-risk situations influences death anxiety. Self-report of previous death-threatening experiences is unrelated to death anxiety (Durlak 1973; Berman 1974). Nurses' death anxiety is not related to the patient death rate on their unit (Shusterman and Sechrest 1973) or within their area of specialization (Lester, Getty, and Kneisl 1974). Parachute jumpers (Alexander and Lester 1972) and widows (Kalish and Reynolds 1974; Rhudick and Dibner 1961) score no higher than controls on death scales, although Swenson (1961) found that widows tend to deny their death anxiety when direct methods are used. The mixed pattern of results obtained on environmental determinants of death anxiety is most likely attributable to the lack of conceptual and methodological rigor in designing and executing research in this area. Researchers should know at what level death anxiety is being assessed and should be sensitive to possible confounding variables when carrying out their research.

FUTURE RESEARCH

This review of the death anxiety literature suggests that future research should move in three directions. First, researchers should be sensitive to the multidimensionality of death anxiety. Much of the confusion of past research may be avoided by recognizing that death anxiety is comprised of several independent components, each of which can be tapped at a public, private, and unconscious level. An immediate goal should be the investigation of the various subcomponents of death anxiety. Some components—such as anxiety over nonexistence and the anxiety over the process of dying (that is, the humiliation, pain, and suffering) in relation to self and others—have been identified. Other components might include anxiety about the impact of one's death on survivors and about having one's plans interrupted.

A second endeavor should be the untangling of discrepancies between conscious and unconscious death anxiety. The consequences of this discrepancy may eventually prove more interesting and important than simple death anxiety per se. One perspective on this problem is presented in a recent excellent review of the psychological death literature by Kastenbaum and Costa (1977). These authors suggest that fear of death and death anxiety are two different and independent phenomena. Thus, an individual may be high on specific fears associated with death and yet exhibit little death anxiety. Viewed from this perspective, there is no reason to expect a consistent relationship between conscious and unconscious death anxiety. At any rate, further attempts at enlarging the list of paper-and-pencil correlates of death anxiety appear to be of little use in understanding or demonstrating its relevance to human behavior.

Third, an effort should be made to demonstrate the functional or behavioral consequences of death anxiety. One such example is Templer's (1972b) study of death anxiety in smokers. Templer found that while nonsmokers and smokers did not differ in death anxiety, smokers with high death anxiety tended to smoke less. Another example is Kastenbaum and Briscoe's (1975) study of street-crossing behavior. The authors demonstrated the feasibility of relating naturalistically observed behavior to unobserved psychosocial variables: they found strong relationships between risk-taking in street-crossing and suicidal tendencies, marital status, and desired and expected life span.

CONCLUSION

Thinking about death has been one of man's major preoccupations. Many early speculations were based on intuition and individual case studies and yielded a rich and complex perspective on what it is that man fears about death and how these fears affect his functioning. Some researchers (Becker 1973; Meyer 1975; Zilboorg 1943) have used this perspective to argue that death anxiety has been the inspiration for many great individual achievements. Turning to the empirical studies of the relationship between death anxiety and a multitude of other variables, we found the existing empirical approach to be somewhat simplistic. Death anxiety does not appear to be a unidimensional concept. Instead, it appears to have many components, each of which can be assessed at different levels. However, recent research shows signs of tapping into the richness of this topic.

REFERENCES

Alexander, I.E., and Adlerstein, A.M. 1958. Affective responses to the concept of death in a population of children and early adolescents. *Journal of Genetic Psychology* 93:167–77.

Alexander, M., and Lester, D. 1972. Fear of death in parachute jumpers. *Perceptual and Motor Skills* 34:338.

Becker, E. 1973. *The denial of death.* New York: Free Press.

Bell, W. 1975. The experimental manipulation of death attitudes: A preliminary investigation. *Omega: Journal of Death and Dying* 6:199–205.

Berman, A. 1974. Belief in afterlife, religion, religiosity, and life-threatening experiences. *Omega: Journal of Death and dying* 5:127.

————. 1973. smoking behavior: How is it related to locus of control, death anxiety, and belief in afterlife. *Omega: Journal of Death and Dying* 4:149–55.

Berman, A., and Hays, J.E. 1973. Relationship between death anxiety, belief in afterlife and locus of control. *Journal of Consulting and Clinical Psychology* 41:318.

Blazer, J. 1973.The relationship between meaning in life and fear of death. *Psychology* 10:33–4.

Boyar, J.I. 1964. "The construction and partial validation of a scale for the measurement of fear of death." Unpublished doctoral dissertation, University of Rochester, Rochester, New York.

Brodman, K., Erdman, A. and Wolff, H. 1956. *Manual for the Cornell Medical Index.* Ithaca, New York: Cornell University Medical College.

Byrne,D. 1964. Repression-sensitization as a dimension of personality. In B.A. Maher (ed.), *Progress in Experimental Personality Research, vol. I.* New York: Academic Press.

Caldwell, D., and Mishara, B.L. 1972. Research on attitudes of medical doctors toward the dying patient: A methodical problem. *Omega: Journal of Death and Dying* 3:341–46.

Christ, P.E.I. 1961. Attitudes toward death among a group of acute geriatric psychiatric patients. *Journal of Gerontology* 16:56–59.

Cohen, R., and Parker, O. 1974. Fear of failure and death. *Psychological Reports* 34:54.

Coleman, J.C. 1972. *Abnormal Psychology and Modern Life.* Glenview, Illinois: Scott Foresman.

Collett, L. and Lester, D. 1969. Fear of death and fear of dying. *Journal of Psychology* 72:179–81.

Corey, L.G. 1961. An analogue of resistance to death awareness. *Journal of Gerontology* 16:59–60.

Crumbaugh, J.C., and Maholick, L.T. 1964. An experimental study in existentialism: The psychometric approach to Frankl's concept of noogenic neurosis. *Journal of Clinical Psychology* 20:200–207.

Degner, L. 1974. The relationship between some beliefs held by physicians and their life-prolonging decisions. *Omega: Journal of Death and Dying* 5:223.

Dickstein, L. 1972. Death concern: Measurement and correlates. *Psychological Reports* 30:563–71.

———. 1975. Self-report and fantasy correlates of death concern. *Psychological Reports* 32:147–58.

Diggory, J.C. and Rothman, D.Z. 1961. Values destroyed by death. *Journal of Abnormal and Social Psychology* 63:205–10.

Donaldson, P.J. 1972. Denying death: A note regarding some ambiguities in the current discussion. *Omega: Journal of Death and Dying* 3:285–90.

Durlak, J. 1972a. Measurement of the fear of death: An examination of some existing scales. *Journal of Clinical Psychology* 28:545–47.

———. 1972b. Relationship between individual attitudes toward life and death. *Journal of Consulting and Clinical Psychology* 38:463.

———. 1973. Relationship between various measures of death concern and fear of death. *Journal of Consulting and Clinical Psychology* 41:162.

Faunce, W.A., and Fulton, R.L. 1958. The sociology of death: A neglected area of research. *Social Forces* 36:205–9.

Feifel, H. 1974. Religious conviction and fear of death among the healthy and the terminally ill. *Journal for the Scientific Study of Religion* 13:353–60.

Feifel, H., and Branscomb, A. 1973. Who's afraid of death? *Journal of Abnormal Psychology* 81:282–88.

Feifel, H., and Hermann, L. 1973. Fear of death in the mentally ill. *Psychological Reports* 33:931–38.

Feifel, H., Freilich, J., and Hermann, L. 1973. Death fear in dying heart and cancer patients. *Journal of Psychosomatic Research* 17:161–66.

Frankl, V.E. 1965. *The Doctor and the Soul.* New York: Knopf.

Fulton, R. 1961. Discussion of a symposium on attitudes toward death in older persons. *Journal of Gerontology* 16:44–66.

Goodman, L. 1975. Winning the race with death, fear of death and creativity. Symposium, American Psychological Association Convention, Chicago, Illinois.

Hall, G. S. 1922. *Senescence.* New York: Appleton.

Handal, P. J., and Rychlak, J. F. 1971. Curvilinearity between dream content and death anxiety and the relationship of death anxiety to repression-sensitization. *Journal of Abnormal Psychology* 77:11–16.

Iammarino, N.K. 1975. Relationship between death anxiety and demographic variables. *Psychological Reports* 17:262.

Jeffers, F.C., Nichols, C. R., and Eisdorfer, C. 1961. Attitudes of older persons to death. *Journal of Gerontology* 16:53–56.

Jones, E.E., and Sigall, H. 1971. The bogus pipeline: A new paradigm for measuring affect and attitude. *Psychological Bulletin* 76:349–64.

Kalish, R.A. 1963. Some variables in death attitudes. *Journal of Social Psychology* 59:137–45.

Kalish, R., and Reynolds, D. 1974. Widows view death. *Omega: Journal of Death and Dying* 5:187.

Kastenbaum, R., and Aisenberg, R. 1972. *The Psychology of Death.* New York: Springer.

Kastenbaum, R., and Briscoe, L. 1975. The street corner: A laboratory for the study of life-threatening behavior. *Omega: Journal of Death and Dying* 6:33.

Kastenbaum, R., and Costa, P.T. 1977. Psychological perspectives on death. In M. R. Rosenzweig and Porter, L.W. (eds.) *Annual Review of Psychology* 8:225–49.

Krieger, S., Epsting, F., and Leitner, L.M. 1974. Personal constructs, threat, and attitudes toward death. *Omega: Journal of Death and Dying* 5:299.

Kübler-Ross, E. 1969. *On Death and Dying.* New York: Macmillan.

Lester, D. 1967a. Experimental and correlational studies of the fear of death. *Psychological Bulletin* 67:27–36.

———. 1967b. Fear of death of suicide persons. *Psychological Reports* 20:1077–78.

———. 1971. Sex differences in attitudes toward death: A replication. *Psychological Reports* 28:754.

———. 1972. Studies in death attitudes. *Psychological Reports* 30:440.

Lester, D., Getty, C., and Kneisl, C. 1974. Attitudes of nursing students and nursing faculty toward death. *Nursing Research* 23:50–53.

Lester, D., and Lester, G. 1970. Fear of death, fear of dying, and threshold differences for death words and neutral words. *Omega: Journal of Death and Dying* 1:175–79.

Lester, D., and Templer, D. 1972. Resemblance of parent-child death anxiety as a function of age and sex of child. *Psychological Reports* 31:750.

Leviton, D. 1973. Death education and change in students' attitudes. *Final Research Report,* National Institute of Mental Health Research Grant MH 21974-01. Washington, D.C.

Lowry, R. 1965. Male-female differences in attitudes toward death. Doctoral dissertation, Brandeis University.

Lucas, R. 1974. A comparative study of measures of general anxiety and death anxiety among three medical groups including patient and wife. *Omega: Journal of Death and Dying* 5:233.

Meyer, J.E. 1975. *Death and Neurosis.* New York: International Universities Press.

Mishara, B., Baker, H., and Kostin, I. 1972. Do people who seek less environmental stimulation avoid thinking about the future and their death? Proceedings of the Annual Convention of the American Psychological Association 7:667–68.

Moody, R.A. 1975. *Life after Life.* Atlanta: Mockingbird Books.

Murray, P. 1974. Death education and its effect on the death anxiety level of nurses. *Psychological Reports* 35:1250.

Nagy, M. 1959. The child's view of death. In H. Feifel (ed.), *The Meaning of Death.* New York: McGraw-Hill.

Nogas, C., Schweitzer, K., and Grumet, J. 1974. An investigation of death anxiety, sense of competence, and need for achievement. *Omega: Journal of Death and Dying* 5:245.

Osarchuck, M., and Tatz, S. 1973. Effect of induced fear of death on belief in afterlife. *Journal of Personality and Social Psychology* 27:256–60.

Pandey, R.E. 1974-75. Factor analytic study of attitudes toward death among college students. *International Journal of Social Psychiatry* 21:7–11.

Pandey, R.E., and Templer, D. 1972. Use of the death anxiety scale in an inter-racial setting. *Omega: Journal of Death and Dying* 3:127–30.

Ray, J.J., and Najman, J. 1974. Death anxiety and death acceptance: A preliminary approach. *Omega: Journal of Death and Dying* 5:311.

Rheingold, J.C. 1967. *The Mother, Anxiety, and Death.* Boston: Little Brown.

Rhudick, P.J., and Dibner, A.S. 1961. Age, personality and health correlates of death concern in normal aged individuals. *Journal of Gerontology* 16:44–49.

Sarnoff, I., and Corwin, S.M. 1959. Castration anxiety and the fear of death. *Journal of Personality* 27:374–85.

Schulz, R., and Aderman, D. 1974. Clinical research and the stages of dying. *Omega: Journal of Death and Dying* 5:137–43.

————. 1977. Physician's death anxiety and survival of patients. Unpublished manuscript.

Schulz, R., Aderman, D., and Manko, G. 1976. Attitudes toward death: The effects of different methods of questionnaire administration. Paper presented at the meeting of the Eastern Psychological Association, New York, April.

Selvey, C. 1973. Concerns about death in relation to sex, dependency, guilt about hostility, and feelings of powerlessness. *Omega: Journal of Death and Dying* 4:209–19.

Shearer, R.E. 1973. Religious belief and attitudes toward death. *Dissertation Abstracts International* 33:3292–93.

Shusterman, L., and Sechrest, L. 1973. Attitudes of RNs toward death in a general hospital. *Psychiatry in Medicine* 4:411–26.

Snyder, M., Gertler, R., and Ferneau, E. 1973. Changes in nursing students' attitudes toward death and dying: A measurement of curriculum integration effectiveness. *International Journal of Social Psychiatry* 19:294–98.

Stroop, J.R. 1938. Factors affecting speed in serial verbal reactions. *Psychological Monographs* 50:38–48.

Swenson, W.M. 1961. Attitudes toward death in an aged population. *Journal of Gerontology* 16:49–52.

Tarter, R., Templer, D., and Perley, R. 1974. Death anxiety in suicide attempters. *Psychological Reports* 34:895–97.

Templer, D. 1970. The construction and validation of a death anxiety scale. *Journal of General Psychology* 82:165–77.

————. 1971a. The relationship between verbalized and nonverbalized death anxiety. *Journal of Genetic Psychology* 119:211–14.

————. 1971b. Death anxiety as related to depression and health of retired persons. *Journal of Gerontology* 26:521–23.

————. 1972a. Death anxiety in religiously very involved persons. *Psychological Reports* 31:361–62.

————. 1972b. Death anxiety: Extraversion, neuroticism, and cigarette smoking. *Omega: Journal of Death and Dying* 3:53–56.

Templer, D., and Ruff, C. 1971. Death anxiety scale means, standard deviations, and embedding. *Psychological Reports* 29:173–74.

Templer, D., Ruff, C., and Franks, C. 1971. Death anxiety: Age, sex and parental resemblance in diverse populations. *Developmental Psychology* 4:108.

Templer, D., Ruff, C., and Simpson, K. 1974. Alleviation of high death anxiety with symptomatic treatment of depression. *Psychological Reports* 35:216.

Tolor, A., and Reznikoff, M. 1967. Relationship between insight, repression-sensitization, internal-external control, and death anxiety. *Journal of Abnormal Psychology* 72:426–30.

Wittmaier, B. 1975. The impact of a death course. Unpublished manuscript, Kirkland College, New York.

Yeaworth, R., Kapp, F. and Winget, C. 1974. Attitudes of nursing students toward the dying patient. *Nursing Research* 23:30–24.

Zilboorg, G. 1943. Fear of death. *Psychoanalytic Quarterly* 12:465–75.

RICHARD A. KALISH and
DAVID K. REYNOLDS

Death and Ethnicity: Encounter with the Death of Self

In the following selection taken from a comprehensive research report, Kalish and Reynolds present findings of an empirical study of attitudes toward death within ethnic subgroups in Southern California. Noting the limitations inherent in generalizing beyond this region, they present their findings for four groups: Blacks, Mexican-Americans, Japanese, and Anglo-Americans. Their summaries indicate that ethnic background is an important factor in attitudes toward dying, death, and bereavement, but they also demonstrate that differences *within* ethnic groups are at least as great as and sometimes greater than those among ethnic groups.

Do people fear death? We don't know. All we can say with certainty is that study after study has shown that people *say* they do not fear death. How valid are these comments? Again, we don't know. University students displayed the same reaction time lags to death words that they did to sex words, while their galvanic skin responses and reaction times to death words were significantly and substantially greater than to neutral words (Alexander, Colley and Adlerstein, 1957). But does this suggest greater fear? It could imply excitement, fascination, or even response to the unexpected.

Most studies of fear of death have been conducted with specific age groups, especially with either university students or the elderly. These are discussed in the chapter on age, so that comparisons can be made with proper age groups. However, a few investigations have cut across age lines. Neither Scott (1896) nor Hall (1897) asked directly about fear of death in their questionnaires, although Hall did say 20 years later, "We long to be just as well, strong, happy, and vital as possible, and strive against everything that impedes this wish or will . . . We love life supremely and cannot have too much of it . . . while we dread all that interferes with it" (p. 569). Feifel

Source: Richard A. Kalish and David K. Reynolds, *Death and Ethnicity: A Psychocultural Study,* ©1976, The Ethel Percy Andrus Gerontology Center, University of Southern California. Published by the University of Southern California Press. Reprinted by permission.

and Jones (1968) combined the seriously ill, the chronically ill and disabled, the mentally ill, and normals into one sample, with roughly equal numbers in each category. Of this conglomerate, 71 percent verbalized no fear of death.

In Hinton's observations of the terminally ill, he felt that "as many as two-thirds of those who died under fifty years of age were clearly apprehensive, whereas less than a third of those over sixty years were as anxious" (1967, p. 84). Of Chenard's Catholic and Unitarian women, 11 percent were very much afraid, 21 percent were not at all afraid, and the rest were split between some fear and little fear (1972).

In a recent national survey, conducted by the Harris Poll organization under the auspices of the National Council on the Aging, individuals in a large sample were asked to respond to the open-ended question: What are the worst things about being over 65 years of age? Fear of death was given as an answer by 9 percent of the total sample, but by only 6 percent of those 50 years of age and older. This compares with 62 percent of the sample who indicated that poor health was one of the worst things about being old and 33 percent who stipulated loneliness. Blacks mentioned fear of death only 2 percent of the time, compared to 10 percent for the non-Blacks (other ethnic groups were not represented in sufficient numbers for breakdowns) (National Council on the Aging, 1975). When the same respondents were asked to list what they considered to be very serious problems of old age, fear of death was not among the 12 most common concerns listed either by those between 18 and 64 or by those 65 and over.

Riley (in Riley et al, 1968) reports that only 4 percent of his national survey sample "gave evidence of fear or emotional anxiety in connection with death" (p. 332). Other studies, although based upon samples limited by geography, age, or education, found comparable results ranging up to around 10 percent or so indicating fear of death. Our respondents were either more frightened of death—or more truthful in their responses. We asked, "Some people say they are afraid to die and others say they are not. How do you feel?" The interviewer coded the response in the categories *terrified/afraid, neither afraid nor unafraid,* or *unafraid/eager.* Only two people could be clearly categorized as *eager*, and about 2 percent gave responses classified by the interviewer as *terrified*. Because of these small numbers, we combined those categories with adjacent ones, as indicated just above.

Using this approach, over a quarter of all respondents were classed as afraid of dying (B 19 percent, J 31 percent, M 33 percent, A 22 percent),* while just over half were unafraid (B 50 percent, J 50 percent, M 54 percent, A 53 percent). About 2½ percent were uncodable, and the rest were classified as neither afraid nor unafraid. Why we received such a low proportion of persons claiming to be unafraid is difficult to say. Perhaps their having already participated in some 30 minutes of death-related discussion heightened their anxieties—or perhaps it enabled them to reply with greater honesty. To be consistent with our policy of assuming face validity of any statements, unless substantial evidence suggests otherwise, we propose that our data represent accurately the feelings of the respondents at the time the question was asked.

*Editor's Note: In the summaries that follow, "B," "J," "M" and "A" indicate the proportion of respondents who were Black, Japanese, Mexican-American and Anglo-American respectively.

One respondent commented, "So many say they are ready (to die), but I don't feel near ready. Judging from the way I got frightened at the earthquake, I'm not near ready." A Mexican-American man said, "I *say* I'm unafraid, but if I had time to think about it, and I knew I would die shortly, I don't know—I guess I would certainly be concerned." And an Anglo-American man put his view succinctly: "You are *nuts* if you aren't afraid of death."

This leads to the question, how stable are attitudes toward death? Ivey and Bardwick (1968) have shown that death anxiety of women varies as a function of their menstrual cycle—as do other kinds of anxiety. We know of no other evidence on this issue. However, we suggest no mystique for death attitudes—they undoubtedly vary as a function of situation, mood, experience, and shifting cultural milieu, just as all other attitudes vary.

Whatever a person's attitude might be regarding death, what has influenced these feelings? For this question we provided the respondent a card with 10 alternatives, plus an eleventh, "OTHER (SPECIFY)." Over one-third of the respondents selected the statement, "The death of someone close," as having influenced them the most (B 26 percent, J 41 percent, M 39 percent, A 35 percent). "My father died when I was 5½ years old. I was very close to him, and when I heard of his death, I ran away from home and went into the woods. I was gone for 2½ days. I felt as if my whole world had collapsed, as if I had no one to turn to any longer. I was desperate. I cried a lot." Second most frequently selected was, "Your religious background" (B 40 percent, J 13 percent, M 21 percent, A 25 percent). Nearly 19 percent stated that having been close to their own death, or believing themselves to be, was their greatest influence. Reading, conversations, the death of an animal, mystical experiences, funerals or other rituals, the media, were all listed by only 5 percent or less of the sample.

Shneidman's survey, while not drawing from a comparable sample, obtained some parallel results. Of his respondents, 35 percent stated that introspection and meditation most influenced their attitudes toward death; we did not include that alternative, but we doubt whether many of our respondents would have selected it. Second and third most frequently mentioned by Shneidman's sample were the death of someone else and religious upbringing (19 percent and 15 percent respectively); these fit quite well with our data. Over one-third of Shneidman's group stated that existential philosophy influenced their present attitudes toward their own death more than such concerns as pollution, violence, television, war, poverty, and so forth. We believe that very few of our respondents would have selected that alternative.

Although 19 percent of the respondents felt that either actually being close to death or thinking they were close to death had the greatest impact upon their attitudes, over twice that many had—at least once—believed that they were close to dying (B 48 percent, J 31 percent, M 49 percent, A 37 percent). Of these, exactly half of the Blacks and Japanese asserted that the experience had affected their lives, slightly under half of the Mexicans and Anglos agreeing also. Unfortunately, responses to the question of how the experience affected them were so scattered, that the categories became too small for serious consideration. Here, too, the response to near death was highly individualistic, varying with circumstances, cultural background, and other experiences before and after the event.

Do people often think about their own death? Kennard (1937) informs us that the Hopi "man who thinks of the dead or of the future life instead of being concerned with wordly activities, is thereby bringing about his own death" (p. 492). Simmons (1945) does not mention any other example of this, but a number of respondents in our study—proportionately more Black Americans than others—referred to being worried that talking about death would bring it about. Scott's sample of 226 adults indicated that only 7 percent never "dwelt on death or suicide," while 60 percent responded in such fashion that they obviously gave at least some thought to the matter (1896). Vernon's student sample showed only 45 percent who said they thought only "rarely" or "very rarely" about their death (1970).

Additional studies add numbers, but little insight. Feifel and Jones (1968), in their investigation of a primarily mentally or physically ill sample, found that 44 percent thought of death "rarely" and 42 percent occasionally. Fulton (1965), using a mail survey with a limited percent of response, also found that 40 percent rarely or never thought about death, while 12 percent dwelled on it frequently or all the time. And in 1963, Riley's national sample (1971) splits into almost equal thirds, stipulating "often," "occasionally," and "hardly ever/never." Shneidman found 5 percent of his respondents thought of their death once a day, while 21 percent contemplated it no more than once a year. In a study of persons 45 years of age and older, drawn from Black, Mexican, and Anglo-American samples also in Los Angeles, 35 percent stated they thought about their own death "not at all," 65 percent "occasionally," and 9 percent "frequently" (Bengtson et al., 1976). Interviews in retirement communities found that fewer than 10 percent stated that they thought of death very frequently, while nearly 15 percent claimed not to think of their own death at all (Mathieu, 1975).

How do our respondents compare? Sadly, almost none of the studies produced directly comparable data. Nonetheless, there is reasonable consistency. Over one in six thinks daily about his death, while over one in four contemplates his termination at least once a week (B 34 percent, J 10 percent, M 37 percent, A 25 percent). On the other hand, 25 percent say they never think of their own death, and over twice that proportion claim that once a year is the most often that thoughts of personal death arise (i.e., combining "Never," "Hardly Ever," and "At least yearly") (B 41 percent, J 69 percent, M 38 percent, A 47 percent). One person makes the valuable point that, "One does think about death, but doesn't remember how often."

If conscious thoughts of one's own death are highly variable in terms of frequency, dreaming about one's own death is much less common, with less than 30 percent admitting that they ever have such dreams. Middleton's (1936) university students reported equivalent figures, only 37 percent indicating such dreams.

Another much-discussed aspect of the process of dying is that of the efficacy of the will-to-live or, conversely, the will-to-die. Weisman and Hacket (1961) discussed the post-operative deaths of six persons, all of whom anticipated their subsequent deaths and none of whom died from obvious medical causes. The professional and popular literature is filled with other examples (e.g., Kalish, 1965). Except for the Mexican-Americans, the overwhelming majority of each group agreed that "People can hasten or slow their own death through a will-to-live or a will-to-die" (B 88 percent, J 85 percent, M 62 percent, A 83 percent).

One Japanese-American funeral director suggested a statistical study to verify his own observations that a highly disproportionate number of deaths occur within one month of the deceased person's birthday. Such research has, in a sense, been conducted. Phillips and Feldman (1973) found a significant reduction in deaths during the month prior to the birth month and a substantial increase in deaths during the month of birth and the month following; this was verified on several independent samples, apparently confirming the perceptions of the funeral director. This information suggests that the dying person has some control over the actual time of his demise. A most graphic case described to the senior author was by a young woman studying for her doctorate whose mother was terminally ill. Although the older woman had been seriously ill for several months, she appeared in good spirits and alert until the day following her daughter's doctoral preliminary orals (the most demanding single day of her graduate program), when the mother died peacefully in her sleep. She had frequently expressed the double concern of wanting to know that her daughter had been successful (she was) and of not wanting to place the burden of a death upon the immensely important event.

Many supernatural and mystical feelings surround death. Thus nearly half of all respondents were affirmative in answering, "Have you ever experienced or felt the presence of anyone after he had died?" (B 55 percent, J 29 percent, M 54 percent, A 38 percent), and one-fourth of these were manifested while awake and were perceived through the senses. This issue and the data are discussed at greater length elsewhere (Kalish and Reynolds, 1973). Pursuing feelings of mysticism surrounding death, over one-third of the Mexicans and between 12 percent and 15 percent of the other groups had experienced the "unexplainable feeling that (they) were about to die." We explicitly eliminated from our count instances in which these feelings occurred during dreams.

Even more persons had had such a feeling about someone else (B 37 percent, J 17 percent, M 38 percent, A 30 percent), and over 70 percent of these respondents stated that the presentiment was validated by actual death on at least one occasion. We feel strongly that these data have an important message to professionals who work with the dying and the bereaved: mystical feelings, "being in touch with his ether," "sensing the vibes," or actually having vivid and realistic contact with the dead, all these experiences are commonplace to large segments of the American public, and it is time they cease being approached as inevitably pathological.

In some settings, people routinely express their desire to die, e.g., at the Japanese-American nursing home, nurses told us that nearly all the patients express such a wish at some time or other during their stay. Other than those suffering severe physical or emotional anguish, however, extremely few people wish to die, whether or not they state that they fear death. What is there about life that they cherish? Diggory and Rothman (1961) described seven values destroyed by death, and they obtained ratings of the importance of these values from over 500 respondents. Shneidman administered the same questions in his *Psychology Today* study. (Shneidman also reports on the same items administered to 120 Harvard and Radcliffe students.) Although the Diggory-Rothman sample was not limited to college students, about two-thirds were

Table 3-4

Here are some reasons why people don't want to die. Tell me whether they are very important to you, important to you, or not important to you. *(Don't know* responses about 3%.)

	B (%)	J (%)	M (%)	A (%)
(080) I am afraid of what might happen to my body after death.				
Very important	3	5	8	5
Important	6	11	9	11
Not important	91	84	83	84
(081) I could no longer care for my dependents.				
Very important	26	42	47	44
Important	26	33	29	29
Not important	48	25	24	26
(082) I am uncertain as to what might happen to me.				
Very important	9	14	11	9
Important	16	19	21	19
Not important	75	66	68	72
(083) I could no longer have any experiences.				
Very important	3	11	7	6
Important	9	26	27	23
Not important	88	63	66	70
(084) My death would cause grief to my relatives and friends.				
Very important	19	14	38	29
Important	55	48	40	50
Not important	26	38	23	21
(085) All my plans and projects would come to an end.				
Very important	10	14	15	14
Important	24	43	34	22
Not important	66	44	51	64
(086) The process of dying might be painful.				
Very important	13	18	30	18
Important	41	38	27	36
Not important	46	44	43	46

under 25 years old, two-thirds were unmarried, and one-fourth were Jewish. Diggory and Rothman also presented the values on a matched pair basis, the respondent being required to select the alternative felt to represent the greatest loss, while we had our respondents indicate whether they felt the value was "very important," "important," or "not-important." Results are, thus, not directly comparable to our study (see Table 3-4).

Our respondents were most concerned by the possibility of causing grief to their friends and relatives (based upon combining "very important" and "important"). Diggory and Rothman also found this to be the most important, but it ranked fifth for Schneidman, perhaps due to the different family roles of his subjects. Over half the Blacks and 75 percent each of our other groups also listed not being able to care for dependents as "important" or "very important," but this concern was ranked much lower by the other studies, depending as they did upon respondents not so likely to have dependents. However, Shaffer's (1970) study of just over 30 individuals who were concerned with making out their wills had results in keeping with ours. Hall (1915) expresses the feeling, "Often the last thought as the soul launches out to cross the bar is for others. There is often a tenacious clinging in thought of . . . a friend, and there is very rarely . . . any concern for the individual's future . . ."(p. 554).

Between one-fourth and one-third of each ethnic group felt that being uncertain as to what might happen to them was important or very important, ranking it fifth, while not being able to have any more experiences distressed well under one-third of our respondents to rank sixth. Shneidman's high-achievement sample placed it first by a wide margin, while Diggory and Rothman's intermediate group listed it fourth. And all studies agreed that what happened to the body after death was least important (see Table 3-5).

Clearly, concern over survivors ranks most highly as a reason for not wanting to die, while the fate of the physical body is obviously of minor importance. Fear of pain was also a major consideration. Somewhat unexpected in these results was the relatively low concern for the inability to continue with plans and projects or to have on-going experiences. If, as Kastenbaum and Aisenberg (1972) contend, cessation of experience is the one characteristic that differentiates death from other occurrences, these respondents certainly do not give the matter much status in their lives. Had we requested that the seven issues be rank-ordered, rather than rated, we could understand better the relegation of loss of experience to such a low level. The question we have, then, is not why the other reasons for not wishing to die were rated so highly, but why these two were not rated equally high. Why do two-thirds of these respondents state that loss of ability to have experiences is not important to them? Why do well over half make the same claim about the end of plans and projects?

One obvious answer is that many respondents do not actually believe that their death will result in the end of self-aware existence. Those who believe in a traditional Christian or Buddhist concept of after-life may not feel they need be concerned about these losses. Another explanation is simply that people are not that enthralled with life. This suggests the possibility that the elderly, who have presumably become disengaged to some extent with life, would care less about these matters than younger

Table 3-5 Comparison of importance of seven values lost by death, as ranked by respondents in three studies, based on lowest proportion of "Unimportant" rating.*

	Kalish and Reynolds	Diggory and Rothman	Shneidman
My death would cause grief to my relatives and friends.	1	1	5
I could no longer care for my dependents.	2	5	3
The process of dying might be painful.	3	3	2
All my plans and projects would come to an end.	4	2	4
I am uncertain as to what might happen to me.	5	6	6
I could no longer have any experiences.	6	4	1
I am afraid of what might happen to my body after death.	7	7	7

*Author's Note: Differences in sampling and methodology are described in the text.

persons. Examination of the data does show that to be the case, but it can only explain away a portion of those who respond in that fashion.

We would opt for a different kind of explanation. When people think of death, they tend to think in terms of the loss of others, of pain, of financial difficulties. They seldom think about ceasing to have experiences, which inevitably constitute life itself. When philosophers and others have stated that people cannot conceptualize their own deaths, they are often referring to cessation, including cessation of experience. To contemplate this is to contemplate nothingness, absence, void—the task is overwhelming. It is to conceive of that which has never—and can never be—experienced. Therefore, the notion is not dealt with and it is not conceptualized as an important reason for not wishing to die. Shneidman's respondents, being younger, more introspective, and more intellectually sophisticated, may have given more thought to this issue.

In our writing this report, we sometimes find ourselves focusing on statistics and theory, rather than exposing ourselves to the personal and existential meaning of pain, of loss, and of death. In this regard, we want to quote from the report of one of our research assistants who effectively combined the research demands of our project with her own desire to offer personal service.

"Mr. Z. was a friendly, gentle, gregarious individual in his early thirties whose physical appearance reminded me a great deal of another patient who had just died of leukemia. In all the time Mr. Z. spoke with me, he never once mentioned his illness by name—it was as though he had been afraid to say the word. On my second visit, he talked a lot about God and made frequent references to passages in the Bible, he spoke about faith and how one has to think of God as being *un Dios Posesiro*. He even read me a passage from the New Testament. I commented that I hadn't seen anyone with such fervent faith in a long time, especially a young Mexican man. I then asked him if he was Protestant. 'Yes, I'm a Seventh-Day Adventist.'

"My third visit. Mr. Z. recognized me and said hello. He told me he wasn't feeling well and was in pain, because some liquid had been drawn from his liver. The whole process was extremely painful, and Mr. Z. was very uncomfortable. He looked at me and said, 'I'd rather be . . .' and then he stopped, without completing the sentence. (Was he afraid that if he put the word *dead* at the end of his sentence, it might become a reality?)

"My fifth visit. Walking into Mr. Z.'s room I could see the anguish and pain he was going through. He restlessly changed from his back to his left side to his right side, all in vain. He was desperately fighting that pain. On top of his nightstand, beside his bed, I noticed a vase with red roses. Mr. Z. noticed me looking at his flowers: 'My wife brought them to me yesterday and look at them—they're all . . . all . . . dead.' He stared emptily, as if all hope for life were gone for himself as well as for his flowers.

"Never having seen anyone in such pain, I felt helpless and upset because I couldn't think of anything to do. I also looked at the roses in desperation. Then my eye caught sight of one rose that had been hidden. It was alive and in full bloom! 'Look!! You were too quick to judge. One is still alive!!' Mr. Z. looked over and smiled.

"My sixth visit. Mr. Z. was in such pain that he could hardly bear it. His only consolation was the news that he did not have cancer, but had a rare blood disease. The nurse had told him that he couldn't have any more medication and that he needed to relax. Then she left. 'Will you stay with me a while?' he asked. I nodded and he stared at me.

" 'Try to lie back and relax.' He tried, but he couldn't. He still kept fighting. In a final attempt, I told him, 'Lie back and hold my hand. Every time the pain comes, squeeze my hand as hard as you can.' He did. I sat with him for about thirty minutes before I felt the pressure on my hand slowly relax. He had fallen asleep."

(From the notes of Patricia Osuna Salazar)

PREDICTING THE FUTURE

We asked our respondents to look into their future for a few moments. How do they predict they will die? and when? Almost all of those who responded (many did not respond: B 37 percent, J 9 percent, M 34 percent, A 21 percent) predicted a natural death for themselves (about 90 percent), and median age at death of 75. (The 25 percentile was 69 years of age, and the 75 percentile was 82, with a range from 27 to over 100.) Over two-thirds of Shneidman's much younger group picked "an old age," but specific year of death was not provided. Significant differences (based on 't' tests) were found between the Blacks and each other ethnic group, with the former expecting to live longer. (A more detailed analysis is presented in Reynolds and Kalish, 1974.) Bengtson, Cuellar, and Ragan (1976), in their study of ethnicity and aging, also found that Blacks had longer subjective life expectancy than Mexican-Americans or Anglos.

But how do they want to die? Relatively few have difficulty answering this one (under 7 percent), and all but a handful want to die a natural death. (We did find that 2 percent of the Blacks and 3 percent of the Anglos wanted to die by suicide, while about 25 percent of the Japanese and 7 percent of the Mexicans wanted to die in an accident.) And when? The median age was 80, with the 25 percentile at 70 (virtually the same as for the expectation of death) and the 75 percentile at 90. The range was from 40 to well beyond 100 again. And 66 percent of Shneidman's respondents also opted for "old age."

Although it is well known that most people now die in hospitals and convalescent centers, many more of our respondents would prefer dying at home. Among the Blacks, the ratio was 2:1, and among the Mexicans, a little lower. However the Japanese and Anglos both preferred dying at home by better than 4:1.

We also asked how the person would spend his last six months, assuming he learned that he was dying from a terminal illness. Answers were coded by the interviewers, and they ranged over a number of categories. About one-fourth would make no change in life style (B 31 percent, J 25 percent, M 12 percent, A 36 percent), and another one-fifth would focus attention on their inner life (e.g., contemplate, pray). However about one-sixth would undergo a marked change in life style, such as traveling, satisfying hedonistic demands, essentially trying to soak up as many experiences as possible (B 16 percent, J 24 percent, M 11 percent, A 17 percent). Nearly 40 percent of the Mexicans and about half that proportion of the others would devote their remaining time to those they love. The categories described above were pre-established, based upon our pilot testing. However, the question was open-ended, and examination of the specific answers given by interviewees shows great diversity. Thus, devoting time to loved ones might mean taking a trip with the wife, returning to live with parents, or baby-sitting with grandchildren. Each of our categories encompassed numerous specific kinds of behavior.

How would these people die? A little more than one-third would fight death, rather than accepting it, with virtually no differences by ethnicity. Explanations varied greatly. A Black high school graduate said, "I believe if you're a Christian, you wouldn't fight—just get yourself ready to go. Ask forgiveness for your sins and put yourself in the hands of the Lord." Another Black woman interpreted the question somewhat differently: "If by fight, you mean seeking any medical aid available or through positive thinking and not giving up, then I would fight." A Mexican-American woman made the differentiation, "If I was in the hospital and feeling very sick, I would just accept death. But if I was out in the world, I would fight it by enjoying life as long as I possibly could." Well over half the Blacks and Japanese, but somewhat under half the Mexicans and Anglos, would tell someone of their pain rather than enduring it in silence. One made the point that, "If it was the doctor, I would tell him of my pain. I think maybe I would tell my husband, but not my son" (who was still a child). A college graduate from the Japanese-American community was more fatalistic: "If it's going to hurt, it's going to hurt. The doctor knows I'm hurting already and if there was a way to prevent it, he would prevent it." An Anglo-American man was more demanding: "I would ask the doctor to give me some codeine or some other pain killer.'' Very similar proportions would refrain from encouraging their families to be with them, if it were inconvenient. A young Japanese-American woman said, ''No, I wouldn't ask them, but I would feel better if they did.'' A Mexican-American woman of about the same age explained, ''I would want my husband and my child there only—not the rest of my family. Not my parents—they would probably cry and have a lot of sympathy for me, but my husband, he'd be strong.'' And nearly 90 percent of the Mexican-Americans, and over half the others, would call for a clergyman. Something has happened to customary ethnic stereotypes in these figures. The stoical Japanese-Americans and the emotive Mexican-Americans appear to reverse expected roles in terms of expressing their feelings of pain; the aggressive, competitive Anglos were no more likely to fight death than the more accepting Mexicans or Japanese. The highly familistic Mexican-Americans do encourage their families to be with them, but not so the highly familistic Japanese-Americans. Our point is certainly obvious: situational factors and competing demands often weigh more heavily than even well-established modal group characteristics.

REFERENCES

Alexander, I.E., Colley, R. S., and Adlerstein, A.M. 1957. Is death a matter of indifference? *Journal of Psychology* 43:277–283.

Bengtson, V.L., Cuellar, J.A., and Ragan, P.K. 1976. Group contrasts in attitudes toward death: Variation by race, age, occupational status, and sex. Submitted for publication.

Chenard, M. 1972. Unpublished doctoral dissertation.

Diggory, James C., and Rothman, Doreen Z. 1961. Values destroyed by death. *Journal of Abnormal and Social Psychology* 63:205–210.

Feifel, Herman, and Jones, R. 1968. Perception of death as related to nearness to death. *Proceedings of the 76th Annual Convention of the American Psychological Association* 3:545–546.

Fulton, R. 1965. The sacred and the secular: Attitudes of the American public toward death, funerals, and funeral directors, in *Death and identity*. Ed. R. Fulton. New York: Wiley, pp. 89–105.

Hall, G. Stanley, 1897. A study of fears. *American Journal of Psychology* 8:147–149.

Hall, G. Stanley, 1915. Thanatophobia and immortality. *American Journal of Psychology* 26: 550–613.

Hinton, John M. 1963. The physical and mental distress of the dying. *Quarterly Journal of Medicine* 32:1–21.

Ivey, M.E., and Bardwick, J.M. 1968. Patterns of affective fluctuation in the menstrual cycle. *Psychosomatic Medicine* 30:336–345.

Kalish, Richard A. 1965. The aged and the dying process: The inevitable decisions. *Journal of Social Issues* 21:87–96.

Kalish, Richard A., and Reynolds, David K. 1973. Phenomenological reality and post-death contact. *Journal for the Scientific Study of Religion* 12:209–221.

Kastenbaum, Robert, and Aisenberg, Ruth B. 1972. *The psychology of death*. New York: Springer.

Kennard, E.A. 1937. Hopi reactions to death. *American Anthropologist* 29:491–494.

Middleton, W.C. 1936. Some reactions toward death among college students. *Journal of Abnormal and Social Psychology* 31:165–173.

National Council on the Aging 1975. *The myth and reality of aging in America*. Washington, D.C.: National Council on the Aging.

Phillips, D.P., and Feldman, K.A. 1973. A dip in deaths before ceremonial occasions: Some new relationships between social integration and mortality. *American Sociological Review* 38:678–696.

Reynolds, David K., and Kalish, Richard A. 1974. Anticipation of futurity as a function of ethnicity and age. *Journal of Gerontology* 29: 224–231.

Riley, J.W., Jr. 1970. What people think about death. In O.G. Brim Jr., Freeman, H.E., Levine, S., and Scotch, N.A., eds. *The dying patient.* New York: Russell Sage Foundation, pp. 30–41.

Riley, Matilda, and Foner, Anne. 1968. *Aging and society: In an inventory of research findings.* New York: Russell Sage Foundation.

Scott, C.A. 1896. Old age and death. *American Journal of Psychology* 8: 54–122.

Shaffer, Thomas L. 1970. *Death, property, and lawyers: a behavioral approach.* New York: Dunellen.

Shneidman, Edwin S. 1971. You and death. *Psychology Today* 5:43.

Vernon, Glenn M. 1970. *Sociology of death: An analysis of death-related behavior.* New York: Ronald Press.

Weisman, Avery D., and Hackett, Thomas P. 1961. Predilection to death: Death and dying as a psychiatric problem. *Psychomatic Medicine* 23:232–256.

TALCOTT PARSONS and
VICTOR LIDZ

selection from
Death in American Society

While the preceding articles reviewed the study of individual attitudes, the next essay turns to an analysis of the cultural context in which those attitudes are embedded. Using a sociological model, Parsons and Lidz demonstrate that the interpretation of death in America has concentrated on two factors: the completion of a normal life cycle and the technological control of random causes. They counter the often-heard generalization that ours is a death-denying society by asserting that American society demonstrates an attitude of acceptance, qualified by a concept of appropriate timing.

The present paper will examine the basic patterns of orientation toward death in American society, their cultural roots, and their relations to the social structure. We hope also to suggest problems for further research, as social science clearly lacks crucial knowledge about the subject, as well as to shed light upon some related aspects of American society and, e.g., attitudes toward life purposes or strivings and toward aging, problems occasioned by the increasing proportion of older people in our population and by the high incidence of suicide, and the nature of current funeral practices.

We shall begin with a foil—the widespread view that the realities of death are characteristically met with "denial" in contemporary American society,[1] an opinion that seems dubious to us. Usually cited as evidence of this opinion are practices such as embalming, the elaborate dressing of corpses, and the use of cosmetics upon them, as well as more extreme ones such as concern with coffins' impermeability to decay and the seeming apathy of many terminal patients about their diseases.

Such practices are commonly interpreted as indications that Americans are "going soft," becoming progressively less capable of facing the harsh reality of the

Source: Talcott Parsons and Victor Lidz, "Death in American Society," *Essays in Self-Destruction*. Edited by Edwin S. Shneidman. New York: Science House, Inc., 1967, 133–140. Copyright © by Jason Aronson, Inc., New York, New York. Reprinted by permission.

actual world. In such interpretations, reality and harshness are often equated, whereas the pleasant things of life are considered not very "real." Americans are said, then, to live in a world of illusion, constructing elaborate defenses against intrusions of reality. Our handling of death is considered only one striking manifestation of a general deplorable tendency.[2]

This paper will present an alternative view, namely that American society has institutionalized a broadly stable, though flexible and changing, orientation to death that is fundamentally not a "denial" but a mode of acceptance appropriate to our primary cultural patterns of activism. We cannot develop our argument until we have reviewed some of the salient characteristics of American society and have discussed some aspects of death and dying. However, it seems appropriate to register immediately a basic difficulty of the denial hypothesis: it would be very anomalous for a society that has no thoroughly institutionalized scientific values to adopt an attitude so drastically discrepant with the realism of science in an area so close to biology and medicine.

Death is a "natural" phenomenon rooted in the conditions of the biological existence of man and all the higher organisms. Moreover, modern biological science has established that death is not only inevitable among higher organisms but is also a positive factor in species' adaptations within the broader physical and organic system.

The differentiation between germ plasm and somatoplasm, which is the crux of the mortality of the higher organisms, enhances both stability and variability of genetic materials in adaptational terms. Bisexual reproduction favors controlled genetic variation by combining two independent genetic lines to produce a new, unique genetic constitution in practically every individual of the offspring generation. However, if the resulting adaptive changes are to accumulate with much efficiency, the parental generation must die off so that its genetic materials can be replaced by those of the offspring. Hence death is positively functional for biological adaptation.[3]

The death of the individual human personality seems to be similarly functional for the sociocultural system to which it belongs. Human kinship systems tend to ascribe reproduction and its correlate in the sociocultural system, the socialization process, to each other, though there is certainly some independent "play" between the two. Through its structuring of marital selection and family maintenance, a kinship system determines both what organic-social components in the society are combined for perpetuation and how the resultant offspring are submitted to the primary learning processes that introduce them to members within the continuing society. In maturing through the life cycle, a new generation comes to internalize the cultural patterns of the society as communicated by the parental generation.[4] It then becomes important that the older generation be "on the way out" so that its offspring can "take over" the controlling positions of the society, perhaps especially those of reproduction and socialization, and can be free to innovate, both socially and culturally.[5] Like genetic patterns, the cultural patterns communicated to specific offspring seem to vary with both generation and the particular "lines" in the kinship system which the parents represent. Clearly, death plays an important part in the genesis and utilization of new variations in the cultural patterns that will have adaptive significance for the society.

Thus death must be regarded as a fundamental aspect of the human condition, not only by us in our roles as social scientists but by all men as members of their various social groups. All who attain even a moderate longevity must undergo the strains of losing at least some persons to whom they have been closely attached. And, by virtue of being human and being oriented in action by long-accumulating, complex symbol systems, all will have anticipatory knowledge of, and must contemplate, their own deaths. Furthermore, it seems that mortality must always be a particularly important example and trenchant symbol of the finitude of the concrete human being. It is the barrier to omnipotence and the limit to capacities that simply cannot be overcome but must be adjusted to and accepted.

Because death inherently has such critical meaning for humans, it must be given an important position in the "constitutive symbolism" of all viable religious systems. In terms of its own fundamental patterns of orientation, each culture must attribute some "ultimate" meaning or reference to death. If a religion is to remain a workable, institutionalized complex, it can *never* simply deny the ultimate relevance of such a basic condition, although it can (and must) select among the many possibilities which are viable within the human condition, including some rather extreme ones.[6] It must provide a framework for interpreting death that is meaningful and appropriate, in relation to other elements of the culture, for defining attitudes regarding both the deaths of others and the prospect of one's own death. Closely associated with such a framework, of course, are the conventions for occasions of death, particularly the complex of funeral practices.[7]

Some massive facts indicate that modern Western society stands very far along in a major evolutionary development in the biological-demographic sphere. It is well known that "nature" is generally prodigal with the potentials of reproduction at the lower levels of evolution. Among the lower species, the ratio of ova produced to ova fertilized is exceedingly high, as is the ratio of fertilized ova to those which develop into mature organisms. The general evolutionary trend is toward reducing these ratios and increasing the species' "investment" in the probability that particular organisms will perpetuate its patterns.[8] For example, the long periods of gestation and postnatal care that characterize mammals are evidence of this trend. Man has a particularly prolonged gestation period and a relatively extreme postnatal dependency, but he also has a generally high rate of successful maturation (and reproduction). Modern societies seem to accentuate this development within the broad range of possibilities that comprises the biologic basis of the human condition.

Most striking is the recent prolongation of the individual life and concomitant reduction in the ratio of, first, conceptions and, then, live births to completions of a relatively maximum life cycle. The dramatic demographic fact is that in modern societies life expectancy at birth has approximately doubled in the last century, from in the thirties to about seventy years. However, this has occurred without a marked change in the typical maximum life span—the proportion of centenarians has increased little, if at all. The essential fact, then, is that a substantially larger proportion of a birth cohort, or cohort of young adults, lives to approximate completion of the life cycle. Premature death, relative to a normality of attaining "old age," has been enormously reduced.

This broad development comprises a gain in control over the effects of death in that we need not fear its caprices so acutely now that we have fair (statistical) assurance of living out our most active days. Nevertheless, in some other senses the problem of death has concomitantly come to be posed even more massively and trenchantly.

Modern societies contain a rapidly increasing class of persons who have attained old age. Over 9 percent of the American population is now over 65 years of age, as opposed to only 4 percent only 60 years ago.[9] A very large proportion of these people have completed their more obvious and important life tasks, as valued by the ordinary criteria of our society. In general, they have retired from their occupational jobs, and their children have matured and become independent and have families of their own. By the nature of their social positions, they are "on the way out" and are living "in the shadow of death," having entered what is—by most *institutional* criteria—a terminal period of their lives. Thus, there is a relatively large group institutionally placed so that, in some sense, it must rather directly confront the problem of inevitable death. Moreover, this situation affects a much wider group, as those associated with the aging, particularly their children, must prepare to lose them in the relatively near future.

Both for the individual as he faces death and for the social groups intimately attached to him, the problem of the *meaning* of death is coming in a new sense to be concentrated about death occurring as the completion of a normal life cycle. This central, irreducible problem is becoming disentangled from the problem of adjusting to deaths that occur earlier in the life cycle, particularly in infancy and early childhood, which was much more general in the premodern period.

This development may be regarded as differentiating two aspects of the historic problem of death: that stemming from the inevitability of death and that pertaining to deaths which are potentially subject to some kind of human control. We generally value very highly efforts to minimize deaths of the latter type and are particularly upset by such deaths when they do occur. This seems to be the underlying reason why we feel deaths in automobile accidents to be so shocking and their rates to warrant so much public concern. Similarly, lapses in control over avoidable deaths that we now take for granted are experienced as especially disturbing—e.g., the great international concern over the Zermatt typhoid epidemic. Similarly, a major rise in deaths due to smallpox or plague would be highly traumatic, very largely because it is now so completely unexpected and considered to be unnecessary.

This basic differentiation within the complex of orientations toward death has some important correlates. We have come to expect that death will occur primarily among the old and only rarely in other groups. Parents no longer frequently experience the deaths of young children, nor do they ordinarily expect that they will. Similarly, the death of young adults, once so closely associated with tuberculosis, is now relatively uncommon—Violetta and Mimi, though characters still as tragic as when *La Traviata* and *La Bohème* were composed, no longer represent a common fate. The fact that people killed in automobile accidents are often the young probably contributes greatly to our concern over such deaths.

With the prevention of premature death being so heavily and broadly emphasized, difficult problems of meaning are raised by instances in which death either is deliberately imposed or could be avoided through greater care. Significantly, the imposition of capital punishment has been declining, even in proportion to convictions for capital crimes, and is being opposed by widespread movements to abolish the death penalty altogether. Similarly, the contemporary world has newly developed general and intense convictions about the ethical unacceptability and irrationality of war.

Death also has a very broad, if complex, association with suffering and violence. On the one hand, it is an ultimate severity on the scales of punishment, violence, and suffering. On the other hand, it is just as ultimate a release from them. Our modern concerns with control clearly bear upon these scales, and the minimization of suffering in general has certainly become highly valued. The deliberate imposition of physical suffering through torture has generated very great humanitarian opposition, so much so that torture is now almost considered basically unacceptable in the main Western tradition, no matter how "good" its cause may be. Throughout our era, torture has been a major focus of the moral objection to totalitarian regimes. Increasingly, the aggressive employment of violence for overt political ends seems to be attracting opposition of a similar moral generality, except in the cases of certain extreme situations. The most massive developments in the control of suffering, however, have been those in modern medicine. These are salient, not only in the prevention and cure of disabling diseases but also in the reduction of the physical suffering that is involved in illness, including mortal illness. Anesthetics and narcotics have been the most important means for this accomplishment (note that even those who are alarmed by contemporary American attitudes toward death object very little to such "denial" of pain) and have enabled modern man almost to exclude physical suffering from the problems which death inevitably presents.

Thus, modern institutions differentiate three components of the more diffuse problem of death from the core phenomenon of "inevitable death": "premature" death that can be avoided by human measures; deliberately imposed death; and the physical suffering that dying may entail. The modern tendency has been to mobilize control measures to minimize the undesirable impact of each of these three components. In a sense, all three comprise the "uncertainty" of death, as distinguished from its inevitability, and it is this adventitious uncertainty that we strive to control. Although it is unlikely that any of the three components will ever be completely eliminated, all have already been sufficiently reduced to be distinguished clearly from the category of the inevitable "natural" death of all individuals. They need be involved in only a small and varying minority of deaths—they are no longer constitutive components of "man's fate." Moreover, when they occur, they may be seen as "irrational" relative to the "normal," natural aspects of death.

Here we may note how radically these ideas contrast with most pre-modern orientations toward death. Many primitive societies evidently regard *all* deaths as a result of the adventitious play of human or magical factors and lack a clear conception of "natural death." Deaths can then be warded off or adapted to on some combination of political and religio-magical grounds, but they cannot be the foci of distinct cultural complexes that discriminate between their "ultimately" and scientifically meaningful aspects. Most of the classical civilizations adopted a rather fatalistic attitude toward death and illness, when early in life as well as in old age.[10] They regarded the loss of a large proportion of a population cohort before maturity as quite normal. Furthermore, they would have considered any very elaborate efforts to save the dying and to mitigate suffering as interference with Divine provision. Thus, the modern development of both a pattern for valuing the prolongation of life and a highly rationalized schema for identifying the controllable components of the death complex must not be taken for granted.

The comparative evidence suggests that the concomitant emergence in modern societies of the two general developments we have noted, the prolongation of actual life expectancy and the orientation toward controlling the "adventitious" components of the death complex, can hardly be fortuitous. It suggests that we should view the modern, differentiated orientation toward death as a component of a much broader orientation system which emphasizes dedication to activity that can be expected on rational grounds to maximize human control over the *conditional* elements of the life situation. A major tradition of sociological research, stemming largely from Max Weber's comparative studies in religion, has shown that such a general orientational system, which may be conveniently called instrumental activism, characterizes modern Western civilization, particularly American society,[11] and underlies much of the modern day's rather spectacular reconstruction of the human condition.[12] A major theme in our analysis as it develops will be that American attitudes and practices regarding death can be interpreted very generally as elements of that reconstruction.

This bears directly on our rejection of the view we have set as a foil, that American attitudes tend to "deny" death. Instrumental activism is a rational orientation in that, when specified to a particular sphere of action, it can develop the type of control that it values only by accurately recognizing the facts and conditions of the relevant situation. Here, the development of science that it has fostered is evidently prototypical—surely science is not grounded primarily in fantasies that deny basic realities of the empirical world, no matter how problematic is any sense in which it simply reflects these realities. It would seem that the modern orientation toward controlling the adventitious aspects of death must involve a very similar realism, both because of its interpenetration with science (e.g., medicine) and because of its need for highly rationalized means for meeting human strains. However, it is evident that the orientation of control cannot apply to the "inevitable" aspect of death, which is its core phenomenon, in quite the same sense. Rather, the differentiation between the adventitious and inevitable aspects of death has rendered the latter still more irreducible—something that must be faced still more squarely than ever before. The sense in which such facing of death has been incorporated in the value pattern of instrumental activism is extremely complex; it can be treated only after we have considered the "ultimate" meaning that Western tradition has given to the fact of death.

NOTES

1. Herman Feifel states that "denial and avoidance of the countenance of death characterize much of the American outlook," by way of summarizing a predominating theme in the book he edited, *The Meaning of Death* (New York: McGraw-Hill, 1959), which contains contributions by many distinguished people in a variety of disciplines. Quotation is from p. xvii.

2. Perhaps the most sociological discussion of funeral practices and such a hypothetical general trend is Peter Berger and Richard Lieban, "Kulturelle Wertstruktur und Bestattungspraktiken in den Vereinigten Staaten," *Kolner Zeitschrift fur Soziologie und Sozial psychologie,* No. 2, 1960.

3. George Gaylord Simpson, *The Meaning of Evolution* (New Haven, Conn.: Yale University Press, 1949).

4. Talcott Parsons, *Social Structure and Personality* (New York: The Free Press, 1964), especially chap. 4.

5. S.N. Eisenstadt has probably made the most important contribution to the understanding of problems in this field. See his *From Generation to Generation* (New York: The Free Press, 1956).

6. Max Weber's *Sociology of Religion,* English ed. (Boston: Beacon Press, 1963) is probably still the best single statement of the broad analytical position we are taking toward religion.

7. These last paragraphs are intended to give death its due in terms of its general implications for action systems. We wish to note, however, that our account is quite distinct from that of much current existentialism, which seems to claim that, very generally, life purposes and a great many life activities gain their meaning *only* from being contrasted with and opposed to death. Analytically, this seems extreme and perhaps hinges upon a rather pejorative use of the term "meaning."

8. See Simpson, op. cit.

9. M. Gendell and H.L. Zetterberg, *A Sociological Almanac for the United States,* 2nd ed. (New York: Scribner's, 1961), p. 42.

10. Buddha, we may recall, viewed sickness, old age, and death, with their attendant suffering, as the aspects of this world that led him to recognize the need for adopting a radical other-wordly orientation.

11. The best statement on the characteristics of the pattern of instrumental activism that is yet in print is given in Talcott Parsons and Winston White, "The Link Between Character and Society," chap. 8 in *Social Structure and Personality*. It should be clear that we are referring to a general orientational pattern that can be specified, in principle, to all contexts of social action. We are not simply talking about the "scientific" orientation.

12. Talcott Parsons, *The System of Modern Society* (Englewood Cliffs, N.J.: Prentice-Hall, 1971).

PHILIPPE ARIÈS

Death
Inside Out

Philippe Ariès enters the discussion of contemporary attitudes about death from a
European vantage point. Rather than focus on distinctions among contemporary
groups, he insists on historical context to provide a perspective for understanding
modern attitudes. The following selection traces a pattern of reversal in the history
of Western attitudes toward the dying person, mourning processes, and funeral
rituals. The reversal that has taken place in these patterns, he suggests, provides a
direct link between two modern crises: that of death and that of individuality.

The attitudes commonly held about death by modern man—whether sociologists,
psychologists or doctors—are so novel and bewildering that scholars have not yet
been able to detach them from their modernity and situate them within a broader
historical perspective. This is what I shall attempt to do in the following chapter,
with respect to three themes: the dispossession of the dying person, the denial of
mourning and the new funeral rites in America.

I. HOW THE DYING PERSON IS DEPRIVED OF HIS DEATH

For thousands of years man has been the sovereign master of his death and the
circumstances attending it. Today he no longer is and these are the reasons why.

First of all, it was always taken for granted that man knew he was going to
die—whether he came by this knowledge on his own or was told by somebody else.
The story-tellers of former times assumed as a matter of course that man is aware of
his forthcoming death. La Fontaine is an example. In those days, death was rarely

Source: Philippe Ariès, "Death Inside Out," translated by Bernard Murchland, reprinted from Peter Steinfels and Robert M. Veatch, eds.,
Death Inside Out: The Hastings Center Report, ©1975, Institute of Society, Ethics and the Life Sciences. Harper and Row. Reprinted by
permission.

sudden, even in cases of accident or war. Sudden death was very much feared not only because it did not allow time to repent but more importantly because it deprived man of his death. Most people were forewarned of their death, especially since most diseases were fatal. One would have had to be a fool not to perceive the signs of death; moralists and satirists took it upon themselves to ridicule those who refused to admit the obvious. Roland was aware that death was about to carry him off; Tristan felt his life ebbing away and knew that he was going to die; Tolstoi's peasant, responding to an inquiry about his health, says: "Death is at hand." For Tolstoi as for La Fontaine, men adopted a familiar and resigned attitude before death. This does not mean that thinking about death remained the same over this long period of history. Nonetheless, some basic similarities survived in certain classes from one age to another despite the emergence of other attitudes.

When the dying person failed to perceive his lot, it fell to others to tell him. A pontifical document of the Middle Ages made this a responsibility of physicians, and for centuries they executed it faithfully. We find one at Don Quixote's bedside: "A physician was sent for, who, after feeling his pulse, took a rather gloomy view of the case, and told him that he should provide for his soul's health, as that of his body was in a dangerous condition." The *Artes Moriendi* of the fifteenth century stipulated a "spiritual" friend for this task (as opposed to a "carnal" friend) who was called the *nuntius mortis,* a title and a role that is more than a little shocking to our modern sensibility.

As we advance through history ascending the social ladder in an urban environment, we find that man adverts less and less to his impending death. He must be prepared for it by others upon whom he consequently becomes more and more dependent. Probably sometime in the eighteenth century, the physician renounced a role that had long been his. By the nineteenth century, the doctor spoke only when questioned and then with certain reservations. Friends no longer intervened as they did in the time of Gerson or even as late as Cervantes. From the seventeenth century onward, the family assumed this responsibility, which may be taken as a sign of the evolution in family sentiment. For example: The year is 1848 and we are with a family called La Ferronnays. Madame La Ferronnays falls sick. A doctor diagnoses her case as serious and shortly afterwards calls it hopeless. The woman's daughter writes: "When she finished her bath and as I was about to tell her what the doctor had said, she suddenly said to me: 'I can no longer see anything and fear I am going to die.' She then recited a short prayer. How consoling those calm words were to me in that terrible moment!" The daughter was relieved because she was spared the painful task of telling her mother that she was going to die. Such relief is a modern trait but the obligation to inform another of imminent death is very ancient.

The dying were not to be deprived of their death. Indeed, they had to preside over it. As one was born in public so too one died in public. This was true not only of kings (as is well known from Saint-Simon's celebrated account of the death of Louis XIV) but of everyone. Countless tapestries and paintings have depicted the scene for us! As soon as someone fell ill, the room filled with people—parents, children, friends, neighbors, fellow workers. All windows and doors were closed.

The candles were lit. When people in the street saw the priest carrying the viaticum, custom as well as devotion dictated that they follow him to the dying person's bed-side, even if the person were a stranger. As death approached, the sick-room became a public place. In this context we understand the force of Pascal's words: "We die alone." They have lost much of their meaning for modern man because we literally do die alone. What Pascal means was that, despite the crowd gathered about, the dying person was, in the end, alone. Progressive doctors in the late eighteenth century were firm believers in the curative powers of fresh air and complained bitterly about this public invasion of the rooms of the dying. To their minds, it would have been far healthier to open the windows, put out the candles, and send everyone home.

The public presence at the last moments was not a pious practice imposed by the Church, as we might think. The clergy, or at least the more enlightened of them, had tried long before the doctors to restrain this mob in order to better prepare the sick person for an edifying end. Beginning with the fifteenth century, the *Artes Moriendi* recommended that the dying person be left alone with God so as not to be distracted from the care of his soul. As late as the nineteenth century, very pious individuals, having submitted to all these customary practices, might request that the many onlookers leave the room so that nothing would disturb their final conversations with God. But these were cases of rare and exemplary devotion. Long-standing custom dictated that death be the occasion of a ritual ceremony in which the priest had his place, but so did numbers of other people. The primary role in this ritual was played by the dying person himself. He presided with controlled dignity; having been a participant himself in many such occasions, he knew how to conduct himself. He spoke in turn to his relatives, his friends, his servants, including "the least of them," as Saint-Simon put it in describing the death of Madame de Montespan. He bade them adieu, asked their forgiveness, and gave them his blessing. Invested with a sovereign authority by approaching death (this was especially true in the eighteenth and nineteenth centuries), he gave his orders and made his recommendations. This was the case when the dying person was a very young girl, virtually a child.

Today, nothing remains of this attitude toward death. We do not believe that the sick person has a right to know he is dying; nor do we believe in the public and solemn character accorded the moment of death. What ought to be known is ignored; what ought to be a sacred moment is conjured away.

A Reversal in Sentiment

We take it for granted that the first duty of the family and the physician is to keep the dying person uninformed about his condition. He must not (exceptional cases apart) know that his end is near; he dies ignorant of his death. This is not merely an accidental feature of our contemporary mores; on the contrary, it has taken on the force of a moral rule. Vladimir Jankélévitch made a clear statement in proof of this at a recent medical conference on the theme: Should We Lie to the

Sick?[1] "In my mind," he declared, "the liar is the one who tells the truth. I am against the truth, passionately against the truth. For me there is one law that takes precedence over all others and that is the law of love and charity." Since traditional morality made it mandatory to inform the dying of their state, Jankélévitch's law presumably has been universally violated until recent times. Such an attitude is the measure of an extraordinary reversal in sentiment and thought. What has happened? How has this change come about? We might suppose that modern societies are so fixed upon the goals of affluence and material well-being, that there is no place in them for suffering, sorrow, or death. But this would be to mistake the effect for the cause.

This change in attitude toward the dying is linked to the changing role of the family in modern society and its quasi-monopoly over our emotional lives. We must seek the cause of modern attitudes toward death in the relationship between the sick person and his family. The latter does not consider it dignified or a mark of self-esteem to speak frankly about the imminence of death. How often have we heard it said of a loved one: "I at least have the satisfaction of knowing that he died without being aware of it." The "without being aware of it" has replaced the "being aware of one's approaching death" of other times, when every effort was made to make the dying aware of what was happening.

In fact, it may be that the dying frequently know perfectly well what is happening, but remain silent to spare the feelings of those close to them. (Of course, the dead do not share these secrets.) In any case, the modern family has abdicated the role played by the *nuntius mortis*, who from the Middle Ages until the dawn of modern times was not a member of the immediate family. As a result, the dying have also abdicated their role. Why? Because they fear death? Hardly. Fear of death has always existed, and was always countered, often with humor. Despite a natural fear of death, society obligated the dying to play out the final scene of farewell and departure. The fear of death, it is said, is ancestral, but so are the ways of overcoming it. No, the fear of death does not account for the modern practice of denying one's own death. Again, we must turn to the history of the family for an explanation.

In the late Middle Ages (the age of Roland which lives on in the peasants of Tolstoi) and the Renaissance, a man insisted upon participating in his own death because he saw in it an exceptional moment—a moment which gave his individuality its definitive form. He was only the master of his life to the extent that he was the master of his death. His death belonged to him, and to him alone. From the seventeenth century onward, one began to abdicate sole sovereignty over life, as well as over death. These matters came to be shared with the family which had previously been excluded from the serious decisions; all decisions had been made by the dying person, alone and with full knowledge of his impending death.

Last wills and testaments provide evidence of this. From the fourteenth to the beginning of the eighteenth century, they were a spontaneous and individual means of expression, as well as a sign of distrust—or, at least, the absence of trust—

toward the family. Today the last will and testament has lost its character of moral necessity; nor, is it any longer a means of warm and personal expression. Since the eighteenth century, family affections have triumphed over the testator's traditional distrust of his heirs. This distrust has been replaced by a trust so absolute that written wills are no longer necessary. Oral wills have recently become binding for the survivors and are now scrupulously respected. For their part, the dying confidently rely on the family's word. This trusting attitude, which emerged in the seventeenth and eighteenth centuries, and developed in the nineteenth, has become, in the twentieth, a prime source of alienation. No sooner does a member of the family fall mortally ill than the rest conspire to conceal his condition from him, depriving him of information, as well as his freedom. The dying person becomes, in effect, a minor like a child or mental defective. His relatives take complete charge of him and shield him from the world. They supposedly know better than he what he must do, and how much he should know. He is deprived of his rights, particularly the formerly sacred right of knowing about his death, of preparing for it, and organizing it. Now he allows this to be done for him because he is convinced that it is for his own good. He gives himself over to the affection of his family. And if, despite all, he divines his condition, he pretends not to know. In former times, death was a tragedy—often lightened by a comical element—in which one played the role of the dying person. Today, death is a comedy—although not without its tragic elements—in which one plays the role of the "one who does not know" he is going to die.

Of itself, the pressure of family sentiment probably would not have changed the meaning of death so drastically, had it not been for the progress of medical science. It is not so much that medicine has conquered disease, however real its achievements in this realm, but that it has succeeded in substituting sickness for death in the consciousness of the afflicted man. This substitution began to take place in the second half of the nineteenth century. When a sick peasant in Tolstoi's *Three Deaths* (1859) is asked how he is, he answers, "death is at hand." On the contrary, in *The Death of Ivan Ilych* (1886), after overhearing a conversation that leaves no doubt in Ivan's mind about his condition, he obstinately believes that his floating kidney and infected appendix will be cured by drugs or surgery. His illness becomes an occasion for self-delusion. His wife supports this illusion, blaming his illness on his refusal to obey the doctor's orders to take his medicine regularly.

Of course, it is true, with advances in medical science, serious illness terminates less frequently in death. And chances of recovery are greatly improved. Even when recovery is partial, one can still count on many years of life. Thus, in our society (where we so often act as though medicine had all the answers, or look upon death as something that happens to others, but never to oneself) incurable disease, and especially cancer, has taken on, in the popular imagination, all the frightening and hideous traits depicted in ancient representations of death. Even more than the skeletons or macabre mummies of the fourteenth and fifteenth centuries, cancer is today the very image of death. Disease must be incurable, and regarded as such, before we can admit the reality of death and give it its true name. But the anguish caused by this kind of honesty is so great that it constrains society to hastily multiply those many inducements to silence that reduce a moment of high drama to the banality of a Sunday afternoon picnic.

As a consequence we die in virtual secrecy, far more alone than Pascal could have imagined. This secretiveness comes from a refusal to openly admit the death of those we love and a proclivity to soften its reality by calling it a disease that may be cured. There is another aspect to this problem that American sociologists have noted. In what one might be tempted to regard as nothing more than illusory conduct, they have shown the de facto presence of a new style of death, in which discretion is the modern form of dignity. With less poetry, this is the kind of death approved of by Jankélévitch in which the hard reality is coated over with soothing words of deception.

A New Model of Death

In their *Awareness of Dying* Glaser and Strauss report on their study of six hospitals in the San Francisco Bay area.[2] They recorded the reactions to death of an interrelated group that included the patient, his family, and the medical personnel (doctors and nurses). What happens when it becomes clear that the patient is near death? Should the family be told? The patient? And when? How long should a life be artificially maintained? At what moment should the patient be allowed to die? How should doctors and nurses act in the presence of a patient who does not know, or at least appears not to know, that he is dying? Or one that does know? Every modern family is certainly confronted by such questions, but in a hospital context an important new factor is present: the power of modern medicine. Today, few people die at home. The hospital has become the place where modern man dies, and this fact lends added importance to the Glaser and Strauss study. But the interest of their book goes beyond its empirical analysis. The authors have in fact uncovered an ideal of death that has replaced its traditional public character, as manifested for example in the theatrical pomp of the Romantic era. We now have a new "style of dying" or rather "an acceptable style of living while dying," "an acceptable style of facing death." The emphasis is on *acceptable*. What is important is that one die in a manner that can be accepted and tolerated by the survivors.

Doctors and nurses (although the latter less so) wait as long as possible before telling the family, and scarcely ever tell the patient himself, because they fear becoming involved in a chain of emotional reactions that would make them lose self-control. To talk about death, and thus admit it as a normal dimension of social intercourse, is no longer socially acceptable; on the contrary, it is now something exceptional, excessive, and always dramatic. Death was once a familiar figure and the moralists had to make it hideous in order to inspire fear. Today, mere mention of the word provokes an emotional tension that jars the routine of daily life. An "acceptable style of dying" is, therefore, a style which avoids "status forcing scenes," scenes which tear one from one's social role and offend our sensibility. Such scenes are the crises of despair the sick go through, their tears, their cries and, in general, any exceptional emotive or noisy outburst that would interfere with hospital routine and trouble others. This is an example of what Glaser and Strauss call, "embarrassingly graceless dying," the very opposite of an "acceptable style of dying." Such a death would embarrass the survivors. This is what must be avoided at all costs and this is the reason why the patient is kept uninformed. What basically matters is not whether the patient knows or does not know; rather, if he does know he must have the consideration and courage to be discreet. He must conduct himself in such a way that the hospital staff is not reminded that he knows and can communicate with him as though death were not in their midst. For communication is necessary. It is not enough for the dying to be discreet; they must also be open and receptive to messages. Their indifference in this matter should be as embarrassing to the medical personnel as an excessive display of emotion. Thus, there are two ways of dying badly: one can be either too emotional or too indifferent.

The authors cite the case of an old woman who was at first well behaved, in accord with acceptable conventions; she cooperated with the doctors and nurses and bore her illness courageously. One day she decided that she had struggled enough, that the time had come to give up. Whereupon she closed her eyes, never to open them again, signifying in this way that she had withdrawn from the world and wished to await her end alone. In former times, this withdrawal would have been respected and accepted as normal. But in a California hospital it disconcerted the medical staff so much that they flew in one of her sons from another city to persuade her to open her eyes on the grounds that she was "hurting everybody." Sometimes patients turn to the wall and refuse to move. We recognize in such acts one of the oldest gestures of man in the face of death. In this way did the Jews of the Old Testament die. So did Tristan who turned toward the wall and exclaimed that he could no longer keep a hold on life. But in such ancestral reactions the California doctors and nurses saw only an antisocial refusal to communicate, a culpable renunciation of the will to live.

Let us note that patients are not blamed in such cases merely because they have demoralized the medical staff, or because of failure to perform their duty but more seriously because they are considered to have lessened the capacity to resist the sickness itself—an eventuality that becomes as fearsome as a "status forcing scene." That is why American and English doctors are today less inclined to keep patients in the dark about their condition. But we must not exaggerate the significance of such signs. They may indicate no more than the pragmatic hope that the patient will respond better to treatment if he knows his condition and will, in the end, die as discreetly and with as much dignity as if he knew nothing. In *Reflections on America,* Jacques Maritain describes the good American's death: The medical staff induces in him a kind of dream-like state in which he thinks that to die amidst these smiling faces and these uniforms, white and immaculate like the wings of angels, is a genuine pleasure, or at least a moment of no consequence—"Relax, take it easy, it's nothing."[3] Take away the professional smile and add a little music, and you have the contemporary philosopher's ideal of the dignified, humanistic death: "To disappear *pianissimo* and, so to speak, on tip toe" (Jankélévitch).

II. THE DENIAL OF MOURNING

We now see how modern society deprives man of his death. Whatever dignity remains must be purchased at the price of not troubling the living. Reciprocally, modern society forbids the living from showing too much emotion over the death of a loved one; they are permitted neither to weep for the departed nor to appear to mourn their passing.

In times past mourning was the ultimate expression of sorrow. It was both legitimate and necessary. Grief over the death of a close one was considered the strongest and most spontaneous expression of emotion. During the Middle Ages, the most hardened warriors and the most renowned kings broke into tears over the bodies of friends and relatives. They wept, as we would say today, like hysterical women. King Arthur is a good example. He often fainted, struck his breast, and tore at his skin until the blood flowed. On the battlefield, he fell to the ground in a swoon before his nephew's body and then set out in tears to find the bodies of his friends. Upon discovering one of them, he clasped his hands and cried out that he had lived long enough. He removed the helmet from the dead man's body and, after gazing upon him for a long time, kissed his eyes and mouth. We find many instances, in those times, of the most extraordinary and uninhibited emotional outbursts. But, with the exception of those few whose sorrow was so great that they had to retire to a monastery, the survivors soon resumed normal life.

From the thirteenth century on, we notice that expressions of mourning begin to lose their spontaneity and become more and more ritualized. The grand gesticulations of the early Middle Ages are now simulated by professional mourners (who can be found in some parts of Europe even today). The Spanish hero, El Cid, requested in his will that there be no flowers or mourners at his funeral, as had been the custom. The iconography of fourteenth- and fifteenth-century tombs depict mourners around the body of the deceased, clothed in black robes with their heads buried in penitent-like cowls. We learn from sixteenth- and seventeenth-century documents that funeral processions were composed largely of substitute mourners: mendicant monks, the poor, and orphans, all clothed for the occasion in black robes furnished by the deceased. After the ceremony, each received a portion of bread and a little money.

Apparently close relatives did not attend the funeral services. Friends were offered a banquet—banquets so excessively festive that the Church tried to suppress the practice. Last wills refer to such festivities less and less, or mention them only in censorious language. We notice that the dying frequently requested and sometimes insisted upon the presence of a brother or a son in the funeral procession. Often this was a child, who was offered a special legacy for his much desired presence. Would this have been the case had the family attended funerals as a matter of course? Under the old regime we know that women did not attend funerals. It is probable that from the end of the Middle Ages with the increasing ritualization of mourning rites, society imposed a period of seclusion upon the immediate members of the family, a seclusion which would have excluded them from the obsequies. They were represented by priests and professional mourners, religious, members of pious organizations, or simply those who were attracted by the alms distributed on such occasions.

The period of seclusion had two purposes. First of all, it gave the bereaved some privacy in which to mourn their loved ones. Protected from the gaze of the world, they waited for their sorrow to pass as a sick person waits for his illness to abate. One, Henri de Campion, makes mention of this in his *Mémoires*. In June, 1659, his wife died in childbirth and the child, a daughter, died shortly afterwards. He wrote:

> I was heartbroken and fell into a pitiful state. My brother and my sister took me to Conches where I remained seventeen days and then returned to Baxferei to put my affairs in order. Not being able to inhabit my house because it reminded me too much of my beloved wife, I bought a property in Conches and lived there until June, 1660 (which is to say until the first anniversary of my wife's death) at which time I perceived that my sorrow had followed me. So I returned to my former home in Baxferei with my children, where I am presently living in great sadness.

Second, the period of seclusion prevented the survivors from forgetting the deceased too soon. It was in fact a time of penance during which they were not permitted the activities and pleasures of normal life. This precaution was not unhelpful in preventing a hasty replacement of the dead person. Nicolas Versoris, a Parisian merchant, lost his wife to the plague on September 3, 1522, one hour after midnight. On December 30 of that same year, he was engaged to a doctor's widow, whom he married as soon as he could, which is to say on January 13, 1523, "the first festive day after Christmas."

This custom continued through the nineteenth century. When someone died the immediate family, servants, and often the domestic animals as well, were separated from the rest of society by drawn curtains and black mourning crepe. By this time, however, the period of seclusion was more voluntary than obligatory: it no longer prohibited close relatives from participating in the funeral service, pilgrimages to the graveside, or the elaborate memorial cults that characterized the Romantic Age. Nor were women any longer excluded from the obsequies. In this regard, the bourgeoisie were the first to break with tradition, followed some time later by the nobility, among whom it had been considered good taste for a widow not to attend her husband's funeral. At first the nobility ceded to the new practices discreetly, usually hidden in some dark corner of the church with ecclesiastical approval. Little by little the traditional custom of seclusion gave way to the new practice of honoring the dead and venerating their tombs. Women's presence at funerals, however, did nothing to radically change the private character of mourning: entirely clothed in black, the *mater dolorosa*, she is hidden from the world's sight except as symbol of sorrow and desolation. Nonetheless, mourning was now more moral than physical in nature. It was less a protection of the dead from oblivion that an affirmation that the living must remember them; that they could not go on living as before. The dead no longer needed society to protect them from the indifference of their close relatives; nor did the dying any longer need written testaments to make their last will known to their heirs.

The new family sentiment of the late eighteenth and early nineteenth centuries thus combined with the ancient tradition of seclusion to transform the mourning period from an imposed quarantine into a right to express, with all due propriety, deeply felt sorrow. This marked a return to the spontaneity of the high Middle Ages while conserving the formal rituals that had been introduced around the twelfth century. If we were to trace the historical curve of mourning it would look like this: until the thirteenth century, a time of uninhibited and even violent spontaneity, followed through the seventeenth century by a long period of ritualization, which gave way in the nineteenth to an age when sorrow was given full and dramatic expression. It is likely that the paroxysm of mourning in the nineteenth century stands in some direct relationship to its attenuation in the twentieth century in somewhat the same way as the "dirty death" of Remarque, Sartre, and Genet in the post-war period emerged as the other side of the "noble death" celebrated by Romanticism. Thus, the significance of Sartre's gesture, more laughable than scandalous, of urinating on Chateaubriand's tomb. It took a Chateaubriand to produce such a Sartre. It is a relationship of the sort that links contemporary eroticism to Victorian sexual taboos.

Mourning Becomes Forbidden

Some form of mourning, whether spontaneous or obligatory, has always been mandatory in human society. Only in the twentieth century has it been forbidden. The situation was reversed in a single generation: what was always commanded by individual conscience, or the general will, is now rejected. And what was, in former times, rejected is now recommended. It is no longer fitting to manifest one's sorrow or even give evidence of experiencing any.

Credit for uncovering this unwritten law of our civilization goes to the British sociologist, Geoffrey Gorer. He was the first to understand that certain facts, neglected or poorly understood by the humanistic moralists, did, indeed, constitute a characteristic attitude toward death in industrial societies. In an autobiographical introduction to his *Death, Grief and Mourning,* Gorer recounts some personal experiences which led him to the discovery that death is the principal taboo of our time.[4] The sociological inquiry he undertook in 1963 on attitudes toward death and mourning in England merely confirmed, detailed, and enriched ideas he had already published in his "The Pornography of Death," a remarkable article based upon his personal experiences and reflection.[5]

Gorer was born in 1910. He recalls that the whole family mourned the death of Edward VII. He learned, as do French children, to take off his hat when a funeral procession passed in the street and to treat those in mourning with special respect—practices which seem strange to the British today. In 1915, his father was lost in the sinking of the *Lusitania,* and Gorer was, in his turn, given special attention. "I was

treated with great kindness, like an invalid; no demands were made on me, I was indulged, conversation was hushed in my presence.'' One day during a walk, he attempted to convey his desolation by telling his Nanny that he would never be able "to enjoy flowers again," whereupon she reprimanded him and told him not to be morbid.

Because of the war his mother was allowed to take a job where she found diversion from her sorrow. She would not have had such a recourse at any earlier date; but at a later date she would not have had the support of the mourning ritual. Thus Gorer experienced in his childhood the traditional manifestations of mourning and they must have made a strong impression on him for they remained vivid in his memory many years later. During his youth in the postwar period, he had no further experience of death. Once he saw a cadaver in a Russian hospital he visited in 1931; unaccustomed to the sight of death, this chance viewing seems to have captured his imagination. Gorer's case was not unusual. Unfamiliarity with death is common today—the long, unnoticed consequence of greater longevity. J. Fourcassié has shown how it is possible for today's children to grow to adulthood without ever seeing anyone die. Gorer was, however, surprised when his inquiry revealed that more people had witnessed death than he would have suspected. But he also observed that they quite spontaneously adopted the same behavior patterns as those who had never seen a death, and forgot it with all possible haste.

Gorer was later surprised when his brother, a well-known physician, fell into a state of depression after his wife's death. Intellectuals in England had already begun to abandon the traditional funeral rites and external manifestations of sorrow as so many primitive and superstitious practices. But Gorer did not at the time see any connection between his brother's pathological despair and the absence of mourning rituals. The situation was different in 1948 when he lost a close friend who left a wife and three children. Gorer wrote:

> When I went to see her some two months after John's death, she told me, with tears of gratitude, that I was the first man to stay in the house since she had become a widow. She was being given some good professional help from lawyers and the like who were also friends; but socially she had been almost completely abandoned to loneliness, although the town was full of acquaintances who considered themselves friends.

Gorer then strongly suspected that the changes that had taken place in mourning customs were neither anecdotal or insignificant. He was discovering the importance and serious consequences of these changes, and a few years later, in 1955, he published his famous article.

Decisive proof came in 1961 when his brother, who had remarried, was diagnosed as suffering from incurable cancer. His brother's doctor, a friend since they were in medical school together, "asked me to decide whether his wife, Elizabeth, should be informed; he had already decided to hide the truth from Peter; and he and his colleagues engaged in the most elaborate and successful medical mystification to hide from Peter's expert knowledge the facts of their diagnosis." He consulted an old and respected friend about his dilemma and was advised that Elizabeth should be told. "One of the arguments he advanced was that, if she were ignorant, she might show impatience or lack of understanding with his probably increasing weakness, for which she would reproach herself later; she could use the final months of their marriage better if she knew them for what they were." The prognosis was for a lingering illness but much to everyone's surprise Peter died suddenly in his sleep. Everyone concerned congratulated themselves that he had died without knowing it, an eventuality widely regarded as a desirable one in our culture. In this family of intellectuals, there would be no funeral vigil and no exposure of the body. Since his death took place at home, the body would have to be prepared. Gorer evokes what took place in colorful language:

> It was arranged for a pair of ex-nurses to come to lay out the body. They imparted a somewhat Dickensian tone; they were fat and jolly and asked in a respectful but cheerful tone, "Where is the patient?" Some half hour later their work was done, and they came out saying, "The patient looks lovely now. Come and have a look!" I did not wish to, at which they expressed surprise. I gave them a pound for their pains; the leader, pure Sarah Gamp, said, "That for us duck? Cheers!" and went through the motions of raising a bottle and emptying it into her mouth.

No mention was made through all of this of either death or the corpse. Peter was still regarded as a "patient" despite the biological transformation that had taken place. Preparing the body for burial is an ancient rite. But its meaning has changed. It formerly had as its object to make the body reflect the ideal image of death prevalent in society; the intention was to create a sense of dependency, to present the body in a helpless state, with crossed hands, awaiting the life to come. The Romantic Age discovered the original beauty that death imparts to the human face and these last ablutions were designed to rescue this beauty from the pain that had generated it. In both cases, the intention was to create an image of death: to present a beautiful corpse but a corpse nonetheless. Today we no longer have a corpse but something almost alive. "The patient looks lovely now." Our fairy's touch has given it the appearance of life. All signs of pain have been erased, not in order to capture the hieratic beauty of the dead or the majesty of those in repose, but to present a cadaver that retains the charms of something living, something "lovely" and not at all repulsive. The preparation of the body is today intended to mask the reality of death and give the pleasing illusion of life. We must remember that in Gorer's England this practice was just emerging, which is why the family could not share the old nurses' enthusiasm for their handiwork. In the United States, on the other hand, embalming is a fine art and corpses are exhibited in funeral homes with great pride.

The Meaning of Cremation

Gorer's family was deluded by neither the beliefs of another age nor the flashy talents of American morticians. Peter's body was to be cremated, and cremation in England (and no doubt in Northern Europe generally) has a special meaning which Gorer's study clearly brought out. Cremation is no longer chosen, as was long the case, in defiance of the Church and traditional Christian customs. Nor is it chosen solely for reasons of convenience or economy, reasons which the Church would be disposed to respect in memory of a time when ashes, like those of Antigone's brother, were as venerable as a body that was buried. The significance of cremation in modern England cuts deeper; it reflects the rational spirit of modern times and is nothing less than a denial of life after death, although this was not immediately apparent from the results of Gorer's inquiry. Of sixty-four persons interviewed, forty favored cremation over burial and they offered two basic reasons for this preference. It was first of all considered the most efficient means of disposing of the body. Thus one of the respondents in the study had her mother cremated because it was "healthier" but stated, "I think for my husband, who was buried, cremation would have been too final."

The second reason is connected to the first: cremation makes cemetery rituals and periodic visitation to the graveside unnecessary. But it should be noted that such practices are not necessarily eliminated by cremation. On the contrary the administrators of crematoriums do everything in their power to enable families to venerate their dead just as they do in the traditional cemeteries. In the memorial rooms of crematoriums one can have a plaque installed which performs a function analogous to that of the tombstone. But of the forty persons interviewed by Gorer, only one had opted for such a plaque and only fourteen wrote their names in the memorial book which is opened each day to commemorate the day of the death. This may be seen as a kind of intermediary solution between complete oblivion and the permanency of the engraved plaque. If families choose not to adopt commemorative practices available to them it is because they see in cremation a sure means of avoiding any form of cultic homage to the dead.

It would be a serious mistake to see in this refusal to commemorate the dead a sign of indifference or insensitivity. The results of Gorer's study and his autobiographical testimony is evidence to the contrary that the survivors are and remain deeply affected by a death in the family. For further proof of this let us turn to Gorer's account of his brother's cremation. Elizabeth, the widow,

> decided not to come to the cremation herself—she could not bear the thought that she might lose control and other people observe her grief; and she wished to spare the children the distressing experience. As a consequence, their father's death was quite unmarked for them by ritual of any kind, and was nearly even treated as a secret, for it was several months before Elizabeth could bear to mention him or have him mentioned in her presence.

Notice that her absence was not due to any of the traditional reasons or to indifference but to a fear of "losing control." This has become a new form of modesty, a convention which requires us to hide what we were formerly obliged to manifest, even if it had to be simulated: one's sorrow.

Notice, too, that children are also affected by this modern mandate. Even in France, where traditional practices are more in evidence, middle-class children rarely attend the funerals of their grandparents. Old people who are several times grandparents are buried by adults who are more rushed and embarrassed than grieved, with no grandchildren present. I was especially struck by this when in the course of my research I came across a number of documents dating from the seventeenth century in which the testator insisted that at least one of his grandchildren be in his funeral procession, although he may have been indifferent to the presence of other relatives. At that time, we might recall, mourners were often recruited among orphans. In numerous representations of the dying, the painter or engraver always included a child among those gathered about the deathbed.

So Elizabeth and her children stayed in their country home on the day of her husband's cremation. Geoffrey joined them that evening, overcome with grief and fatigue. His sister-in-law welcomed him in her usual self-assured manner. She told him that she had passed a pleasant day with the children. "They had taken a picnic to the fields where the grass was being cut for silage." Elizabeth, who was born in New England, quite naturally adopted the conduct she had been taught in America and which the English expected of her: she acted as if nothing had happened and so made it easier for others to do the same and thus permit social life to continue without even momentary interruption by death. Had she risked a public demonstration of her sorrow, society would have censored her like a fallen woman. She was, moreover, avoided by her and Peter's friends. They treated her, she said, "like a leper." Only if she acted as though nothing of consequence had happened was she again socially acceptable. Gorer observes that "at the period when she most needed help and comfort from society she was left alone." It was in the months following Peter's death that he decided to undertake a study of the modern refusal to mourn and its traumatizing effects.

From the Cabbage Patch to the Flower Garden

Gorer argues that this state of affairs began with the decline of social support for funeral rituals and the special status of the mourning period. He perhaps accords too much importance to the two World Wars as catalysts in this evolution. New conventions made their appearance gradually, almost imperceptibly in such a way that their originality went unnoticed. Even today they are not formalized in the manner of traditional customs. Yet they are just as powerful an influence on behavior. Death has become a taboo, an unmentionable subject (as Jankélévitch says over and over again in his book on death), something excluded from polite conversation. Gorer mounts impressive evidence to show that in the twentieth century death has taken the place of sex as the principal taboo. He writes that in our time,

> there has been an unremarked shift in prudery; whereas copulation has become more and more "mentionable" . . . death has become more and more "unmentionable" as a natural process. . . . The natural processes of corruption and decay have become disgusting, as disgusting as the natural processes of birth and copulation were a century ago; preoccupation about such processes is (or was) morbid and unhealthy, to be

discouraged in all and punished in the young. Our great-grandparents were told that babies were found under gooseberry bushes or cabbages; our children are likely to be told that those who have passed on (fie! on the gross Anglo-Saxon monosyllable) are changed into flowers, or lie at rest in lovely gardens. The ugly facts are relentlessly hidden; the art of the embalmers is an art of complete denial.

Children used to be told that a stork brought them but they could be present at deathbeds and attend funerals! Sometime after the middle of the nineteenth century, their presence caused a kind of malaise and there was a tendency to at least limit their participation when in fact it was not prohibited altogether. Children were present at the deaths of Emma Bovary and Ivan Ilych but they were permitted only a brief visit and then escorted from the room on the pretext that the agonies of the dying would be too much for them to bear. Although their presence at the deathbed was gradually prohibited, they were allowed their traditional place at the obsequies, clothed from head to foot in black.

Today children are initiated at an early age into the physiology of love and birth, but when they express curiosity about why they no longer see their grandparents they are told (at least in France) that they have gone on a long trip or (in England) that they are resting among the flowers. It is no longer a case of babies being found under the cabbages but of grandparents who disappear among the flowers! Relatives of the deceased are thus forced to feign indifference. Society demands of them a form of self-control similar to that demanded of the dying themselves. For the one as for the other, what is important is to show no sign of emotion. Society as a whole behaves like a hospital staff. Just as the dying must control their feelings and cooperate with the doctors and nurses, so must the bereaved hide their sorrow, reject the traditional period of seclusion (because this would betray their feelings), and carry on their normal activities without so much as missing a step. Otherwise, they would be ostracized by society, a form of seclusion that would have consequences quite different from the traditional mourning period. The latter was accepted by all as a necessary transition period and carried with it forms of behavior that were equally ritualistic such as obligatory visits of condolence, letters of sympathy, and the succors of religion. Today the bereaved are treated like sexual deviants, those afflicted with contagious diseases, or other asocial types. Whoever wishes to spare himself this stigma must hide his true feelings in public and reveal them only to his closest friends. As Gorer puts it, one weeps in private just as we undress and go to sleep in private, "as if it were an analogue of masturbation."

Society today refuses to recognize that the bereaved are sick people who need help. It refuses to associate mourning with illness. The traditional custom was in this respect more comprehensive, perhaps more "modern," more sensitive to the pathological effects of repressed moral suffering. Gorer considers it a mark of cruelty to deprive anyone of the beneficence guaranteed by the ancient custom. In their mourning, Gorer notes, those stricken by the death of a loved one need society's help more than at any other time, but it is precisely then that society withdraws its assistance and refuses to help. The price of this failure is very great in misery, loneliness, despair, and morbidity. This prohibition of a decent period of mourning forces the bereaved to bury himself in work; or to push himself to the very limits of sanity by pretending that the deceased is still living, that he never went away; or, what is worse, to imagine that he himself is the dead person, imitating his gestures, his voice, his idiosyncrasies, and sometimes simulating the symptoms of the sickness that carried him off. This is clearly neurotic behavior. We see in such behavior instances of those strange manifestations of exaggerated grief which seem new and modern to Gorer but are nonetheless familiar to the historian of customs. They once found an outlet in rituals which were acknowledged, recommended, and, indeed, even simulated during the prescribed period of mourning in traditional societies. But it must be admitted that only the appearances are the same. In former times such rituals had the purpose of liberating. Even when, as often happened in the Romantic Age, they exceeded the limits of custom and became pathological, they were not repressed as something monstrous but were patiently tolerated. This tolerance appears in a striking manner in a novel by Mark Twain in which a woman refuses to accept the death of her husband and each year lives out his impossible return. Her friends conspire to support this illusion. Today we can't imagine anyone participating in such a dark comedy. Twain's characters acted out of kindness and generosity but their action would be viewed by today's society as something embarrassing and shamefully morbid, indeed, a sign of mental illness. We thus ask ourselves, with Gorer, whether or not a large part of contemporary social pathology does not originate in our refusal to confront the reality of death—in society's denial of mourning and the right to weep for the dead.

III. NEW FUNERAL RITES IN THE UNITED STATES

Based on the foregoing analysis, we might be tempted to conclude that our suppression of the reality of death is part of the very structure of contemporary civilization. The elimination of death from conversation and from the communications media goes hand-in-hand with the priority of material well-being as the principal trait of industrial societies. This is especially the case in Northern Europe and America, the main geographical areas of modernity, although there are exceptions where older thought-patterns still prevail. I am thinking of some sectors of Catholic France and Italy, of Presbyterian Scotland, and of the lower classes even in countries that are industrially advanced. Modernity depends on social conditions as much as geography and even in the most progressive countries is limited to the educated classes, whether believers or sceptics. Where modernity has not penetrated we find that eighteenth- and nineteenth-century Romantic attitudes toward death still prevail, such as the cult of the dead and veneration in cemeteries. We should not be misled by the survival of such attitudes, however; while they characterize large numbers of people, they are seriously threatened today. They are doomed to inevitable decline, along with the earlier, less developed mentalities with which they are linked. They are also jeopardized by a model of future society which would continue the process of emptying death of all existential meaning, a model that already dominates middle-class families, whether liberal or conservative. We need not be entirely pessimistic about this evolution because it is probable that the denial of death is so bound up with industrial civilization that the one will disappear with the other. Nor is the denial of death universally the case, as we pointed out, because it is not found in many sectors of society. I am not thinking now of backward parts of Old Europe but of that stronghold of modernity, the United States. America has been the first among modern societies to attenuate the tragic sense of death. There we can observe firsthand the new attitudes toward death. Some of these were satirized in *The Loved One,* Waugh's novel, written in 1948.[6] In 1951, Roger Caillois saw in them an example of hedonistic sleight of hand:

> Death can be faced without fear, not because of some moral ability to transcend the fear it provokes, but because it is inevitable and because in fact there is no reason to dread it. *What we must do is simply not think or talk about it.*[7]

Everything we have said about death in the preceding pages—the alienation of the dying person, the denial of mourning, etc.—holds true for America with the one exception of burial practices. The Americans have not simplified funeral rites as much as the English. To understand this singularity we must continue our earlier account of how modern man dies, with the emphasis now on the time between death and burial. The time before death and after burial, together with the peculiar mourning rites modern man affects, is no different in American than in any other modern society. The difference comes in the intermediary period. We recall how the two nurses charged with preparing the body of Gorer's brother admired their own work. But in England this kind of enthusiasm is not shared by society at large. What matters to the English is to get rid of the body as decently and quickly as possible. That is why they favor cremation.

In America, on the other hand, the art of laying out the body forms part of a series of new rites that are both complicated and sumptuous. These include: the embalming of the body, its exhibition in a funeral parlor, visitation by friends and relatives, flowers and music, solemn obsequies, and finally, interment in a cemetery that looks like a park. The latter is embellished with monuments and is intended for the moral edification of visitors who are more like tourists than pilgrims. There is no point in describing these rites further. They are well known to a wide public as a result of Waugh's book, which has been made into a film, and Jessica Mitford's *The American Way of Death.*[8] Such books are misleading, however, insofar as they suggest that these rituals are no more than a form of commercial exploitation or a perversion of the cult of happiness held dear by Americans. More deeply, they testify to a refusal to have death emptied of all meaning, a refusal to let death pass without solemnizing the occasion ritualistically. This is one reason why cremation is less widespread in the United States.

American society is very attached to these rituals, although they seem somewhat ridiculous to Europeans and American intellectuals (whose attitudes are reflected in Mitford's book). So much so that for a time death is something familiar, something one can talk about. Ads of this sort are common in America: "The dignity and integrity of So-and-So Funeral Home costs no more. Easy access. Private parking for over one hundred cars.'' Of course, there is no doubt that death is a consumer product. But what is noteworthy is that it has become so, together with all the publicity attendant upon its commercial status, despite the banishment of death elsewhere in society. American attitudes toward the immediately deceased constitute an exception to modern attitudes toward death in general. In this case, they break the normal pattern of modernity and grant the deceased the social space traditional societies had always reserved for them, space that has been practically eliminated in industrial societies. In their way, Americans are carrying on the tradition of bidding a solemn farewell to the dead, and this in spite of the iron-clad rule of expediency that governs conduct in technological and consumer societies. In France many of the hospitals date from the seventeenth century (when the sick were subjected to humiliating and coarse treatment at the hands of vagabonds and delinquents) and the bodies of the dead are still kept in cold rooms like so much meat. The French are, consequently, in a good position to appreciate the need for a time of recollection and solemnity that strikes a balance between the anonymity of a collective morgue and the finality of burial.

In another age such a time could have been observed in the home. But modern attitudes are set against having the corpse too close to the living. In Europe the intelligentsia rarely keep the body in the house, even if the death occurs there. This is partly for hygienic reasons, but more because of a nervous fear of losing control. The American solution is to deposit the body in a neutral place, halfway between the anonymity of the hospital and the privacy of the home. This place is called a funeral home, a special building that is in charge of a kind of innkeeper who specializes in welcoming the dead. The time spent here is a compromise between the decent but hasty and deritualized services of Northern Europe and the more archaic ceremonies of traditional mourning. The new funeral rites created by the Americans are also a compromise between their desire to observe a period of solemnity after death and their general acceptance of society's taboos. That is why these rituals are so different from those we are used to and why, consequently, they strike us as somewhat comical, even though they retain some traditional elements. The half-closed coffin exposing the upper half of the body is not an invention of American morticians. It is a practice dating from the Middle Ages and can still be found in Mediterranean areas like Marseilles and parts of Italy. A fifteenth-century fresco in the church of St. Petronius in Bologna depicts the remains of Saint Mark reposing in a coffin of this type.

The Mortician's Art

Still, it must be borne in mind that these funeral home rituals have quite radically changed the meaning of death. In fact, it is not death that is celebrated in these rituals; it is rather death transformed into the appearance of life by the mortician's art. Formerly embalming was intended primarily to impart something of the incorruptibility of the saints to the dead, especially those who had been celebrated and venerated in life. One of the miracles required for sainthood is an uncorrupted body. By helping to make the body more incorruptible, embalming was looked upon as a way of cooperating in the work of sanctification.

In modern America chemical techniques for preserving the body make us forget death by creating an illusion of life. What friends and relatives pay respect to amidst the banks of flowers and the soothing music is the lifelike appearance of the deceased. The idea of death is banished from this ritual as is all deep sorrow. Roger Caillois grasped this point so well when he noted that those fully clothed corpses give the impression that they are merely taking a nap. While it is a fact that this illusion is dispensed with in those sectors of English society described by Gorer and in the American intelligentsia, it is also a fact that the general public goes along with it and this is no doubt evidence of a profound trait in the American character.

The idea of making a dead person appear alive as a way of paying one's last respects may well strike us as puerile and preposterous. As is often the case in America, this practice is part and parcel of a syndrome that includes commercial interests and the language of advertising. But it also testifies to a rapid and unerring adaptation to complex and contradictory conditions of sensibility. This is the first time in history that a whole society has honored the dead by pretending that they were alive.

Something like this happened once before in history, but involved one person only. I refer to Louis XIV, King of France. When he died he was embalmed, clothed in the purple robes of his consecration, laid out on a bed that looked something like a judge's bench—all as though he would wake up at any moment. Banquet tables were set up, no doubt reminiscent of the ancient funeral festivities but more a symbol of the rejection of mourning. The king did not die in the minds of his subjects. Dressed in festive garments, like a rich Californian in a funeral parlor, he received his court for a last time. The idea of the continuity of the Crown dictated a funeral rite that was, in effect, much like those of contemporary America despite a time difference of several centuries, and like them it may be regarded as a compromise between the desire to honor the dead and the desire to put them out of mind as something unmentionable.

The Americans, who believe in their way of death (including the practices of their funeral directors) as they do in their way of life, give these rituals a further justification that is very interesting because it bears out in an unexpected way Gorer's theory about the traumatizing effects of the denial of mourning. Jessica Mitford reports this case: "Recently a funeral director told me of a woman who needed psychiatric treatment because her husband's funeral was with a closed casket, no visitation, and burial in another state with her not present." (In effect, this represents the practice of the progressive Englishman.) "The psychiatrist called him (the funeral director) to learn about the funeral or lack of one. The patient was treated and has recovered and has vowed never to be part of another memorial-type service," that is to say a simplified commemoration of the dead.[9]

Funeral directors, whose interests are threatened by a trend toward simplicity, draw upon expert psychological opinion to defend their business. They argue that by replacing sorrow with sweet serenity they are providing an important public service.

Because it tempers the anguish of the bereaved and designs cemeteries for the happiness of the living, the funeral industry sees itself as having a beneficient moral and social function. In America today cemeteries play a role that was intended for future necropolises by French urban-planners at the end of the eighteenth century when a royal edict prohibited burial within the city walls. As a result, provisions for new cemeteries had to be made, and a vast literature described what they should be like and what in particular Père Lachaise of Paris (which became the model of all modern cemeteries in both Europe and America) should be like. One is struck by the resemblance between these eighteenth-century texts and the prose of modern American funeral directors and the moralists who support them. Mitford's book offers abundant evidence of this similarity. America is rediscovering the tone and style of the Age of Enlightenment. Rediscovering? Perhaps we should say that they have never lost them. Some historians of American society think that the Puritanism of the eighteenth century impeded the development of a hedonistic attitude toward death and that contemporary optimism does not predate the twentieth century. Whether the influence is direct, then, or a repetition, after a century's interlude, in either case the similarity is striking.

Had it not been for the influence of Romanticism, Père Lachaise would have become another Forest Lawn, the famous cemetery in Los Angeles caricatured by Waugh. Romanticism thwarted a development in this direction and its influence still persists in the popular representations of death and in graveside cults. On the other hand, we get the impression that in America the Romantic influence was short-lived and that the spirit of the Enlightenment, although diminished by Puritanism, was more influential. If this is the case, Puritanism would have had the same braking effect in America as Romanticism did in Europe, but would have died out earlier, thus fostering a mentality much like that of the Enlightenment, the seedbed of so many modern attitudes. We cannot help thinking that in this matter as in so many others (in constitutional law, for example) America is closer to the eighteenth century than Europe is.

The Crisis of Death and the Crisis of Individuality

We conclude that in the last third of the twentieth century something of monumental significance is taking place of which we are just becoming aware: death, that familiar companion of yore, has disappeared from our language. His name is anathema. A kind of vague and anonymous anxiety has taken the place of the words and symbols elaborated by our ancestors. A few writers like Malraux and Ionesco make some attempt to restore death's ancient name which has been obliterated from our language and social conventions. But in normal existence it no longer has any positive meaning at all. It is merely the negative side of what we really see, what we really know, and what we really feel.

This represents a profound change in attitude. In truth, death did not occupy a large place in the minds of men during the high Middle Ages or for some time afterwards. It was not outlawed by edict as it is today; rather its power was weakened by reason of its extreme familiarity. But from the twelfth century onwards, people became more and more preoccupied with death, at least this was the case among the clergy and the educated classes. This concern emerged gradually in connection with two distinct themes: in the twelfth and thirteenth centuries in connection with the theme of the Last Judgment and in the fourteenth and fifteenth centuries in connection with the theme of the art of dying. The *Artes Moriendi* depicted the whole universe in the death-room: the living of the earth, the blessed of heaven, and the damned of hell, all in the presence of Christ and his heavenly court. The life of the dying person was thus summed up for all time and, whoever he might be, he was in this restricted space and for this brief moment the very center of the natural and supernatural worlds. Death was the occasion for individual self-awareness.

We know from several sources that the late Middle Ages was a time of emerging individuality, when men began to define themselves as entities distinct from the collective representations of the human race. It was a time of rampant individualism in religion, in economics (the beginnings of capitalism), and in culture at large. The most conclusive evidence of this individualism is, in my opinion, to be found in the wills and last testaments of the time. These became a literary form in their own right and a means of individual self-expression. When a will is reduced to a mere means of disposing of the deceased's wealth as it is today, it is a sign of a decline or at the very least of a change in our conception of individuality. The progress of science, the affirmation of the rights of man, and the rise of the middle class in the eighteenth century testify that that age was also a heyday of individualism. But it was an individualism already in eclipse, for in the unnoticed intimacy of daily life, individual freedom was already threatened, on the one hand, by family constraints and, on the other, by the demands of professional life. The clear correspondence between the triumph over death and the triumph of individuality during the late Middle Ages invites us to ask whether a similar but inverse relationship might not exist today between the "crisis of death" and the crisis of individuality.

NOTES

1. Vladimir Jankélévitch, *Médecine de France* [177] (1966) 3-16; reprinted in *La mort* (Paris: Flammarion, 1966).
2. B.G. Glaser and A.L. Strauss, *Awareness of Dying* (Chicago: Aldine, 1965).
3. Jacques Maritain, *Reflections on America* (New York: Scribner's, 1958).
4. Geoffrey Gorer, *Death, Grief and Mourning* (New York: Doubleday, 1965).
5. Ibid., pp. 192–99. See Gorer, for this article and subsequent quotes.
6. Evelyn Waugh, *The Loved One* (London: Chapman and Hall, 1950).
7. Roger Caillois, *Quatre essais de sociologie contemporaine* (Paris: Perrin, 1951).
8. Jessica Mitford, *The American Way of Death* (New York: Simon and Schuster, 1963).
9. Ibid., p. 93.

PAUL RAMSEY

selection from
The Indignity of
'Death with Dignity'

In the preceding article, Ariès argued that whatever dignity remains for death is purchased at the price of not troubling the living. In the following article, Ramsey takes
up the same theme but works from a theological perspective to challenge the logic of
death with dignity. He insists that death poses a basic contradiction to the uniqueness of an individual human life and urges the reader to avoid too-easily-formed
attitudes of acceptance. Death, he claims, means *finis* (simply an end) and not
necessarily *telos* (a goal or end imbued with meaning). Dread of death and the true
humanism thus become dependent variables.

Never one am I to use an ordinary title when an extraordinary one will do as well!
Besides, I mean to suggest that there is an additional insult besides death itself
heaped upon the dying by our ordinary talk about "death with dignity." Sometimes
that is said even to be a human "right"; and what should a decent citizen do but
insist on enjoying his rights? That might be his duty (if there is any such right), to the
commonwealth, to the human race or some other collective entity; or at least,
embracing that "right" and dying rationally would exhibit a proper respect for the
going concept of a rational man. So "The Indignity of Death" would not suffice for
my purposes even though all I shall say depends on understanding the contradiction
death poses to the unique worth of an individual human life.

The genesis of the following reflections may be worth noting. A few years ago,[1]
I embraced what I characterized as the oldest morality there is (no "new morality")
concerning responsibility toward the dying: the acceptance of death, stopping our

Source: Paul Ramsey, "The Indignity of 'Death With Dignity,'" reprinted from Peter Steinfels and Robert M. Veatch, eds., *Death Inside
Out: The Hastings Center Report,* ©1975, Institute of Society, Ethics and the Life Sciences. Harper and Row. Reprinted by permission.

medical interventions for all sorts of good, human reasons, *only* companying with the dying in their final passage. Then suddenly it appeared that altogether too many people were agreeing with me. That caused qualms. As a Southerner born addicted to lost causes, it seemed I now was caught up in a triumphal social trend. As a controversialist in ethics, I found agreement from too many sides. As a generally happy prophet of the doom facing the modern age, unless there is a sea-change in norms of action, it was clear from these premises that anything divers people agree to must necessarily be superficial if not wrong.

Today, when divers people draw the same warm blanket of "allowing to die" or "death with dignity" close up around their shoulders against the dread of that cold night, their various feet are showing. Exposed beneath our growing agreement to that "philosophy of death and dying" may be significantly different "philosophies of life"; and in the present age that agreement may reveal that these interpretations of human life are increasingly mundane, naturalistic, antihumanistic when measured by *any* genuinely "humanistic" esteem for the individual human being.

These "philosophical" ingredients of any view of death and dying I want to make prominent by speaking of "The Indignity of 'Death with Dignity'." Whatever practical agreement there may be, or "guidelines" proposed to govern contemporary choice or practice, these are bound to be dehumanizing unless at the same time we bring to bear great summit points and sources of insight in mankind's understanding of mankind (be it Christian or other religious humanism, or religiously-dependent but not explicitly religious humanism, or, if it is possible, a true humanism that is neither systematically nor historically dependent on any religious outlook).

DEATH WITH DIGNITY IDEOLOGIES

There is nobility and dignity in caring for the dying, but not in dying itself. "To be a therapist to a dying patient makes us aware of the uniqueness of each individual in this vast sea of humanity."[2] It is more correct to say that a therapist brings to the event, from some other source, an awareness of the uniqueness, the once-for-allness of an individual life-span as part of an "outlook" and "on-look" upon the vast sea of humanity. In any case, that is the reflected glory and dignity of caring for the dying, that we are or become aware of the unique life here ending. The humanity of such human caring is apt to be more sensitive and mature if we do not lightly suppose that it is an easy thing to convey dignity to the dying. That certainly cannot be done simply by withdrawing tubes and stopping respirators or not thumping hearts. At most, those omissions can only be prelude to companying with the dying in their final passage, if we are fortunate enough to share with them—they in moderate comfort—those interchanges that are in accord with the dignity and nobility of mankind. Still, however noble the manifestations of caring called for, however unique the individual life, we finally must come to the reality of death, and must ask, what can possibly be the meaning of "death with dignity"?

At most we convey only the liberty to die with human dignity; we can provide some of the necessary but not sufficient conditions. If the dying die with a degree of nobility it will be mostly their doing in doing their own dying. I fancy their task was easier when death as a human event meant that special note was taken of the last words of the dying—even humorous ones, as in the case of the Roman emperor who said as he expired, "I Deify." A human countenance may be discerned in death accepted with serenity. So also there is a human countenance behind death with defiance. "Do not go gentle into that good night," wrote Dylan Thomas. "Old age should rage and burn against the close of day; Rage Rage against the dying of the light." But the human countenance has been removed from most modern understandings of death.

We do not begin to keep human community with the dying if we interpose between them and us most of the current notions of "death with dignity." Rather do we draw closer to them if and only if our conception of "dying with dignity" encompasses—nakedly and without dilution—the final indignity of death itself, whether accepted or raged against. So I think it may be profitable to explore "the indignity of 'death with dignity'." "Good death" (euthanasia) like "Good grief!" are ultimately contradictions in terms, even if superficially, and before we reach the heart of the matter, there are distinctions to be made; even if, that is to say, the predicate "good" still is applicable in both cases in contrast to worse ways to die and worse ways to grieve or not to grieve.

"Death is simply a part of life," we are told, as a first move to persuade us to accept the ideology of the entire dignity of dying with dignity. A singularly unpersuasive proposition, since we are not told what sort of part of life death is. Disease, injury, congenital defects are also a part of life, and as well murder, rapine, and pillage.[3] Yet there is no campaign for accepting or doing those things with dignity. Nor, for that matter, for the contemporary mentality which would enshrine "death with dignity" is there an equal emphasis on "suffering with dignity," suffering as a "natural" part of life, etc. All those things, it seems, are enemies and violations of human nobility while death is not, or (with a few changes) need not be. Doctors did not invent the fact that death is an enemy, although they may sometimes use disproportionate means to avoid final surrender. Neither did they invent the fact that pain and suffering are enemies and often indignities, although suffering accepted may also be ennobling or may manifest the nobility of the human spirit of any ordinary person.

But, then, it is said, death is an evolutionary necessity and in that further sense a part of life not to be denied. Socially and biologically, one generation follows another. So there must be death, else social history would have no room for creative novelty and planet earth would be glutted with humankind. True enough, no doubt, from the point of view of evolution (which—so far—never dies). But the man who is dying happens not to be evolution. He is a part of evolution, no doubt: but not to the whole extent of his being or his dying. A crucial testimony to the individual's transcendence over the species is man's problem and his dis-ease in dying. Death is a natural fact of life, yet no man dies "naturally," nor do we have occasions in which to practice doing so in order to learn how. Not unless the pursuit of philosophy is a practice of dying (as Plato's *Phaedo* teaches); and that I take to be an understanding of the human being we moderns do not mean to embrace when we embrace "death with dignity."

It is small consolation to tell mortal men that as long as you are, the death you contribute to evolution is not yet; and when death is, you are not—so why fear death? That is the modern equivalent to the recipe offered by the ancient Epicureans (and some Stoics) to undercut fear of death and devotion to the gods: as long as you are, death is not; when death is, you are not; there's never a direct encounter between you and death; so why dread death? Indeed, contrary to modern parlance, those ancient philosophers declared that death is *not a part of life;* so, why worry?

So "death is not a part of life" is another declaration designed to quiet fear of death. This can be better understood in terms of a terse comment by Wittgenstein: "Our life has no limit in just the way in which our visual field has no limit."[4] We cannot see beyond the boundary of our visual field; it is more correct to say that beyond the boundary of our visual field *we do not see*. Not only so. Also, we do not see the boundary, the limit itself. There is no seeable bound to the visual field. *Death is not a part of life* in the same way that the boundary is not a part of our visual field. Commenting on this remark by Wittgenstein, James Van Evra writes: "Pressing the analogy, then, if my life has no end in *just the way* that my visual field has no limit, then it must be in the sense that I can have no experience of death, conceived as the complete cessation of experience and thought. That is, if life is considered to be a series of experiences and thoughts, then it is impossible for me to experience death, for to experience something is to be alive, and hence is to be inside the bound formed by death."[5] This is why death itself steadfastly resists conceptualization.

Still, I think the disanalogy ought also to be pressed, against both ancient and contemporary analytical philosophers. That notion of death as a limit makes use of a visual or spatial metaphor. Good basketball players are often men naturally endowed with an unusually wide visual field; this is true, for example, of Bill Bradley. Perhaps basketball players, among other things, strive to enlarge their visual fields, or their habitual use of what powers of sight they have, if that is possible. But ordinarily, every one of us is perfectly happy within the unseeable limits of sight's reach.

Transfer this notion of death as a limit from space to time as the form of human perception, from sight to an individual's inward desire, effort and hope, and I suggest that one gets a different result. Then death as the temporal limit of a life-span is something we live toward. That limit still can never be experienced or conceptualized; indeed death is *never* a part of life. Moreover, neither is the boundary. Still it is a limit we conative human beings know we live *up against* during our life-spans. We do not live toward or up against the side-limits of our visual-span. Instead, within that acceptable visual limit (and other limits as well) as channels we live toward yet another limit which is death.

Nor is the following analogy for death as a limit of much help in deepening understanding. ". . . The importance of the limit and virtually *all* of its significance," writes Van Evra, "derives from the fact that the limit serves as an ordering device"—just as absolute zero serves for ordering a series; it is not *just* a limit, although nothing can exist at such a temperature. The analogy is valid so far as it suggests that we conceive of death not in itself but as it bears on us while still alive. As I shall suggest below, death teaches us to "number our days."

But that may not be its only ordering function for conative creatures. Having placed death "out of our league" by showing that it is not a "something," or never a part of life, and while understanding awareness of death as awareness of a limit bearing upon us only while still alive, one ought not forthwith to conclude that this understanding of it "exonerates death as the purported snake in our garden." Death as a limit can disorder no less than order the series. Only a disembodied reason can say, as Van Evra does, that "the bound, not being a member of the series, cannot defile it. The series is what it is, happy or unhappy, good or bad, quite independently of any bound as such." An Erik Erikson knows better than that when writing of the "despair and often unconscious fear of death" which results when "the one and only life cycle is not accepted as the ultimate life." Despair, he observes, "expresses the feeling that the time is short, too short for the attempt to start another life and to try out alternate roads to integrity."[6]

It is the temporal flight of the series that is grievous (not death as an evil "something" within life's span to be balanced, optimistically or pessimistically, against other things that are good). The reminder that death is *not a part of life*, or that it is only a boundary never encountered, is an ancient recipe that can only increase the threat of death on any profound understanding of human life. The dread of death is the dread of oblivion, of there being only empty room in one's stead. Kübler-Ross writes that for the dying, death means the loss of every loved one, total loss of everything that constituted the self in its world, separation from every experience, even from future possible, replacing experiences—nothingness beyond. Therefore, life is a time-intensive activity and not only a goods-intensive or quality-intensive activity. No matter how many "goods" we store up in barns, like the man in Jesus' parable we know that this night our soul may be required of us (Luke 12:13-21). No matter what "quality of life" our lives have, we must take into account the opportunity-costs of used time. Death means the conquest of the time of our lives—even though we never experience the experience of the nothingness which is natural death.

"Awareness of dying" means awareness of *that;* and awareness of that constitutes an experience of ultimate indignity in and to the awareness of the self who is dying.

Birth and death (our *terminus ad quo* and our *terminus ad quem*) are not to be equated with any of the qualities or experiences, the grandeur and the misery, in between, which constitutes "parts" of our lives. While we live toward death and can encompass our own dying in awareness, no one in the same way is aware of his own birth. We know that we were born in the same way we know *that* we die. Explanations of whence we came do not establish conscious contact with our individual origin; and among explanations, that God called us from the womb out of nothing is as good as any other; and better than most. But awareness of dying is quite another matter. That we may have, but not awareness of our births. And while awareness of birth might conceivably be the great original individuating experience (if we had it), among the race of men it is awareness of dying that is uniquely individuating. To encompass one's own death in the living and dying of one's life is more of a task than it is a part of life. And there is something of indignity to be faced when engaging in that final act of life. Members of the caring human community (doctors, nurses, family) are apt to keep closer company with the dying if we acknowledge the loss of all worth by the loss of him in whom inhered all worth in his world. Yet ordinary men may sometimes nobly suffer the ignobility of death.

By way of contrast with the "A Living Will" framed by the Euthanasia Society, the Judicial Council of the AMA in its recent action on the physician and the dying patient had before it two similar letters. One was composed by the Connecticut Delegation:

TO MY FAMILY, MY PHYSICIAN, MY CLERGYMAN, MY LAWYER—

If the time comes when I can no longer actively take part in decisions for my own future, I wish this statement to stand as the testament of my wishes. If there is no reasonable expectation of my recovery from physical or mental and spiritual disability, I, ..., request that I be allowed to die and not be kept alive by artificial means or heroic measures. I ask also that drugs be mercifully administered to me for terminal suffering even if in relieving pain they may hasten the moment of death. I value life and the dignity of life, so that I am not asking that my life be directly taken, but that my dying not be unreasonably prolonged nor the dignity of life be destroyed. This request is made, after careful reflection, while I am in good health and spirits. Although this document is not legally binding, you who care for me will, I hope, feel morally bound to take it into account. I recognize that it places a heavy burden of responsibility upon you, and it is with the intention of sharing this responsibility that this statement is made.

A second letter had been composed by a physician to express his own wishes, in quite simple language:

TO MY FAMILY, TO MY PHYSICIAN—

Should the occasion arise in my lifetime when death is imminent and a decision is to be made about the nature and the extent of the care to be given to me and I am not able at that time to express my desires, let this statement serve to express my deep, sincere, and considered wish and hope that my physician will administer to me simple, ordinary medical treatment. I ask that he not administer heroic, extraordinary, expensive, or useless medical care or treatment which in the final analysis will merely delay, not change, the ultimate outcome of my terminal condition.

A comparison of these declarations with "A Living Will" circulated by the Euthanasia Society reveals the following signal differences: neither of the AMA submissions engages in any superfluous calculus of "comparative indignities";[7] neither associates the reality of death with such things as birth or maturation; both allow death to be simply what it is in human experience; both are in a general sense "pro-life" statements, in that death is neither reified as one fact among others nor beautified even comparatively.[8]

Everyone concerned takes the wrong turn in trying either to "thing-ify" death or to beautify it. The dying have at least this advantage, that in these projects for dehumanizing death by naturalizing it the dying finally cannot succeed, and death makes its threatening visage known to them before ever there are any societal or evolutionary replacement values or the everlasting arms or Abraham's bosom to rest on. Death means *finis*, not in itself *telos*. Certainly not a telos to be engineered, or to be accomplished by reducing both human life and death to the level of natural events.

"Thing-ifying" death reaches its highest pitch in the stated preference of many people in the present age for *sudden* death,[9] for death from unanticipated internal collapse, from the abrupt intrusion of violent outside forces, from some chance occurrence due to the natural law governing the operation of automobiles. While for a comparative calculus of indignities sudden *unknowing* death may be preferred to suffering knowingly or unknowingly the indignity of deterioration, abject dependence, and hopeless pain, how ought we to assess in human terms the present-day absolute (noncomparative) preference for sudden death? Nothing reveals more the meaning we assign to human "dignity" than the view that sudden death, death as an eruptive natural event, could be a prismatic case of death with dignity or at least one without indignity. Human society seems about to rise to the moral level of the "humane" societies in their treatment of animals. What is the principled difference between their view and ours about the meaning of dying "humanely"? By way of contrast, consider the prayer in the Anglican prayer book: "From perils by night and perils by day, perils by land and perils by sea, and *from sudden death*, Lord, deliver us." Such a petition bespeaks an age in which dying with dignity was a gift and a task (*Gaube und Aufgaube*), a liberty to encompass dying as a final act among the actions of life, to enfold awareness of dying as an ingredient into awareness of one's self dying as the finale of the self's relationships in this life to God or to fellowman—in any case to everything that was worthy.

TRUE HUMANISM AND THE DREAD OF DEATH

I always write as the ethicist I am, namely, a Christian ethicist, and not as some hypothetical common denominator. On common concrete problems I, of course, try to elaborate analysis at the point or on a terrain where there may be convergence of vectors that began in other ethical outlooks and onlooks. Still one should not pant for agreement as the hart pants for the waterbrooks, lest the substance of one's ethics dissolve into vapidity. So in this section I want, among other things, to exhibit some of the meaning of "Christian humanism" in regard to death and dying, in the confidence that this will prove tolerable to my colleagues for a time, if not finally instructive to them.

In this connection, there are two counterpoised verses in the First Epistle of St. John that are worth pondering. The first reads: "Perfect love casts out fear" (which being interpreted means: Perfect care of the dying casts out fear of one's own death or rejection of their dying because of fear of ours). The second verse reads: "Where fear is, love is not perfected" (which being interpreted means: Where fear of death and dying remains, medical and human care of the dying is not perfected). That states nothing so much as the enduring dubiety and ambiguity of any mortal man's care of another through his dying. At the same time there is here applied without modification a standard for unflinching care of a dying fellowman, or short of that of any fellow mortal any time. That standard is cut to the measure of the perfection in benevolence believed to be that of our Father in Heaven in his dealings with mankind. So there is "faith-ing" in an ultimate righteousness beyond the perceptible human condition presupposed by those verses that immediately have to do simply with loving and caring.

Whatever non-Christians may think about the *theology* here entailed, or about similar foundations in any religious ethics, I ask that the notation upon or penetration of the human condition be attended to. Where and insofar as fear is, love and care for the dying cannot be perfected in moral agents or the helping professions. The religious traditions have one way of addressing that problematic. In the modern age the problematic itself is avoided by various forms and degrees of denial of the tragedy of death which proceeds first to reduce the unique worth and once-for-all-ness of the individual life-span that dies.

Perhaps one can apprehend the threat posed to the dignity of man (i.e., in an easy and ready dignifying of death) by many modern viewpoints, especially those dominating the scientific community, and their superficial equivalents in our culture generally, by bringing into view three states of consciousness in the Western past.

The burden of the Hebrew Scriptures was man's obedience or disobedience to covenant, to Torah. Thus sin was the problem, and death came in only as a subordinate theme; and, as one focus for the problematic of the human condition, this was a late development. In contrast, righteousness and disobedience (sin) was a subordinate theme in Greek religion. The central theme of Greek religious thought and practice was the problem of death—a problem whose solution was found either by initiation into religious cults that promised to extricate the soul from its corruptible shroud or by belief in the native power of the soul to outlast any number of bodies. Alongside these, death was at the heart of the pathos of life depicted in Greek tragical drama, against which, and against the flaws of finitude in general, the major character manifested his heroic transcendence. So sin was determinative for the Hebrew consciousness; death for the Greek consciousness.

Consciousness III was Christianity, and by this, sin and death were tied together in Western man's awareness of personal existence. These two foci of man's misery and of his need for redemption—sin and death—were inseparably fused. This new dimension of man's awareness of himself was originally probed most profoundly by St. Paul's Letter to the Romans (5–7). Those opaque reflections, I opine, were once understood not so much by the intellect as along the pulses of ordinary people in great numbers, in taverns and market places; and it represents a cultural breakdown without parallel that these reflections are scarcely understandable to the greatest intelligences today. A simple night school lesson in them may be gained by simply pondering a while the two verses quoted above from St. John's Epistle.

The point is that according to the Christian saga the Messiah did not come to bring boors into culture. Nor did he bear epilepsy or psychosomatic disorders to gain victory over them in the flesh before the interventions of psychoneurosurgery. Rather is he said to have been born *mortal* flesh to gain for us a foretaste of victory over sin and death where those twin enemies had taken up apparently secure citadel.

Again, the point for our purposes is not to be drawn into agreement or disagreement with those theological affirmations, and it is certainly not to be tempted into endless speculation about an after-life. Crucial instead is to attend to the notation on the human condition implied in all that. Death is an enemy even if it is the last enemy to be fully conquered in the Fulfillment, the eschaton; meanwhile, the sting of death is sin. Such was the new consciousness-raising that Christianity brought into the Western world. And the question is whether in doing so it has not grasped some important experiential human realities better than most philosophies, whether it was not attuned to essential ingredients of the human condition vis-à-vis death— whatever the truth or falsity of its theological address to that condition.

The foregoing, I grant, may be an oversimplification; and I am aware of needed corrections more in the case of Hebrew humanism than in the case of Greek humanism. The New Testament word, "He will wipe away every tear from their eyes, and death shall be no more, neither shall there be mourning nor crying nor pain any more, for the former things have passed away," (Rev. 21:3,4) has its parallel in the Hebrew Bible: "He will swallow up death forever, and the Lord God will wipe away tears from all faces . . ." (Isa. 25:8). Again, since contemplating the Lord God may be too much for us, I ask only that we attend to the doctrine of death implied in these passages: it is an enemy, surely, and not simply an acceptable part of the natural order of things. And the connection between dread of death and sin, made most prominent in Christian consciousness, was nowhere better stated than in Ecclesiastes: "This is the root of the evil in all that happens under the sun, that one fate comes to all. Therefore, men's minds are filled with evil and there is madness in their hearts while they live, for they know that afterward—they are off to the dead!"

One can, indeed, ponder that verse about the source of all evil in the apprehended evil of death together with another verse in Ecclesiastes which reads: "Teach us so to number our days that we may apply our hearts unto wisdom." The first says that death is an evil evil: it is experienced as a threatening limit that begets evil. The second says that death is a good evil: that experience also begets good. Without death, and death perceived as a threat, we would also have no reason to "number our days" so as to ransom the time allotted us, to receive life as a precious gift, to drink the wine of gladness in toast to every successive present moment. Instead, life would be an endless boredom and boring because endless; there would be no reason to probe its depths while there is still time. Some there are who number their days so as to apply their hearts unto eating, drinking and being merry—for tomorrow we die. Some there are who number their days so as to apply their hearts unto wisdom—for tomorrow we die. Both are life-spans enhanced in importance and in individuation under the stimulus of the perceived evil of death. Knowledge of human good or of human evil that is in the slightest degree above the level of the beasts of the field are both enhanced because of death, the horizon of human existence. So, debarment from access to the tree of life was on the horizon and a sequence of the events in the Garden of Paradise; the temptation in eating the fruit of the tree of knowledge of good and evil was because that seemed a way for mortal creatures to become like gods. The punishment of that is said to have been death; and no governor uses as a penalty something that anyone can simply choose to believe to be a good or simply receive as a neutral or dignified, even ennobling, part of life. So I say death may be a good evil or an evil evil, but it is perceived as an evil or experienced indignity in either case. Existential anxiety or general anxiety (distinguishable from particular fears or removable anxieties) means anxiety over death toward which we live. That paradoxically, as Reinhold Niebuhr said, is the source of all human creativity and of all human sinfulness.

Of course, the sages of old could and did engage in a calculus of comparative indignities. "O death, your sentence is welcome," wrote Ben Sira, "to a man worn out with age, worried about everything, disaffected and beyond endurance" (Ecclus. 41:2,3). Still death was a "sentence," not a natural event acceptable in itself. Moreover, not every man grows old gracefully in the Psalms; instead, one complains:

> Take pity on me, Yahweh,
> I am in trouble now.
> Grief wastes away my eye,
> My throat, my inmost parts.
> For my life is worn out with sorrow,
> My years with sighs;
> My strength yields under misery,
> My bones are wasting away.
> To every one of my oppressors
> I am contemptible,
> Loathsome to my neighbors,
> To my friends a thing of fear.
> Those who see me in the street
> Hurry past me.
> I am forgotten, as good as dead, in their hearts,
> Something discarded. (Ps. 31:9–12)

What else is to be expected if it be true that the madness in men's hearts while they live, and the root of all evil in all that happens under the sun, lies in the simple fact that every man consciously lives toward his own death, knowing that afterward he too is off to the dead? Where fear is—fear of the properly dreadful—love and care for the dying cannot be perfected.

Unless one has some grounds for respecting the shadow of death upon every human countenance—grounds more ultimate than perceptible realities—then it makes good sense as a policy of life simply to try to outlast one's neighbors. One can, for example, *generalize*, and so attenuate our neighbors' irreplaceability. "If I must grieve whenever the bell tolls," writes Carey McWilliams, "I am never bereft: some of my kinsmen will remain. Indeed, I need not grieve much—even, lest I suggest some preference among my brethren, should not grieve much—for each loss is small compared to what remains."[10] But that solace, we know, is denied the dead who have lost everything making for worth in this their world. Realistic love for another irreplaceable, noninterchangeable individual human being means, as Unamuno wrote, care for another "doomed soul."

In this setting, let us now bring into consideration some empirical findings that in this day are commonly supposed to be more confirmatory than wisdom mediated from the heart.

In the second year anatomy course, medical students clothe with "gallows humor" their encounter with the cadaver which once was a human being alive. That defense is not to be despised; nor does it necessarily indicate socialization in shallowness on the students' part. Even when dealing with the remains of the long since dead, there is special tension involved—if I mistook not a recent address by Renée Fox—when performing investigatory medical actions involving the face, the hands, and the genitalia. This thing-in-the-world that was once a man alive we still encounter as once a communicating being, not quite as an object of research or instruction. Face and hands, yes; but why the genitalia? Those reactions must seem incongruous to a resolutely biologizing age. For a beginning of an explanation, one might take up the expression "carnal knowledge"—which was the best thing about the movie bearing that title—and behind that go to the expression "carnal *conversation*," an old, legal term for adultery, and back of both to the Biblical word "knew" in "And Adam *knew* his wife and begat. . . ." Here we have an entire anthropology impacted in a word, not a squeamish euphemism. In short, in those reactions of medical students can be discerned a sensed relic of the human being bodily experiencing and communicating, and the body itself uniquely speaking.

Notably, however, there's no "gallows humor" used when doing or observing one's first autopsy, or in the emergency room when a D.O.A. (Dead on Arrival) is brought in with his skull cleaved open. With regard to the "newly dead" we come as close as we possibly can to experiencing the incommensurable contrast between life and death. Yet those sequential realities—life and death—here juxtaposed never *meet* in direct encounter. So we never have an impression or experience of the measure and meaning of the two different worlds before which we stand in the autopsy and the emergency room. A cadaver has over time become almost a thing-in-the-world from which to gain knowledge of the human body. While *there* a little humor helps, to go about acquiring medical knowledge from autopsies requires a different sort of inward effort to face down or live with our near-experience of the boundary of life and death. The cleavage in the brain may be quite enough and more than enough to *explain* rationally why this man was D.O.A. But, I suggest, there can be no gash deep enough, no physical event destructive enough to account for the felt difference between life and death that we face here. The physician or medical student may be a confirmed materialist. For him the material explanation of this death may be quite sufficient rationally. Still the heart has its reasons that the reason knows not of; and, I suggest, the awakening of these feelings of awe and dread should not be repressed in anyone whose calling is to the human dignity of caring for the dying.

In any case, from these empirical observations, if they be true, let us return to a great example of theological anthropology in order to try to comprehend why death was thought to be the assault of an enemy. According to some readings, Christians in all ages should be going about bestowing the gift of immortality on one another posthaste. A distinguished Catholic physician, beset by what he regarded as the incorrigible problems of medical ethics today, once shook his head in my presence and wondered out loud why the people who most believe in an after-life should have established so many hospitals! That seems to require explanation, at least as against silly interpretations of "otherworldiness." The answer is that none of the facts or outlooks cited ever denied the reality of death, or affirmed that death ever presents a friendly face (except comparatively). The explanation lies in the vicinity of Christian anthropology and the Biblical view that death is an enemy. That foundation of Western medicine ought not lightly to be discarded, even if we need to enliven again the sense that there are limits to man's struggle against that alien power.

Far from the otherworldliness or body-soul dualism with which he is often charged, St. Augustine went so far as to say that "the body is not an extraneous ornament or aid, but a part of man's very nature."[11] Upon that understanding of the human being, Augustine could then express a quite realistic account of "the dying process":

> Wherefore, as regards bodily death, that is, the separation of the soul from the body, it is good to none while it is being endured by those whom we say are in the article of death [dying]. For the very violence with which the body and soul are wrenched asunder, which in the living are conjoined and closely intertwined, brings with it a harsh experience, jarring horribly on nature as long as it continues, till there comes a total loss of sensation, which arose from the very interpenetration of flesh and spirit.[12]

From this Augustine correctly concludes: "Wherefore death is indeed . . . good to none while it is actually suffered, and while it is subduing the dying to its power. . . ." His ultimate justifications attenuate not at all the harshness of that alien power's triumph. Death, he only says, is "meritoriously endured for the sake of winning what *is* good. And regarding what happens after death, it is no absurdity to say that death is good to the good, and evil to the evil."[13] But that is not to say that death as endured in this life, or as life's terminus, is itself in any way good. He even goes so far as to say:

> For though there can be no manner of doubt that the souls of the just and holy lead lives in peaceful rest, yet so much better would it be for them to be alive in healthy, well-conditioned bodies, that even those who hold the tenet that it is most blessed to be quit of every kind of body, condemn this opinion in spite of themselves.[14]

Thus, for Biblical or later Christian anthropology, the only possible form which human life in any true and proper sense can take here or hereafter is "somatic." That is the Pauline word; we today say "psychosomatic." Therefore, for Christian theology death may be a "conquered enemy"; still it was in the natural order—and as long as the generations of mankind endure will remain—an enemy still. To pretend otherwise adds insult to injury—or, at least, carelessness.

There are two ways, so far as I can see, to reduce the dreadful visage of death to a level of inherently acceptable indifference. One way is to subscribe to an interpretation of "bodily life" that reduces it to an acceptable level of indifference to the person long before his dying. That—if anyone can believe it today, or if it is not a false account of human nature— was the way taken by Plato in his idealized account of the death of Socrates. (It should be remembered that we know not whether Socrates' hands trembled as he yet bravely drank the hemlock, no more than we know how Isaac experienced dying when "fullness of years" came upon him. Secondary accounts of these matters are fairly untrustworthy.)

Plato's dialogue *The Phaedo* may not "work" as a proof of the immortality of the soul. Still it decisively raises the question of immortality by its thorough representation of the incommensurability between mental processes and bodily processes. Few philosophers today accept the demonstration of the mind's power to outlast bodies because the mind itself is not material, or because the mind "plays" the body like a musician the lyre. But most of them are still wrestling with the mind-body problem, and many speak of two separate languages, a language for mental events isomorphic with our language for brain events. That's rather like saying the same thing as Socrates (Plato) while claiming to have gone beyond him (Soren Kierkegaard).

I cite *The Phaedo* for another purpose: to manifest one way to render death incomparably welcomed. Those who most have mature manhood in exercise—the lovers of wisdom—have desired death and dying all their life long, in the sense that they seek "in every sort of way to dissever the soul from the communion of the body"; "thought is best when the mind is gathered into herself and none of these things trouble her—neither sounds nor sights nor pain nor any pleasure—when she takes leave of the body. . . ." That life is best and has nothing to fear that has "the habit of the soul gathering and collecting herself into herself from all sides out of the body." (Feminists, note the pronouns.)

Granted, Socrates' insight is valid concerning the self's transcendence, when he says: "I am inclined to think that these muscles and bones of mine would have gone off long ago to Megara and Boeotia—by the dog, they would, if they had been moved only by their own idea of what was best. . . ." Still Crito had a point, when he feared that the impending dread event had more to do with "the same Socrates who has been talking and conducting the argument" than Socrates is represented to have believed. To fear the loss of Socrates, Crito had not to fancy, as Socrates charged, "that I am the other Socrates whom he will soon see, a dead body." Crito had only to apprehend, however faintly, that there is not an entire otherness between those two Socrates *now*, in this living being; that there was unity between, let us say,

The other way to reduce the dreadful visage of death is to subscribe to a philosophy of "human life" that reduces the stature, the worth, and the irreplaceable uniqueness of the individual person (long before his dying) to a level of acceptable transiency or interchangeability. True, modern culture is going this way. But there have been other and better ways of stipulating that the image of death across the human countenance is no shadow. One was that of Aristotelian philosophy. According to its form-matter distinction, reason, the formal principle, is definitive of essential humanity. That is universal, eternal as logic. Matter, however, is the individuating factor. So when a man who bears a particular name dies, only the individuation disintegrates—to provide matter for other forms. Humanity goes on in other instances. Anything unique or precious about mankind is not individual. There are parallels to this outlook in Eastern religions and philosophies, in which the individual has only transiency, and should seek only that, disappearing in the Fulfillment into the Divine pool.

These then are two ways of denying the dread of death. Whenever these two escapes are *simultaneously* rejected—i.e., if the "bodily life" is neither an ornament nor a drag but a part of man's very nature; and if the "personal life" of an individual in his unique life-span is accorded unrepeatable, noninterchangeable value—then it is that Death the Enemy again comes into view. Conquered or Unconquerable. A true humanism and the dread of death seem to be dependent variables. I suggest that it is better to have the indignity of death on our hands and in our outlooks than to "dignify" it in either of these two possible ways. Then we ought to be much more circumspect in speaking of death with dignity, and hesitant to—I almost said—thrust that upon the dying! Surely, a proper care for them needs not only to know the pain of dying which human agency may hold at bay, but also care needs to acknowledge that there is grief over death which no human agency can alleviate.

NOTES

1. Paul Ramsey, "On (Only) Caring for the Dying," *The Patient as Person* (New Haven: Yale University Press, 1971).
2. Elisabeth Kübler-Ross, *On Death and Dying* (New York: Macmillan, 1969), p. 247.
3. Schopenhauer's characterization of human history: if you've read one page, you've read it all.
4. Wittgenstein, *Tractatus,* 6.4311.
5. James Van Evra, "On Death as a Limit," *Analysis* 31 (April 1971): 170–76.
6. Erik Erikson, "Identity and the Life Cycle," *Psychological Issues,* I (New York: International University Press, 1959).
7. What, after all, is the point of promoting, as if it were a line of reasoning, observations such as that said to be inscribed on W.C. Field's tombstone: "On the whole I'd rather be here than in Philadelphia"?
8. I may add that while the House of Delegates did not endorse any particular form to express an individual's wishes relating prospectively to his final illness, it recognized that individuals have a right to express them. While it encouraged physicians to discuss such matters with patients and attend to their wishes, the House nevertheless maintained a place for the conscience and judgment of a physician in determining indicated treatment. It did not subsume every consideration under the rubric of the patient's right to refuse treatment (or to have refused treatment). That sole action-guide can find no medical or logical reason for distinguishing, in physician actions, between the

dying and those who simply have a terminal illness (or have this "dying life," Augustine's description of all of us). It would also entail a belief that wishing or autonomous choice makes the moral difference between life and death decisions which then are to be imposed on the physician-technician; and that, to say the least, is an ethics that can find no place for either reason or sensibility.

9. Cf. the report of a Swedish survey by Gunnar Biörck, M.D., in *Archives of Internal Medicine,* October, 1973; news report in *The New York Times,* Oct. 31, 1973.

10. Wilson Carey McWilliams, *The Idea of Fraternity in America* (Berkeley: University of California Press, 1973), p. 48.

11. Augustine, *City of God,* Book I, Chapter XIII.

12. Ibid., Book XIII, Chapter VI.

13. Ibid., Book XIII, Chapter VIII.

14. Ibid., Book XIII, Chapter XIX.

Questions

1. Define the following terms and give examples of each where appropriate. Terms marked with an asterisk are psychological, sociological, or medical terms the authors of the selections expect readers to know. If you are not familiar with their meanings, consult the appropriate dictionary.

*test validation	*correlation	*nuntius mortis*
death anxiety	*projective test	*approach-avoidance
*denial	cognitive style	eschaton
adaptive changes	*socialization	Puritanism
*germ plasm	*identity	the Enlightenment
*somatoplasm	premature death	Romanticism
*operational definition		

2. Schulz supports the widely held belief that death anxiety is, on occasion, constructive in that it may serve as inspiration for great individual achievements. Drawing from literature, philosophy, music, art, and film, suggest works that might be offered as evidence of this theory.

3. What are the functional applications of the ability to measure death anxiety? In what groups might it be particularly interesting to study levels of death anxiety? In what situations would you expect differences in levels of death anxiety to influence behavior?

4. Kalish found that age was an important variable in assessing the impact of ethnicity in death-related attitudes. Using Kalish's article, construct an interview schedule and administer it to several members of a generation different from your own. Try, if possible, to obtain a range of ethnicity in your respondents.

5. The ability to "make sense of" death depends in large measure on the degree to which we find it appropriate. (Parsons and Lidz suggest death at the end of a complete life cycle as one way.) The following statements suggest different ways of justifying death. What factors make death acceptable to the speakers? Compare each attitude to your own idea of appropriate death.

   a. Mother, 42, speaking of her son who died suddenly at age 19 as a result of a previously undetected congenital heart defect:

      "He died at the right time. He had decided on his major, made the track team, and had just fallen in love. Life had never been better for him. He seemed to have found himself. In another year, things might have fallen apart."

   b. Woman, 55, at a study group discussion of funeral practices:

      "My family will not have to fight about my funeral. I have worked hard and I have got it all paid for. I have always made do with second best, but this I am going to do right."

   c. Male student, 28, in seminar on death and dying:

      "What's all this talk about appropriate death? If I have lived my life well, why should the circumstances of my death matter to me?"

6. In his reference to wills, Ariès uses changes in social customs as an indicator of attitudinal shifts. What other long-established social customs might be studied as indicators of such change?

7. Ramsey pits the notion of acceptance too-easily-achieved against the reality of the dying person's experience. Identify several approaches that Ramsey claims obscure an understanding of the reality of death.

8. a. Ariès describes the moral obligations of the *nuntius mortis* and notes that the role of the dying person has undergone a reversal with respect to the management of death. Yet many contemporary writers would claim a subsequent shift. Would you want to be informed of your own death? Why or why not? If so, by whom?

   b. Results of surveys such as the one conducted by Kalish indicate that while many people claim they would like to be informed of a terminal illness, relatively few would be willing to assume the role of *nuntius mortis.* Would you? For whom?

9. Ariès develops a specialized notion of "acceptable death." What are its characteristics, and how does it differ from the concept of "appropriate death" put forward by Parsons and Lidz? What would Ramsey say about "appropriate death"? "Acceptable death"?

Projects for Further Study

1. Terminal illness has become a popular subject for movies and television. Watch three different medical series on television during a one-week period and observe both the portrayal of death and its effects on the participants: patient, family, nurse, and doctor. Profile the dying patient in terms of age, sex, occupation, personal and social attractiveness and social status. What is the cause of death? Where does the patient die? Note the attitudes of each person toward death. Based upon your analysis, what do you feel television presents as appropriate death? As inappropriate death?

2. Cultural attitudes determine what one does to "put his house in order" before death. Our society has very different expectations, for instance, from a community in medieval times or more recent Eskimo culture. Research the types of arrangements that are expected and available in our society. Include psychological, financial, legal, and religious factors in your research.

3. Debate the following proposition: The more acceptable that death is in itself, the less worth will be ascribed to the dying life.

4. Read *The Loved One* by Evelyn Waugh and develop a summary of the ways in which the society presented there "attenuates the tragic sense of death." Based on your own experiences of the handling of death, identify points of similarity and dissimilarity with the world of *The Loved One.*

Structured Exercises

Before beginning these exercises, please read "Note to the Instructor" on page xiii.

1. *Coat of Arms.* The discussion of death is closely tied to values in life. This exercise is meant to help students examine what values they hold in life. Have each student draw the outline of a large shield or "coat of arms" on a sheet of paper and divide it into six fields. In each field, have students draw a picture to represent the answer to each of the following questions:
   a. If you were to die right now, what do you think your friends would miss most about you? Draw a picture to show what they might miss.
   b. Think of something about which you feel very strongly, something for which you would be willing to give your life. Draw it.
   c. What was the closest you ever came to losing your life? Draw a picture to represent that event.
   d. Think of someone who was close to you who died. Draw a picture to show what you miss most about that person.
   e. What are you doing to help yourself live a long, healthy life? Illustrate this on your coat of arms.
   f. Imagine that you have one year left to live. Draw something to represent what you would do in that year, what kind of activity you would pursue.

   After completing their drawings, have students discuss their choices with each other in pairs. Then have the pairs return to the large group for a summary of similarities and differences. Finally, have the group as a whole consider the implications of the range of values represented.

2. *Kidney Machine Decision.* To help a class experience how their own attitudes, values, and past experiences with death would influence their decision making, the class can be divided into groups of five to

seven. Copies of the *Kidney Machine Description Sheet* can be distributed to each group. An additional piece of information, the *Kidney Machine Psychological Reports Sheet,* is included in Appendix A1. Its use is optional. If it is to be used in this exercise, the student should not turn to the additional material until the middle of the decision-making process. The groups will need time to read through the materials and about 30 minutes to arrive at a solution. Each group can list the criteria the participants used in decision making. At the end of the allotted time, the groups can evaluate their work in terms of the following:

a. Whom did they choose? Why?
b. Did they feel they had enough information about each candidate to make a decision?
c. What effect did the psychological data have on their decision?
d. To what extent were they motivated to *avoid* making a decision, (e.g., leaving the decision to chance in some way)?
e. Were any novel or unusual solutions proposed?
f To what extent did their group try to "objectify" their decision, i.e., by rating candidates or devising a formula? Were such efforts helpful?

The decisions of all the groups can then be shared for a discussion of criteria. If time allows, the class can then discuss what factors in subjects' profiles would change on their decision.

KIDNEY MACHINE DESCRIPTION SHEET

Located at Swedish Hospital in Seattle, Washington, is the famous kidney machine. A marvel of technological ingenuity, it is the only hope of life for people with a rare kidney disease.

In actuality, the machine functions as a kidney for people who have lost the use of their own. By connecting themselves to the machine for twenty-four hours each week, people with renal failure can remain alive indefinitely—or until they are killed by some other ailment not connected with their kidneys.

There are several problems associated with using this machine, for there are many more people who need it than there is time available on the machine. In fact, only about five people can be placed on it at any one time. Doctors examine all potential patients and determine those who could profit most from connection to the machine. They screen out those with other diseases, for whom the machine would be only a temporary expedient, and they turn their list of recommended patients over to the hospital administration. At present, the doctors have submitted the names of five persons for *one* place on the machine.

The committee assembled to make the decision has been given a brief biography of each person appearing on the list. It is assumed that each person has an equal chance of remaining alive if allowed to use the machine. Thus, the committee is asked to decide which *one* of these may have access to the machine.

You are asked to act as if you were a member of this committee. Remember, there is only one vacancy, and you must fill it with one of these five people. You must agree, *unanimously,* on the single person who is permitted to remain alive, and you must decide your own criteria for making this choice.

The only medical information you have is that people over forty seem to do more poorly on the machine than those under forty (although they do not necessarily find it useless). It is up to you.

KIDNEY MACHINE BIOGRAPHICAL SHEET

Alfred: White, male, American, age 42. Married for 21 years. Two children (boy 18, girl 15), both high school students. Research physicist at University medical school, working on cancer immunization project. Current publications indicate that he is on the verge of a significant medical discovery.

On the health service staff of local university, member of county medical society, member of Rotary International, and Boy Scout leader for 10 years.

Bill: Black, male, American, age 27. Married for five years. One child (girl, 3), wife six months pregnant. Currently employed as an auto mechanic in local car dealership.

Attending night school and taking courses in automatic-transmission rebuilding. No community service activities listed. Plans to open auto-transmission repair shop upon completion of trade school course.

Cora: White, female, American, age 30. Married for eleven years. Five children (boy 10, boy 8, girl 7, girl 5, girl 4 months). Husband self-employed (owns and operates tavern and short-order restaurant). High school graduate. Never employed.

Couple has just purchased home in local suburbs, and Cora is planning the interior to determine whether she has the talent to return to school for courses in interior decoration. Member of several religious organizations.

David: White, male, American, age 19. Single, but recently announced engagement and plans to marry this summer. Presently a sophomore at large eastern university, majoring in philosophy and literature. Eventually hopes to earn Ph.D. and become a college professor.

Member of several campus political organizations, an outspoken critic of the college "administration," was once suspended briefly for "agitation." Has had poetry published in various literary magazines around the New York area. Father is self-employed (owns men's haberdashery store), mother is deceased. Has two younger sisters (15, 11).

Edna: White, female, American, age 34. Single, presently employed as an executive secretary in large manufacturing company, where she has worked since graduation from business college. Member of local choral society; was alto soloist in Christmas production of Handel's *Messiah.* Has been very active in several church and charitable groups.

Source: © Gerald M. Phillips. "Kidney Machine." *1974 Annual Handbook for Group Facilitators.* Edited by J. William Pfeiffer and John E. Jones. La Jolla, California: University Associates Publishers, Inc., 1974, 78–83. Used by permission of Gerald M. Phillips.

For Further Reading

The following books and journal article provide in-depth coverage of the topics introduced in this chapter.

Becker, E. *The Denial of Death.* New York: Free Press, 1973.

Carse, J.P. *Death and Existence.* New York: Wiley, 1980.

Choron, J. *Death and Western Thought.* New York: Collier Books, 1963.

Feifel, H., ed. *New Meanings of Death.* New York: McGraw-Hill, 1977.

Fulton, R., ed. *Death and Identity,* rev. ed. Bowie, Md.: Charles Press, 1976.

Kalish, R.A., ed. *Death and Dying: Views from Many Cultures.* Farmingdale, N.Y.: Baywood, 1980.

Kastenbaum, R. *Death, Society and Human Experience.* Saint Louis: C.V. Mosby, 1977.

Kastenbaum, R., and Costa, P.T., Jr. Psychological Perspectives on Death. *Annual Review of Psychology, 28,* 1978, 225–249.

Lofland, L.H. *The Craft of Dying.* Beverly Hills, Ca: Sage, 1978.

Shneidman, E.S. *Deaths of Man.* New York: Quadrangle, 1973.

Stannard, D.S. (ed.). *Death in America.* Philadelphia: University of Pennsylvania Press, 1975.

Toynbee, A., ed. *Man's Concern with Death.* New York: McGraw-Hill, 1969.

Vernon, G. M. *Sociology of Death: An Analysis of Death-Related Behavior.* New York: Ronald Press, 1970.

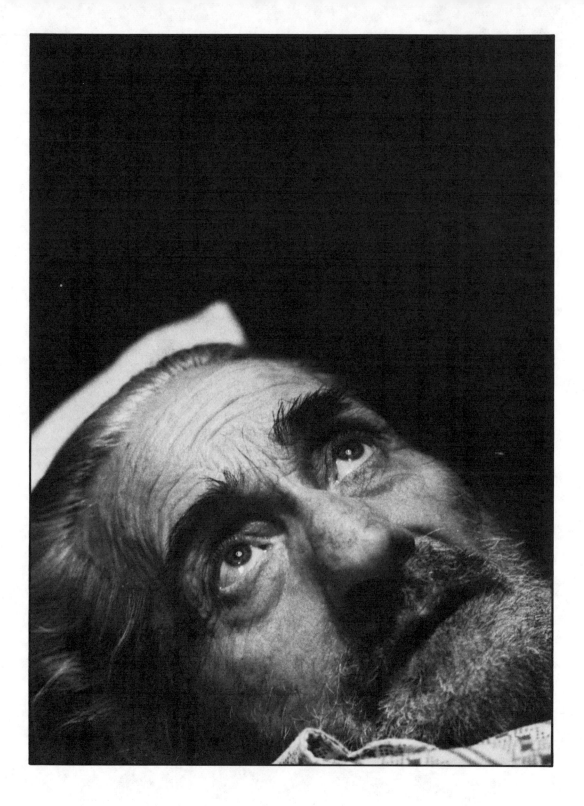

Chapter Two

The Experience of Dying

The person who is dying passes through a social transition from being alive to being dead. Yet all too often, as soon as the dying person enters that transition, he is treated as if he were already dead: left alone and forced to conspire in the fiction that "nothing is wrong." More and more, we are coming to recognize that the interval of dying can be a time for the resolution of conflicts, achievement of personal closure, and even a time for continued psychological growth. But if a person is to make his dying a time for growth, he must be informed and allowed to assume a more active role than has been customary in recent times.

EARLY VOICES

When social scientists began the study of death, they did so "at a distance," focusing more on organizational structures in the hospital than on the dying patient himself. Individual humanists like physician Sir William Osler, at the beginning of this century, and, more recently, psychotherapists like Kurt Eissler and Lawrence and Eda LeShan recognized the needs of the dying and urged their peers in medicine, psychiatry, and psychology to remain with dying patients even when nothing more than palliative care was possible. But the advice of those perceptive individuals was directed to a professional audience that was limited and often skeptical about the patient's willingness or ability to confront death.

DIALOGUE WITH THE TERMINALLY ILL

When Elisabeth Kübler-Ross first attempted to involve terminally ill patients in a seminar for hospital staff in 1965, she repeatedly heard, "We have no dying patients." Yet, once encouraged to discuss their feelings about impending death, many patients were grateful for the opportunity, speaking honestly and freely. Faced with the openness of the patients, the hospital staff realized that they would have to confront their own feelings about death and dying before they could face death directly with their patients. The resulting demand for seminars, classes, and special training has moved thanatology, the study of death, into the health curriculum. Significant changes in health care have taken place both within hospitals and in alternative social structures like hospice programs.

POPULAR RESPONSE

The public interest in studies of the terminally ill has been so great that shortly after the publication of *On Death and Dying* (1969), Kübler-Ross came to be regarded as a spokesperson for the "death and dying movement." Her work created a widened audience for the earlier research that had seldom been noticed beyond professional circles. The one-time public silence on the subject of death has been shattered. Now the media frequently treat such themes as the unique and complex character of the dying person, the value of the terminal patient's discussing death with his family, and the rewards (as well as the costs) of sharing another person's dying.

DYING: TRANSITION VS INSTITUTION

Indeed, the current interest in death and dying is so great as to threaten saturation. Given the machinery to prolong dying and the steadily increasing study of the dying patient, there is a danger that the experience of dying will not only be recognized but also be institutionalized, in much the same way as society has institutionalized death. Dying, like mourning, could become a scripted performance with expected roles. Montaigne warned against such an imbalance: "If we have not known how to live, it is wrong to teach us how to die, and to give the end a different shape from the whole."

OVERVIEW OF THE CHAPTER

To encounter the personal experience of dying is to give substance to theoretical understanding which would otherwise remain abstract. Chapter Two begins with a first-person account of a heart attack by a patient who is confronting complex reactions to impending death. The next two readings examine from the vantage point of clinical experience the process of facing death through terminal illness. In "Help in the Dying Process," E. Mansell Pattison, a psychiatrist, uses the crisis-intervention model to structure the crisis occasioned by the knowledge of death. Sorting out a range of fears evoked by the expectation of death, he frames specific problems the dying face and identifies ways for the helper to aid in the resolution of those problems. The goal is an appropriate death; that is, a death which is integrated into the meaning of the particular life as it was lived. Next, psychiatrist Elisabeth Kübler-Ross describes her early and influential work on the stage theory of dying. In "What Is It Like to Be Dying?" she sets out to answer the question from the patient's point of view in order to provide better information on which helpers can base their efforts.

Clinical experience, however, is only one ground for understanding, as psychologist Robert Kastenbaum shows in his objective assessment of Kübler-Ross's theory. In "Do We Die in Stages?" he urges expanded research both to validate the stage theory and to identify its limitations. As Kastenbaum notes, stage theories are by their nature generalized patterns; so, for contrast, individual statements are presented in the form of two modern poems. In the first, "Do Not Go Gentle into That Good Night" by Dylan Thomas, the persona rages against easy acceptance of death. In "To Waken an Old Lady," William Carlos Williams establishes a contrary perspective by presenting human experience in the metaphoric terms of nature imagery.

This chapter closes with two papers which draw back to view the interaction between the dying individual and the organizational structure within which the dying occurs. In "Reaction to Extreme Stress: Death by Impending Execution," psychiatrists Harvey Bluestone and Carl McGahee present brief case studies of prisoners condemned to execution. The reactions displayed by individual inmates demonstrate a wide variety of approaches to death. In "Awareness of Dying," sociologists Anselm Strauss and Barney Glaser analyze organizational strategies used by hospital staff to manage the patient's knowledge of impending death. They offer advantages and disadvantages to both patient and staff for each of the awareness contexts they present, and they conclude by urging the benefits of open awareness of death in the hospital structure.

This essay began by focusing on *dying* as the social transition that takes one from being alive to being dead. However, the readings in the chapter indicate that the living–dying interval is not as clear-cut as it might seem. The limits of the definition are pressed in the following Encounter in which it becomes clear that a heart attack may result in a rebirth, or the death of a lifestyle, or physical death, or simply a suspended sentence.

Encounter

AUTOBIOGRAPHY OF
A HEART ATTACK

The first sign was vomiting and diarrhea, but I didn't know I had a heart attack because the flu was going around. It was about eight on a Saturday morning, and I'd gone downstairs to get myself a cup of coffee. Fran, my wife, was still asleep and when I went back up, I just kept on going and vomiting, but I still didn't think I was having a heart attack. I figured I had just come down with the bug.

But when I got back in bed, I just couldn't get comfortable. I didn't have any pain, but I just felt poor even in bed. Fran said I felt cold and clammy, and I figured I ought to call the paramedics.

They were there in minutes, and after giving me an IV and checking me all over they told me I was in trouble. I knew that already, but they wouldn't tell me what was wrong. They've got to be careful that way. I still didn't think I had a heart attack, but I knew my body was getting ready for some big battle, what with it being cleaned out at both ends.

A lot of people, including me, at least before my heart attack, think that the only signs of a heart attack are chest pains and pains shooting down your arm, but that isn't always true. It depends on what part of your heart is affected. Mine was the left ventricle. Also, a lot of people have "silent attacks." They never feel any symptoms, and after a time they keel over because the heart never had a chance to repair itself.

I was so sedated in the CCU (Coronary Care Unit) that I wasn't apprehensive at all. I remember a few friends and relatives coming by, but I didn't feel I was deathly ill. You know, I was sedated 20 out of the 24.

I didn't get anxious until I was out of CCU and in a regular ward with a monitor. The man in the room with me, we got to know each other pretty well, was in bad shape and was being transferred to St. Vincent's for open heart surgery. At that time St. Vincent's

Source: As told to Dana Prom Smith. Reprinted by permission of Dana Prom Smith, Senior Associate, St. Paul's Foundation.

was taking all the high risk cases. I called his home the next day, and they told me he died on the table. That kind of got me. I hadn't really thought about dying.

There are three critical stages. If you make it the first twenty-four hours, you're over the first hurdle because you aren't dead. Then you've got to get through the next four or five days. You've got to get enough scarring to stop a blowout because if you blow, you're gone. And then you've got to keep the stress down to let the heart keep on scarring. During this time you begin to walk, but they keep you on Valium. I don't like that stuff because I don't trust drugs.

About this time things start getting grim because you become aware you'll never be the same again.

Some people begin to treat you like an invalid, and then you hear that some of the men at work are saying that "old Charlie isn't ever going to come back." They figure that if you're out for a month, you're out forever. I didn't like that at all. When I got home even some of the women tried to help me down the stairs as if I were a cripple. I didn't like that either.

I never thought I wouldn't make it, though. I don't know why, but I guess it's because I've had a couple of close calls before and squeaked by. You know, when you're in a crisis, that's not the time to give up, it's the time to hold on and keep your head.

A heart attack is hard on your sex life. You just can't get worked up too much if you're worried about your pulse rate and blood pressure, and then the medication depresses your ability and desire. It took a little time to work around that one. I like sex as much as the next man, but I sure didn't want to die for it.

The thing that bothered me the most was the way I had to change my life. Some things turned out for the better, because with better diet and exercise I've had fewer colds and casual illnesses, but the truth is that you never fully recover because you're about ninety percent of what you used to be. Mostly that doesn't bother me because most of us function way below our capacities.

But I can never be more than an hour away from a hospital or doctor. I can't chance accidents like capsizing in a boat because the cold water might be too big a shock for my heart. I can't go hiking in the mountains. You live on the margin.

I guess you're apprehensive as long as you live. I knew I could go back to work, and when I finally put in a full eight-hour day, I felt a lot better. I came home dog-tired, but I knew I'd made it, but still nothing was going to be the same anymore. That damned clot had changed everything.

1. How did the heart attack change life for this speaker? Consider three or four ways in which your own life would change were you to experience a similar attack.

2. Apply the concept of appropriate death of the speaker appropriate? Inappropriate?

3. Acceptance of death often depends on a person's readiness to begin the grief work before the death occurs, whether it is his own death or that of another person. Based on the account above, what indications of readiness were present before the heart attack? After the heart attack?

E. MANSELL PATTISON

Help in the
Dying Process

Even a brush with death such as the heart attack described in the Encounter sets up a psychological trajectory for the rest of one's life. In the following article, Pattison distinguishes between the fact of death and the process of dying. He views the living–dying interval as a psychological crisis period which reactivates anxieties and conflicts central to the organization of the individual's personality. Pattison's framework, which differentiates among the fears normally encountered in the dying process, enables him to describe criteria for appropriate death and to make specific recommendations for psychological support during this time.

"There's nothing more I can do for you, you're going to die." Having failed to preserve life, the physician leaves, for what has he to do with death?

And what has the psychotherapist to do with death? It has been suggested that physicians have failed to provide assistance to the dying because of unresolved conflicts towards death that lie buried in the unconscious of the medical profession. There is ample experimental and clinical evidence to support that assertion.[1,2] Yet little comment has been made on the attitudes of psychotherapists toward death, particularly as it affects clinical practice. Thus Wahl[3] observed:

> It is interesting to note that anxiety about death, when it is noted in the psychiatric literature, is usually described solely as a derivative and secondary phenomenon, often as a more easily endurable form of the "castration fear." . . . It is important to consider if these formulations also subserve a defensive need on the part of psychiatrists themselves.

The problem was inadvertently stated by a psychiatrist reporting on his research on aging.[4]

Source: E. Mansell Pattison. "Help in the Dying Process." *Voices*, V (Spring, 1969), 6–14.

> I myself tend to adhere to the concept of death as an accident, and therefore find it difficult to reconcile myself for myself or for others . . . people do not forgive themselves easily for having failed to save their own or others' lives.

One can observe the failure to face death in many psychotherapeutic situations. Consider how often a patient's threat of suicide cows the therapist. Or the therapist who puts himself in physical danger with a dangerous patient without noting the real danger. Or the reluctance to allow a patient to expose his deepest threatening and psychotic thoughts which intimate the annihilation of personality. I recall the long discussions I had as a young psychiatrist working in a prison. How could we work therapeutically with men serving life sentences? To what purposes? They seemed dead in contrast to our bright anticipatory lives.

I am struck by the fact that most psychotherapists feel sorely prepared to deal with death. This was brought home to me in a very personal way. Shortly after I published an article on dying,[5] I received the following letter from a well-known psychotherapist:

> Dear Dr. P.: I noticed your article on dying, I read it, enjoyed it and 'forgot' about it, until last month when my wife developed acute cancer to which she succumbed in three weeks. I would like you to know how immeasurably your article helped me (and her, indirectly), during that trying period. It is impossible to put into words—all I can say is that I had comfort during and after her dying in the knowledge that I could and did contribute some psychic comfort to her. Not only does your article have obvious personal significance to me, but I feel the wisdom in it should be reaching others in the profession.

I was deeply moved by this, but I know that my wisdom was borrowed from others. Yet how to deal with death has not been part of the curriculum of "training for life." Every psychotherapist ought to read Allen Wheelis' parable,[6] "The League of Death," for Wheelis says to his fellow psychotherapists (as I read him) that we cannot face life until we can face death.

But we must move on, for our psychotherapeutic concern is not with death (that we can only assimilate) but rather with the process of dying. Indeed our preoccupation with death often precludes our looking at the process of dying—the period of life between knowledge of death and the point of death. How do we help people during this period of "dying life?"

A Seattle physician, Dr. Merrill Shaw, had a rectal cancer which had slowly gnawed away until death was only a few weeks away. Yet at that point he addressed the American Academy of General Practice with words of relevance:

> The period of inactivity after a patient learns there is no hope for his condition can be a period of great productivity. I regard myself as fortunate to have had this opportunity for a 'planned exit.' Patients who have been told there is no hope need help with their apprehension. Any doctor forfeits his priesthood of medicine, if, when he knows his patient is beyond help, he discharges the patient to his own services. Then the patient needs his

physician more than anybody else does. The doctor who says merely, 'I'll drop in to see you once in a while, though there's nothing more I can do,' is of no use to the patient. For the patient goes through a period of unnecessary apprehension and anxiety.

The problem is that we do not perceive the healing task in existential terms, but rather in death-defensive terms. If we cannot pretend that we defeat death (and all treatment is in a sense a delaying-action), then we give in to ennui. But was it not Oliver Wendell Holmes who reminded us that "the physician's task is to cure rarely, relieve sometimes, and comfort always"?

The real help that can be given in the "living-dying" process of dying was brought home to me personally by another letter:

> Dear Dr. P.: Quite by accident I read your treatise on dying. Because I am so grateful for your guidance I am writing not only to thank you but to suggest that the article be made available to relatives who care for patients . . . My husband has been treated for chronic glomeruli nephritis for nine years. For the past five years he has had biweekly dialysis which equates to a living-dying stage of long duration. In these times when there is no doctor-patient relationship in this type of indirect care the entire burden of sharing the responsibility of death falls to the member of the family caring for the nephritic. Your listing of the fears was so apparent when I read your paper, yet when my husband experienced them I was unprepared to see them or even acknowledge them. Whenever a patient is accepted on a kidney program he knows he is dying. Would it not be a kindness to the person caring for him to have access to your fine article?

THE PROCESS OF DYING SUBSEQUENT
TO THE CRISIS OF KNOWLEDGE OF DEATH

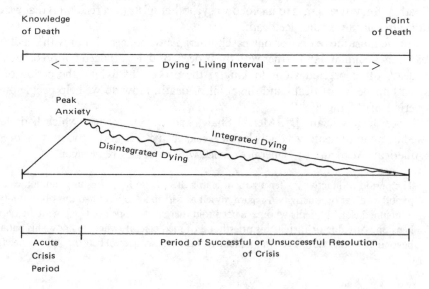

Again, I was touched by a person and learned from her. It is not death that is so much the problem, but how to handle the process of dying. This can be seen in the following diagram. Note that the knowledge of death often precedes the point of death by many days, weeks, months, years. The *knowledge of death* produces a crisis in the life of the person. Will the crisis lead to a disintegrating process of dying? Or can we help the person to deal with the crisis of knowledge of death and help the person to attain an integrated process of dying?[7]

The concepts of crisis intervention can be applied here to the *knowledge of death*.[8] This crisis can be seen as having five characteristics:

1. This stressful event poses a problem which by definition is insoluble in the immediate future. Dying in this sense is most stressful because it is ultimately insoluble and one to which we have to bow rather than solve.
2. The problem taxes one's psychologic resources since it is beyond one's traditional problem-solving methods. One is faced with a new experience with no prior experience to fall back on, for although one lives amidst death, that is far different from one's own death.
3. The situation is perceived as a threat or danger to the life goals of the person. Dying interrupts a person in the midst of life and even in old age it abruptly confronts one with the goals that one had set for one's own life.
4. The crisis period is characterized by a tension which mounts to a peak, then falls. As one faces the crisis of death, anxiety begins to mount, rises to a peak during which the person either mobilizes his coping mechanisms to deal with this anxiety or experiences disorganization and capitulation to his anxiety. In either event, one then passes to a state of diminishing anxiety as one approaches death. Hence, the peak of acute anxiety usually occurs considerably before death.
5. The crisis situation awakens unresolved key problems from both the near and distant past. Problems of dependency, passivity, narcissism, inadequacy, identity, and more, are all reactivated by the process of dying. Hence, one is faced not only with the problem of death per se, but a host of unresolved feelings from one's own lifetime and its inevitable conflicts.

The importance of dying as a crisis is that the crisis is experienced as an overwhelming insuperable feeling of personal inadequacy in dealing with the dying process. There is bewilderment, confusion, indefinable anxiety, and unspecified fear. The person is faced with a total problem that he does not have resources to deal with, and the ensuing anxiety makes it impossible to deal with any of the part-aspects. *Here lies our opportunity to intervene, for although we cannot deal with the ultimate problem of death, we can help the person to deal with the various parts of the process of dying.* By focusing on these part-problems, the dying person can cope with himself and with his dying in some measure to resolve the crisis in a rewarding fashion that enhances his self-esteem, dignity, and integrity. The dying person can take pride then in having faced his crisis of dying with hope and courage and come away having dealt successfully with the crisis. One might call this healthy dying!

Now let us turn to each of these part-aspects of the experience of dying:

THE FEAR OF THE UNKNOWN

That which is strange and which we cannot anticipate strikes a deep fear within ourselves. This fundamental anxiety might be termed a *basic death anxiety*. A case report by Janice Norton illustrated this well.[9]

> Three days before a patient's death and a few hours before she became terminally comatose, we had a long conversation about her dying. She told me her only remaining fear was that dying was strange and unknown to her, that she had never done it before. Like birth, it was something that only happened once to any individual, and that similarly one might not remember what it was really like, only know that it had once happened. She no longer worried about what was to happen to her after death, any more than an infant being born might worry about what his future life might be; she felt that she might be unnecessarily concerned with the actual process of death itself. She then asked me if I had been with other patients when they died and seemed relieved by my affirmative answer. One very comforting recurring thought to her was that throughout the centuries many people had died before her; more importantly, it had occurred to her that I would share this experience with her, although not at this time. I agreed that this was certainly so and added that I hoped I might equal her courage. She was pleased by this and then she reminisced about our relationship.

THE FEAR OF LONELINESS

Sickness of itself isolates one from the rest of humanity and the more so when one is dying. It is a commonplace observation that as death approaches others literally depart. This detachment is not only a psychologic phenomenon, but is also a reflection of our urban technology where the process of dying has become dehumanized and mechanized. There is inevitable separation in death, and yet our culture is perhaps one of the first in the history of humanity to reinforce the isolation of dying.

Now as John Donne said, "No man is an island," and our spirits feed on the food of human companionship. As experiments in sensory deprivation have vividly shown us, the human deprived of contact with other humans quickly disintegrates and loses his ego integrity. For the dying person, the mere fact of institutionalization has already set the stage for human deprivation that leads to a type of anaclitic depression. It is not the depression of the loss of a loved one, but depression resulting from the loss of necessary nurturing persons. Without this support, one rapidly falls into a confusional syndrome of human deprivation which we term loneliness. Indeed, it appears that this fear of loneliness is most paramount and immediate when a person first faces the prospect of death.

FEAR OF LOSS OF FAMILY AND FRIENDS

Related to the actual separation that begins to occur is the real event of losing one's family and friends through one's own death just as much as if they themselves were dying. Hence, there is a real grief for this loss which must be mourned and worked through. Being able to resolve this separation can lead to a sense of attainment for both the patient and the family before death actually occurs. Failure to recognize this loss or being blocked in the grief process may make it difficult for the dying person to distinguish between his own problem of death and the natural and necessary process of grief which can be resolved before death.

FEAR OF LOSS OF BODY

Our bodies are very much part of our self-image so that when illness distorts our body image there is not only a loss of function but a loss of self. This narcissistic blow to the integrity of oneself results in shame, and feelings of disgrace and inadequacy, for vital parts of the integral self-image are lost. Here again, one comes to genuine grief for the loss of part of oneself. In addition, the loss of body leads to the perception of self as disfigured and unlovely, hence unlovable. So the physically ill fear that they will no longer be loved by their families, will be rejected, and left alone. It bears comment that patients seem better able to tolerate external disfigurement than internal disease. Although external disfigurement may be difficult to bear, it seems to pose less threat than unknown and unspecified processes that the person cannot see and thereby keep track of. Hence, the hidden cancer or the failing heart may provoke more anxiety than the external symptoms of disease.

FEAR OF LOSS OF SELF-CONTROL

Debilitating disease makes one less capable of control of one's self, particularly when mental capacity is also affected. This is particularly relevant in our society. We are a hyperrational culture in which the ideal man is one who has full conscious willful rational control of himself. A tremendous fancy! As a result, we become anxious and feel threatened by anything that poses loss of consciousness or control. This is one of the reasons that our society is so ambivalent about the use of psychedelic drugs, tranquilizing, or energizing drugs, or even alcohol—they diminish our rationalistic self-control. So, too, our culture is skeptical and wary of any type of mystical experiences. Loss of self-control that might be quite acceptable among Eastern mystics is quite foreign to our Western human experience. It is rare that Americans experience any sort of self-acceptable loss of control. So when they come to the loss of control and rationality in the process of dying they have nothing in their past by which to measure or deal with this internal experience.

In studies by Goldstein 25 years ago it was shown that patients with brain disease often were troubled more by their own reaction to their mental deficits than by the deficit itself. Likewise, for the dying it is a giving up of total conscious willful control of the self that poses a threat to the ego. One is placed in a position of dependency as well as inadequacy so that in a sense the ego is no longer master of its own fate nor the captain of the self. So it is important to encourage and allow the dying person to retain whatever decisions and authority he can, to sustain him in retaining control of small daily tasks and decisions, and to let him find reward and meaning in whatever self-control is available to him.

FEAR OF LOSS OF IDENTITY

The loss of human contact, the loss of family and friends, the loss of one's body and control are all tied in with the sense of one's identity. Human contacts affirm who we are, family contacts affirm what we have been, and the control of our bodies affirms one's own self. There is a threat to the ego by losing the feelings for one's own body just as there is a threat to the ego by losing contact with family and cultural tradition.

In the dying process, one is faced with the crisis of maintaining an integrity of ego in the face of forces toward dissolution and annihilation of the person. Erikson sums it up as the crisis between *integrity versus despair:*[10]

> It is the acceptance of one's own and only life cycle and of the people who have become significant to it as something that had to be and that, by necessity, permitted of no substitutions. It thus means a new different love of one's parents, free of the wish that they should have been different, and an acceptance of the fact that one's life is one's own responsibility. It is a sense of comradeship with men and women of distant times and of different pursuits, that have created orders and objects and sayings conveying human dignity and love. Although aware of the relativity of all the various life styles which have given meaning to human striving, the possessor of integrity is ready to defend the dignity of his own life style against all physical and economic threats. For he knows that an individual life is the accidental coincidence of but one life cycle with but one segment of history; and that for him all human integrity stands and falls with the one style of integrity of which he partakes.

Despair, in contrast, is the consequence of the loss of self-esteem—the failure to maintain respect for oneself, for what one has been. Erikson's apt phrase is: "To be—through having been." Speaking of his own death, Willie Loman, the salesman, says: "A man must not be allowed to fall into his grave as a dead dog." It is not that you die, but how you die—and hope and courage contribute to maintaining a respect for self until death.

Allied with the idea of integrity then is the desire for both a reunion and a continuity. The reunion has to do with fantasies of return to a primal maternal figure as well as reunion with specific loved ones. And perhaps in some sense the fantasies of the reunion with one's parentage and one's race is a reaffirmation of the fact that one is part of a continuing line of human existence.

With our emphasis on individualism and cultural discontinuity, this sense of affinity is perhaps less available to us in American culture than it is to other peoples. Man as part of the enduring community, as part of the extended and continuing family of man is reflected in the following lines by an African poet, Birago Diop:

Listen more often
To things than to beings;
The fire's voice is heard
Hear the voice of water.
Hear in the wind
The bush sob
It is the ancestor's breath.
Those who have died have never left,
They are in the woman's breast
They are in the wailing child
And in the kindling firebrand
The dead are not under the earth,
They are in the forest, they are in the home
The dead are not dead.

Likewise, there is the desire for the maintenance and the continuity of one's life via one's family and the human race by bequeathing parts of oneself and one's possessions to those who will stay behind. This is most obvious in the tradition of leaving a will. But more personal is the fact that the dying person often finds meaning and significance in the maintenance of his own integrity by sharing of his belongings with those who are most immediately close to him. The most concrete example is the bequest of parts of one's body. We make good cultural use of this through eye banks, bone banks, and so on. As an example, some years ago as an intern I took care of a man with undiagnosed cancer of the neck. He was obviously debilitated and rapidly progressing toward death. We talked many times of the meaning of death and of his life and what he had done and what he would like to have done. He was interested in my plans and my future and hoped that I would learn from his case things that would be of value to me as I continued in my life in medicine. He was discharged and returned to the hospital several months later near the point of death. The surgeons wished to obtain a neck biopsy but the patient refused until he had talked with his doctor, namely me. So I shortly got a call from the professor of surgery asking if I would please see the patient as their consultant! The patient was much relieved when he saw me and wanted my professional opinion as to whether I thought that the surgery professors were right in their management of his case. When I explained to him that biopsy would probably not change the course of his disease nor prevent him from dying in the immediate future, but that it would help us in our understanding of the disease process and would help me in my training and education, he was very happy to comply, feeling that he had something that he could give and share with me, namely his disease process and his body. In this sense he had given to me part of himself that would remain with me after his death.

FEAR OF REGRESSION

Finally, there is a fear of those internal instincts within oneself that always push us to retreat from the outer world of reality to a primal world of fantasy and bliss.

Throughout life, our ego fights against this internal pull to an eternal primordial existence. Freud called in Thanatos—instinct to death. Whatever the theoretical grounds, it does appear that the dying person begins to return to a state of being at one with the world where there is a helpless and timeless existence, where I (the ego) and you (outer world) no longer are differentiated. At this point, one is rapidly approaching the state of surrender to the process of renunciation of life and return to union with the earth out of which we have sprung. Indeed, psychic death is now acceptable, desirable and now at hand.

THE SEQUENCE OF DYING

What I have sketched out here is a rough and tentative outline of the sequence of dying. First is facing a seemingly impossible crisis that threatens to overwhelm the self. Mankind seems to have always recognized that no one has the capability to face this crisis alone, and so we have cultural customs whereby we actually and literally help people to die! Given our interest, support, and guidance, the dying person may turn to use his available capacities to deal with the several distinct part-processes of dying. He can face death as unknown with the realization that he cannot know, and instead consider the process of dying that he can know and deal with. He can learn to endure the inevitable degrees of separation that begin to occur if he is not actually deprived of human contact. He can face the loss of relatives, friends, and activities and actively mourn their loss and become reconciled to it if this grief is defined and accepted. He can tolerate the loss of self-control if it is not perceived by himself and others as a shameful experience, and if he can gain control of himself to the degree that he is able. He can retain dignity and self-respect in the face of the completion of his life cycle, gradually relinquish the unattainable and respect himself for what he has been. Then one can place one's life in a perspective of both reunion and continuity with one's personal history and human tradition. If this is accomplished, then one can move toward an acceptable regression where the self gradually returns to a state of non-self.

THE APPROPRIATE DEATH

If the dying person is provided the opportunity and assistance, then the experience of dying can be a part of living. Weisman and Hackett[11] speak of appropriate death whose criteria closely approximate the clinical sequence outlined above.
1. Conflict is reduced.
2. Compatibility with the ego ideal is obtained.
3. Continuity of important relationships is preserved or restored.
4. Consummation of basic instincts and wishes of fantasy re-emerge and are fulfilled.

The importance of an appropriate death is that dying is not an extraneous foreign process but rather it is a process integrated into the style, meaning and sequence of that which has gone before. The concrete nature of each man's appropriate death will be different, but can be appropriate for him.

HELP IN THE EXPERIENCE OF DYING

From this clinical sequence, we can define certain patterns of assistance toward appropriate death.

1. Sharing the responsibility for the crisis of dying for the patient so that he has help in dealing with the first impact of anxiety and bewilderment.
2. Clarifying and defining the realities of the day-to-day existence which can be dealt with by the patient. These are the realities of his life.
3. Making continued human contact available and rewarding.
4. Assisting in the separation from and grief over the realistic losses of family, body image, and self control, while retaining communication and meaningful relationships with those who will be lost.
5. Assuming necessary body and ego functions for the person without incurring shame or depreciation, maintaining respect for the person, and helping him maintain his self-respect.
6. Encouraging the person to work out an acceptance of his life situation with dignity and integrity so that gradual regression may occur without conflict or guilt.

Death is a crisis event, and can be understood in the clinical terms of crisis intervention therapy. The question facing the clinician is more than whether or not, or how, to tell a patient he is dying. Death is not the primary problem, but rather how one faces death and goes about the process of dying. Although we cannot deal with the ultimate problem of death, we can help the person to deal with the various parts of the process of dying.

The clinician can use specific measures to help the patient with each of these part-aspects of dying so that an appropriate death can occur. An appropriate death is not an extraneous foreign process, but rather a process integrated into the style, meaning, and sequence of that which has gone before. Only when the clinician has come to face death within himself can he begin to practice the high therapeutic art of helping people to die.

NOTES

1. B.G. Glaser and A. Strauss. *Awareness of Dying* (Chicago: Aldine, 1966).
2. B.G. Glaser and A. Strauss. *Time for Dying* (Chicago: Aldine, 1968).
3. C.W. Wahl. "The Fear of Death" in *Death and Identity*, ed. R. Fulton (New York: Wiley, 1965).
4. A.I. Goldfarb. *Death and Dying: Attitudes of Patient and Doctor,* GAP Symposium No. 11, Oct. 1965.
5. E.M. Pattison. "The Experience of Dying," *Amer. J. Psychother.* 21 (1967):32.
6. A. Wheelis. "The League of Death" in *The Illusionless Man* (New York: Norton, 1966).
7. M. Shaw. "Dying of Cancer, 'Horror' Attitude Most Harmful," *Seattle Times,* March 24, 1954.
8. H.J. Parad, ed. *Crisis Intervention: Selected Readings* (New York: Family Service Assn., 1965).
9. J. Norton. "Treatment of a Dying Patient," *Psychoanal. Stud. Child.* 18 (1963):541.
10. E.H. Erickson. "Identity and the Life Cycle," *Psychological Issues* 1, No. 1, 1959.
11. A.D. Weisman and T.D. Hackett. "Predilection to Death: Death and Dying as a Psychiatric Problem," *Psychosom. Med.* 23 (1961): 232.

ELISABETH KÜBLER-ROSS

What Is It Like
to Be Dying?

Philosophy has always concerned itself with death, and great literature speaks of the
enduring conflicts common to all ages. Only recently, as death has been pushed further
and further away from everyday life, has it become a subject of study for the social
sciences. Sociologists have compiled bodies of data on the organization of death and
dying, and Elisabeth Kübler-Ross has done much to establish dying as a discipline of its
own within psychiatry and psychology. In the following article she summarizes her best
known work with the dying. Although she readily admits that all patients do not follow
"a classical pattern" and that a patient may well remain in one "stage" or another, by
outlining a psychological process of dying, she provides a structure for understanding
the reactions and needs of the dying person. Kübler-Ross emphasizes, as Pattison did,
how those close to the dying patient must work to understand their own attitudes
toward death in order to be able to help the patient.

What is it like to be dying? Not from the nurse's point of view, nor from the doctor's,
nor the family's, but from the patient's point of view: what is it like? Because, if we
have some idea of what the answer might be, then we're going to be in a better position to help.

At the University of Chicago Billings Hospital, some of us have made it our
business to find out a little more about what it is like to be dying. Before sharing this
information with you, though, let me first raise another question: why—at this time, in
this society—must we have so many books on death and dying, so many lectures and
seminars on the subject? After all, we should be experts on dying. It is the one thing
that has been with mankind as long as man himself. So why has it suddenly become
such a big issue?

Death has always been a fearful thing to men. We have a hard time conceiving of
our own death. We believe with the psalmist who says, "A thousand shall fall at thy

side, and ten thousand at thy right hand: *but* it shall not come nigh thee." Deep down, we believe, or would like to believe, that we are immortal. We cannot conceive of dying a natural death at the end of our lives, just falling asleep one night and not waking up. Instead, when we have to conceive death, we see it as something malignant and catastrophic: a destructive intervention from the outside that hits us suddenly and finds us unprepared.

Death in the old days came in the form of epidemics: produced by nature, not by man. Man tried to master epidemics, he mastered illness, he developed antibiotics and vaccinations, he learned to prolong life, he was able to master many, many causes of death. But in his fear of death and his need to master things, he has also developed weapons. If he has the choice to kill or be killed, he chooses to kill.

In the old days, an enemy in the battlefield could be seen. You had a chance to defend your family, your tribe, or your honor; you could choose a good weapon or a good hill. You had a chance to survive.

But today, out of man's need to be stronger, to defy death, he has developed bigger and more horrible weapons. One reason for our present death-denying society, I believe, is that man has now created weapons of mass destruction—man-made, mind you, not like nature's epidemics. He has developed weapons which, in a very concrete way, represent our fear of death, the catastrophic death that hits us from the outside when we are not prepared. You can't see, you can't smell, and you can't hear this enemy, whether it be chemical or bacteriological warfare, atom bombs, or even pollution.

What do we do when we have created such weapons of mass destruction? We cannot defend ourselves physically against them, we have to defend ourselves psychologically. We can pretend that nobody will push the wrong button. We can build ourselves bomb shelters in the garden, or we can build anti-missiles and have the illusion that we are safe.

But none of these defenses really works. What works partially is that we can deny that we are finite. That it shall happen to thee and thee but not come nigh to me. We can pretend that we are not finite by developing "deep freeze societies," where we freeze those who die and put them into some sort of mausoleum and promise the next of kin to defrost them in 50 or 100 years from now. These societies really exist; they serve the need to deny that people actually die.

We see this same need and tendency in the hospital. When we are assigned to dying patients, we feel very, very uncomfortable. In fact, even when we know that a patient is dying, we have a hard time facing that fact and acknowledging it—not in the head but in the gut. And our patients very often die with more difficulty than they used to.

In the old days, people were more likely to die at home rather than in the hospital. When a person is at home, he's in his own familiar environment, with his family and his children around him. Dying, under these circumstances, is not only easier and more comfortable for the patient, but it also does something for his family—especially the children, who can share in the preparatory grief for a person who is dying in the house. Such a child will grow up and know that death is part of life.

But if the sick person is shipped off to the hospital, with visits limited to perhaps five minutes every hour in the intensive treatment unit, it is not the same experience. And children are not allowed to see those patients, those parents. In Europe, even now, there is no embalming, no make-believe sleep, no slumber rooms, no euphemisms. All this, I think, helps us to face death as part of life. But today, in the United States, we have a long way to go before we can accept death as part of life. Dying, as many patients have expressed to us, has become not only more lonely and more isolated, but very often more impersonalized, dehumanized, and mechanized.

Some five years ago, four theology students asked me if I couldn't help them in a project. They had to write a paper on crisis in human life, and they had chosen dying. That's the biggest crisis people have to face, they said, and they asked, "How do you go about it? How do you do research on dying? You can't experience it. You can't experiment with it, you can't verify it, you can't do all the things that one ought to do with a good research project."

So I suggested to them that it would be very simple to ask dying patients, "What is it like? How does it feel? What fears, needs, fantasies do you have? What kind of things are we doing that are helpful? What kind of things do we do that are detrimental?" The students agreed, and I volunteered to work with them and to find a seriously ill patient for our first interview.

How naive I was: I discovered that there was not a single dying patient in a 600-bed hospital! I went from ward to ward and told the nurses and doctors that I would like to talk to a terminally ill patient.

"What about?"

"About dying."

"Oh, we have nobody dying."

If I pushed, they said, "He's too weak" or "too sick" or "too tired" or "he doesn't feel like talking." A lot of not only denial and rationalization but also hostility and some very aggressive behavior emerged. One nurse asked me, "Do you enjoy playing God?" and another: "Do you get a kick out of telling a 20-year-old that he has one week to live?" And, of course, there was much well-meant protectiveness for the patients.

I had had the same experience a few years earlier in another hospital. There, the only way I was able to find a dying patient was to go through the wards and look at the patients and guess that somebody was very sick. That way I saw an old man who looked very sick and who was reading a paper with a headline, "Old Soldiers Never Die." I asked him if he wasn't afraid to read that, and he said, "Are you one of those doctors who can't talk about it when you can't help us no more?" So I gave him a pat on the back and said, "You're the right kind of man and I want to talk with you."

Eventually, though, we started to receive an ever-increasing number of referrals. Our first patient was perhaps the most troubling one—to me, anyway. I went to see this old man the day before I was to see him with the students. He put his arms out and with pleading eyes said, "Please sit down *now*." With the emphasis on *now*. But I did what we always do. I could only hear my own needs, I was frustrated and tired of running around, and tomorrow was the day I was supposed to see him with the students. So I told him "No, I can't stay now, I'll be back tomorrow," and I left.

When I came back with the students the next day, it was too late. He was in oxygen, he could hardly breathe, and the only thing he was able to say was, "Thank you for trying, anyway." And he died a short time later. He helped us a lot, however, although not in any verbal way. What he told us was that when a terminally ill patient says, "Sit down *now*," you have to sit down *now*. Because somehow these patients sense that *now* is the time that they can talk about it. There may not be such a time again, so even if you can sit down only two or three minutes, you will feel better, and so will the patient.

The students and I had so many feelings when we left that man's room that we did something that we have continued to do for almost five years now: we went to my office and shared our gut reactions. Not nice things. Not the kinds of things that one ought to say and feel: those come from your head. But how does it feel in the gut? That's what we talk about. We try to get to know each other's feelings—to understand them, not to judge them. We try to help each other express them so that we can learn to listen to our gut reaction and to differentiate between the patient's needs and our own.

So far, we have interviewed over 400 terminally ill patients. By "terminally ill," I mean patients with a serious illness which may end fatally. They don't necessarily die the next day or the next week. Many of them have gone home or have had a remission. Some have lived only 12 hours, and others have lived for a year or two.

What have we learned from them? We have learned that our patients all know when they are dying, and I think that's consoling for us to know. Half of them have never been told that they have a serious illness. We are often asked what or whether a patient should be told. Actually, I don't think any patient should be told that he is dying. He will tell *you* that when you dare to listen, when you are able to hear it.

But patients should, I think, with very few exceptions, be told when they have a serious illness. Our patients say that they would like to be told this under two conditions: one is that the person telling them allows for some hope, and the second is that "you are going to stick it out with me—not desert me—not leave me alone." If we can, indeed, "stick it out" with them, then I think that we can help them the most.

We have learned, too, that dying patients generally go through a series of stages. The stages don't always follow one another; they overlap sometimes and sometimes they go back and forth.

Most patients, when told they have a serious illness, react with shock and denial. "No, it can't be me. It's not possible." Only three of our 400, however, maintained this denial to the very end, although many have maintained denial in the presence of other people—usually family or staff members—who need denial themselves. If a family needs denial, the patient will not talk to them about the seriousness of his illness or how he feels. But if they, or we, can tell him that we are ready to talk about it, that we are willing to listen, he will drop the denial quite quickly and will talk about his situation.

Our patients usually drop part of their denial when they have to take care of unfinished business or financial matters, especially when they begin to worry about their children. But they also drop their denial if they know that the person with them will help them to express the multitude of feelings that emerge when they face the given reality.

Perhaps the second most important and common response is anger. When a person can no longer say, "No, not me," the next question is usually "Why me?" The patient should be allowed to express this, and you don't have to have an answer because none of us will ever have an answer to that question. Just listen.

At this stage these patients will be very difficult; not only with the family (they visit too early or too late or with too many people or not enough people), but also with the nurses. You come in and shake a pillow and the patient complains, "Why are you bothering me now? I just want to take a nap." When you leave him alone, he protests that you don't straighten out his bed. The physician doesn't have the right prescriptions or the right diet or the right tests. In short, these are extremely "difficult and ungrateful" patients.

What do you do when you have a patient like that? What is your gut reaction? Remember, the harder you try, the harder the time he gives you. What do you do? You withdraw, you get angry at him, maybe you wait twice as long until you answer his light.

In one study, they measured the time it took nurses to answer the patients' lights. And they discovered that patients who were beyond medical help—terminally ill patients—had to wait twice as long as the others.

That, too, you have to try to understand and not judge. It is very hard to be around patients like this for very long, especially if you try to do your best and all you get is criticism and abuse. What we have found to be most helpful to the patients and ourselves is not to get angry back at them or take their abuse personally (which we normally do) but to try to find out what they are so angry about.

We asked our patients about this. What came out was that the peppier, the more energetic, the more functioning you are when you come into that room, the more anger you often provoke. And the patient says angrily to you, "*You* can walk out of here again, you know. *You* can go home again at five and see your kids. *You* can go to work." They're not angry at you as a person, but at what you represent—life, functioning, pep, energy, all the things they are in the process of losing or have already partially lost.

We tried to see if it would help if we poured fuel on the fire, if we let them ventilate, let them express their anger. If we can say to them, "You know, I would be angry, too. Get it off your chest. Scream if you feel like screaming," then they will express their rage and anger, but it never comes out as loud and frightening as you might think.

The best example is the mother of a small child who died. She looked very numb, so I said to her, "You look as though you need to scream." And she said, "Do you have a screaming room at the hospital?" She was serious. I said, "No, but we have a chapel," which was a silly answer because she immediately replied, "I need just the opposite. I need to scream and rage and curse. I've just been sitting in the parking lot and cursing and screaming at God. 'God, why do you let this happen to my child?

Why do you let this happen to me?' '' And I said, "Do it here. It's better to do it *with* somebody than out in a parking lot all alone.''

And that's what I mean by the stage of anger, of rage, of a sense of impotence, of helplessness. You can help not only the patient to express this rage and anger, but the family, too, because they go through the same stages. And, from a practical point of view, the nursing staff will be saved many, many steps. The nurse will be called less, the patient will be more comfortable.

Sometimes the patient gets to this point—loses his anger—without any external help, and you wonder what happened. Very often it is because he has entered the state of bargaining. Most bargaining is done with God. "If you give me one more year to live, I will be a good Christian or I will donate my kidney or this or that." Most of the time it is a promise, in exchange for some prolongation of life.

We had one patient who depended on injections around the clock to control her terrible pain. She was one of our most difficult patients, and it became very hard to keep on visiting her. Then one day she was very friendly and she said, "You know, if you help me get out of this hospital for one single day, I will be a good patient." She wanted that one day to get up and get dressed and attend her son's wedding. This was finally possible, and she left, looking like a million dollars.

And we began to wonder, "What is it like? How must it feel to ask only for one single day? It must be terribly difficult to come back to the hospital."

When she returned, she wasn't happy to see me. Before I could ask a single question she said, "Dr. Ross, don't forget I have another son." That's the briefest, quickest example of the bargaining stage I know.

In the denial stage it's "No, not me!" In the anger, "Why me?" In the bargaining, "Yes, me, but. . . ." When the patient finally drops the "but," then it's "Yes, me." And "Yes, me" means that he has the courage to acknowledge that it has indeed "come nigh" to him, and he is naturally very depressed.

After a while, these patients become silent. It's a kind of grief which is difficult for us to accept—where they don't talk much any more, where they don't want any more visitors. How do we react to them when we come into their rooms and find them crying or silently mourning? What do we do? Can we tolerate this?

This is sometimes even more difficult to bear than the angry patients. As long as they complain about all the things they have lost, it's something we can grasp. But when they become quiet and the tears are running down—and especially if it's a man—then it's very hard. We have a tendency to say, "What a beautiful day outside. Look at those lovely flowers. Cheer up. It's not so bad."

It *is* bad. If I were to lose one beloved person, everybody would allow—even expect—me to grieve. It would be perfectly normal because I would have lost one person I loved. But the dying patient is about to lose not just one beloved person but everyone he has ever loved and everything that has been meaningful to him. That is a thousand times sadder. If the patient has the courage to face this, then he should be allowed to grieve; he has a right to it.

We call this the preparatory grief. If he can prepare himself slowly, if he is allowed to grieve and, if necessary, to cry, then he becomes able to decathect, to separate himself. He will have the courage to ask for no more relatives to come after a while, no more children. And at the very end he will want perhaps only one loved person—someone who can sit silently and comfortably by his side, without words, but just touching his hand or perhaps stroking his hair or just being there.

That's when a patient has reached the stage of acceptance. And acceptance is not resignation! Resignation is a bitter kind of giving up ("What's the use?"), almost a defeat. But acceptance is a good feeling. "I have now finished all of my unfinished business. I have said all of the words that have to be said. I am ready to go."

These patients are not happy, but they are not terribly sad. They usually have very little physical pain and discomfort, and they slip into a stage which very often reminds us of the beginning of life: when a person has physical needs and needs only one person to give him some tender, loving care and compassion—who can be with him but doesn't have to talk all the time. It's the comfort of being together that counts.

"Do you have to be a psychiatrist to work with these people?" I am often asked. No. Many of our patients are angry when a psychiatric consultation is called because they have dared to become depressed. What I have talked about so far is the normal behavior of a dying patient, and it doesn't take a psychiatrist to help him. It doesn't take much time, either—only a very few minutes.

Last fall, we saw a young man who was the father of three small children. He had never been sick, never been in the hospital before, and now he was admitted with acute leukemia. Every day when I saw him, he was on the verge of talking. He wanted to talk but he couldn't. So he would say, "Come back tomorrow." And I would come back the next day, but he would say again, "Come back tomorrow."

Finally, I said to him, "If you don't want to talk about it, that's alright." He quickly responded: "No, if I don't do it now, I'll never be able to do it. Why don't you come back tomorrow morning very early, before rounds, before anybody else comes? I have to get it out." (We never talked, by the way, about what "it" meant, but both of us knew.)

The next day I came very early and the nurses told me that this patient had been dying during the night, that he had put up a physical fight for about three and a half hours, that he was really not in a condition to talk. But when I promise a patient I will see him, I keep that promise even if he is comatose or not in a position to communicate. So I went to his room and, to my surprise, he almost sat up in his bed. "Come on in," he said; "close the door and sit down." And he talked as he had never talked before.

He said, "I have to tell you what happened last night, you will never believe it." (I'm using his own words because I want to show you what we mean about talking about dying. Patients do not always use the word "dying" but you can talk about dying in many languages.)

"Last night," he continued, "I put up a fight for several hours. There was a big train going rapidly down the hill towards the end, and I had a big fight with the train master. I argued and fought with him. And I ordered him to stop this train one tenth of an inch short."

Then he paused and asked me, "Do you know what I am talking about?" I said, "I guess the train that goes rapidly down toward the end is your life. And you had a big fight with the train master—for just a little bit more time." Then I smiled and added, "You made it." (That's bargaining. He bargained for one tenth of an inch.)

At that moment his mother came in and I said, "How can I help you with the tenth of an inch?" using his language since I didn't know on what level this mother and son communicated. And he said, "Try to help me convince my mother that she should go home now and bake a loaf of bread and make my favorite vegetable soup; I want to eat that once more." And the mother did go home and he did get his bread and soup—his last solid food. He died about three days later.

I think this man went through all the stages of dying in this overnight struggle. He tried to maintain his denial as long as possible—and then he dropped it in that one night. The anger, the bargaining and the depression, preceded the final stage of acceptance.

My last example is a woman whose story illustrates what hope means and how the nature of hope changes from the healthy to the sick to the dying. If we can elicit the patient's hope and support *his* hope, then we can help him the most.

This woman came to our hospital feeling very sick and weak, and her doctor said that she should go to a specialist in another hospital. So she hoped at that time that it was nothing serious, that it could be treated, that she would get well. After a while she was told that she had a serious kidney disease; then she hoped for treatment that would cure it. Next, she was told her life could be prolonged if she were accepted on a dialysis program for indigent people. This, too, was something for her to hope for—but she was rejected.

The social worker and the nurses, who were really fond of this woman, could not accept this. It was hard for them to visit her after dialysis had been denied, so they asked us to see her in our death and dying seminar.

The patient was very relieved when we were frank and told her why we wanted to see her. Many little but unfortunate things had happened to her at the hospital to which she was sent—hurriedly and unprepared—to be considered for dialysis. Confusion and misunderstanding grew until finally, when all the doctors stopped at her bedside on rounds, she realized that this was the moment of truth.

"A big cloud came over me," she said, "and I had the idea that I had a kidney operation and didn't need those doctors. When I woke up they were gone." In other words, she had a fantasy that she didn't need the doctors to save her life. Considered to be psychotic and hallucinating, she was rejected for dialysis.

We explored a lot of feelings about that, and then we discussed with her what kinds of things we could do now to make whatever time she had left more meaningful or more bearable.

She said, "Don't be so upset. When I die, it will be just like going from this garden to God's garden." But something was really bothering her, she added. She didn't know quite what it was and it was hard to talk about it.

Two days later, I said to her, "You know, there was something that bothered you, and that's what we call unfinished business. What is it?" And she kept saying,

"I'm bad, I'm bad, I'm bad." Because what she was really saying was that she had to confess something that she felt guilty about, but she didn't know the origin of this guilt. And we searched like two children who are looking in the dark for something they have lost.

Finally, I gave up and I said, "God only knows why you should be bad," which was a genuine gut reaction on my part. And she looked up and said, "That's it: God. I called on God for help for the last few days. 'God help me. God help me.' And I heard Him say in the back of my mind, 'Why are you calling me now, why didn't you call me when things were all right?' What do you say to that, Dr. Ross?" And my gut reaction was to take off. Why couldn't a priest be here? Or a minister? Or somebody? But not me.

But you can't give a patient like this a phony answer. You have to be you and you have to be honest. So I struggled, and finally I said, "Just imagine that the children are playing outside and the mother is in the house and the little boy falls and hurts his knee. What happens?" And she said, "The mother goes out and helps him back on his feet and consoles him." I said, "OK, and he is all right now. What happens next?" And she said, "The boy goes back to his play and the mother goes back in the house." "He has no use for her now?" I asked, and she said "No," and I said, "Does the mother resent this terribly?" She looked at me almost angrily and said, "A mother? A mother wouldn't resent that." And I said, "If a mother wouldn't resent that, do you think that our Father would?"

Then the happiest, most beautiful smile came over her face, and she asked me something I'll never forget: "What is your concept of death?" (I felt like saying, "How dare you ask me!" It shall not "come nigh" to me, even after seeing so many dying patients.) So I said something about liking her idea about the garden, but she just shook her head and asked again, "What is your concept of death?" Then I looked at her face and said, "Peace." That was a genuine answer. And she said, "I'm going very peacefully, now, from this garden into the next one."

This patient taught us how hope can change: from hoping it's nothing serious, then hoping for treatment, then hoping for a prolongation of life. And finally hoping that "If I'm not accepted in this garden, I hope I'll be accepted in the next garden."

It is the patient's hope that we should support. I had known this woman less than an hour, yet I learned from her. And I think I helped her.

It didn't take much time. But what it did take, and will always take, is a sense of comfort in the face of death. What all of us have to learn is to accept death as part of life. When we have learned this, then maybe we can help our patients learn it, too.

ROBERT KASTENBAUM

Do We Die in Stages?

In developing the stage progression approach to the dying experience, Kübler-Ross provided an effective vocabulary for discussions of dying. Evaluating her work and noting the limitations of any stage theory, Kastenbaum raises the issue of standards of evidence for clinical research. He calls for empirical research to validate the stage theory of dying and to identify significant variables in its application.

DO WE DIE IN STAGES?

The concept of stages is abundantly familiar in developmental theory and research. Freud, Erikson, and Piaget are perhaps the most influential of the theorists who have offered stage-progression approaches, but there are many others also available to choose from. Stage theories are characterized by emphasis upon qualitative differences that are thought to appear in a relatively fixed sequence. Change along a simple quantitative dimension is usually not regarded as the stuff of stage theory. The 12-year-old is taller than the 6-year-old, but it is the contention that he *thinks differently* that constitutes the grounds for locating him in a different stage.

Popular as a technique for observations and for teaching, stage theory might also be expected to surface in the area of dying and death, which until recent years has attracted few researchers, theoreticians, and clinical specialists. With the publication in 1969 of Elizabeth Kübler-Ross's *On Death and Dying*, such a theory did become available and widely disseminated. It is this approach that will be described and examined in the next section.

A. A Stage Theory of the Dying Process

1. The Five Stages Kübler-Ross proposes that the dying person passes through five stages. These begin with the impact of mortal tidings, and terminate as life itself terminates. Individuals may differ in the rapidity through which they move

Source: Excerpt from Robert Kastenbaum, "Is Death a Life Crisis?" in Nancy Datan and Leon H. Ginsberg, eds., *Life-Span Developmental Psychology: Normative Life Crises*, ©1975, Academic Press. Reprinted by permission.

from stage to stage. Further, some people do not reach the final stage at all. One can be caught or arrested at a particular stage of dying, as in any stage in life-span development. The stages are normal modes of responding to the harsh reality of death. Further, there can be some slipping back and forth between stages, and the coexistence of two stages.

Denial is the first stage. The person is, in effect, saying "No!" to death. This stage takes place whether terminal status is communicated by medical authorities or surmised by the individual himself. Denial can be displayed in straightforward fashion or obliquely. By words and actions the person resists acknowledging the reality of impending death.

Anger comes next. The lid blows off. Angry feelings may be vented upon family, medical staff, the environment. Even God is not exempt. It is as though somebody must be blamed for the overwhelming disaster, which is no longer denied. The typical question the person is struggling with at this time is "Why me?" Frustration builds and anger overflows as the question resists satisfactory answer.

Bargaining is the middle stage. The person attempts to make a deal with fate. He changes his strategy and asks for a favor. Kübler-Ross compares this maneuver with the child whose request for an overnight visit with a friend has been turned down. After stamping his foot, "No!" and expressing anger, the child eventually comes around to ask, "If I am very good all week and wash the dishes every evening, then will you let me go? [Kübler-Ross, 1969, p. 72]." The terminally ill patient attempts to bargain for an extension of life, a postponement of the death event. Much of the bargaining is likely to proceed covertly between the dying person and God, but the process sometimes can be seen as well in interactions with others.

Depression sets in "when the terminally ill patient can no longer deny his illness, when he is forced to undergo more surgery or hospitalization, when he begins to have more symptoms or becomes weaker and thinner, he cannot smile it off anymore. His numbness or stoicism, his anger and rage will soon be replaced with a sense of great loss [Kübler-Ross, 1969, p. 75]." The depressive state may involve feelings of guilt and unworthiness, fear of dying, and attenuation of communication with family and others.

Acceptance is the final stage. The struggle is over. Tired and weak physically, the patient nevertheless is no longer sunk in the anguish of depression. "Acceptance should not be mistaken for a happy stage. It is almost void of feelings. It is as if the pain had gone, the struggle is over, and there comes a time for 'the final rest before the long journey' as one patient phrased it [Kübler-Ross, 1969, p. 100]."

2. Context of the Stage Theory   Kübler-Ross illuminates her presentation of each stage with brief synopses of terminally ill people she has interviewed, and transcribed dialogue between the patient and herself. This sharing of clinical material helps the reader to grasp the essence of the various stages. Moreover, it provides a person with "something to go on" or "something to look for" when entering into a relationship with a dying person oneself. She also comments upon some of the ways in which family or staff might respond helpfully to the dying person in each stage. The difficult problem of relating to the dying person when anger is the dominant affect, for example, receives her attention. A separate chapter is devoted to examples from her therapeutic efforts with the dying.

Interwoven through all five stages is the phenomenon of *hope,* which also is discussed in a separate chapter. Perhaps her key point here is that

> In listening to our terminally ill patients we were always impressed that even the most accepting, the most realistic patients left the possibility open for some cure, for the discovery of a new drug, of the last minute success in a research project. . . . It is this glimpse of hope which maintains them through days, weeks, or months of suffering. It is the feeling that all this must have some meaning, will pay off eventually if they can only endure it for a little while longer. It is the hope that occasionally sneaks in, that all this is just like a nightmare and not true . . . [Kübler-Ross, 1969, p. 123].

B. Stage Theory of Dying as a General Contribution

The stage theory of dying has made a number of contributions to our culture's general orientation toward dying and death. Not the least of these is the awakening or legitimation of interest in a topic that has been taboo to many Americans, whether laymen or professonals (Feifel, 1959). Kübler-Ross has reached the feelings of people who previously did not know where to begin in relating themselves toward their terminally ill friends, family or patients. *On Death and Dying* became for many their first exposure to systematic description of the dying process, and their first guide for their own explorations. Although books on death have been published before and after, it is this contribution by Kübler-Ross that established the topic as one of general concern.

Thoughts and feeling stirred by this book have added to the impetus of a nationwide death education movement. The existence of stage theory also has provided a coin of communication: The social worker from Utah meeting the nurse from New York can both talk about Stage 3, and the student of death education has his or her five stages to copy down and memorize.

The book, then, has opened the subject of death and dying to many people and provided a basis for communication. This stepping-over-the-threshold is significant action, when we reflect that even experienced health professionals often place physical and emotional distance between themselves and the palpabilities of dying and death. The humanism and the case material account for part of this effect. What about the stage theory itself? It is my impression that the stage theory gained rapid acceptance because it is a clear, understandable schema that provides structure and reduces anxiety for the reader. Death becomes subsumed under dying, and dying transformed from a vague, overpowering, and terrifying mass to a delimited, coherent, orderly sequence. There are rules now to govern this part of the universe that has for so long been considered out of bounds. The reader, researcher, or health professional thus can approach the topic with less anxiety and foreboding.

It is not surprising that many people have felt remarkably better after becoming acquainted with the stage theory of dying. Anxiety and lack of cognitive structure are replaced by the security of knowledge. The reader now knows what happens during the process of dying, has greater feeling for the patient's situation, and has some idea about what might be done to be of value to the patient or his family. There is no doubt that stage theory has increased the dialogue, both oral and written, about care of the dying person. And there is little doubt that more people have taken heart to draw closer to the dying person. Not all the consequences have been favorable, however, and some of the problems involved will be examined in what follows.

C. Stage Theory of Dying as a Contribution to Knowledge

We raise now a sampling of those questions that come to mind in evaluating any model of human behavior. Particular attention will be given to issues that link the stage theory of dying with other developmental approaches.

1. Overview   The stage theory of dying draws primarily upon the clinical experiences of psychiatrist author Elizabeth Kübler-Ross. In her words, this theory is intended "to summarize what we have learned from our dying patients in terms of coping mechanisms at the time of a terminal illness [Kübler-Ross, 1969, p. 33]." The theory is intended to encompass feelings and behaviors of the dying person from awareness of terminality to the death event itself. In company with other stage theories, the stage theory of dying specifies a strongly directional set of transitions with each way station characterized by fairly distinct phenomena. The source, intention, and general nature of Kübler-Ross's theory do not present any difficulties. Personal experience with dying patients is obviously a sensible basis for deriving the principles of a theory or general formulation. The stage theory of dying comes into being as a means of summarizing and sharing those experiences. And the idea that the process of dying can be usefully viewed in terms of some orderly progression of adaptive states does not tax credibility. In broad outline, then, the theory deserves consideration as a plausible approach toward understanding the dying process. Does it also deserve acceptance as the "true account" or the "most useful" theory? This is quite another question.

2. The Data Base   Experiences with approximately 200 terminally ill people provided the basis for the stage theory of dying; since that time Kübler-Ross has interviewed approximately another 200 terminally ill in her own setting, and has seen many others as consultant-lecturer. It is clear that her theory is grounded in relevant information.

However, virtually every operation that might be performed on clinical information for conversion into research data has been neglected. The sample itself has not been described. Terms have not been defined. Transcripts have not been subjected to analysis and no interrater reliability procedures that might demonstrate the existence of the five stages have been performed. The interaction between the method of data gathering and the results has not been discussed. The most basic types of statistical information have not been provided. (How many patients, for example, were seen for what periods of time? How many, in fact, did die while the interview series was in process? How many were interviewed only on a single occasion? etc.).

There are sensitive issues here that could easily be distorted. Systematic research and finesse may be unreasonable to expect when a person is helping to pioneer an emotion-laden growing edge of knowledge and concern. One-to-one with a dying person, a psychiatrist or other interested person has more pressing concerns than the abstract demands of science. Kübler-Ross had to discover her own pathway to understanding the terminally ill, and then had the generosity of spirit to share it with others.

But all of this does not permit us to relax standards of evidence. Perhaps a theory has emerged whose ties with its original data base are personal and difficult to share or open for objective evaluation. This circumstance in itself neither supports nor undercuts the specifics of Kübler-Ross's theory. However, the rapid acceptance of the stage theory of dying has quite outdistanced any attempt to examine the theory empirically or logically. It is taken typically as proven fact. But the fact is that the theory was not offered with a close and coherently developed data base at the start, and no effort has been made to test out the theory as it continues to become more widely disseminated and applied. Few who center their approach to dying and death around the stage theory of dying see it as in need of analysis, examination, evaluation. It is useful in some way, therefore it is self-perpetuating. Moreover, as will be seen later, those who find this theory less than useful tend to drop it without necessarily subjecting either the theory or their own uses of it to searching analysis. In short, there is conviction that the stage theory of dying is an empirically valid formulation of human experience during the dying process, when little effort has been expended to study the relationship between theory and fact. The present criticism is not directed at the paucity of information brought forth to support or test the stage theory of dying, but the attitude that research is superfluous.

As a person who has some experience with the terminally ill, I appreciate the fact that companionship, caring, and intervention cannot wait until scientific formulations have been purified and validated. Sounding the caution about a particular theory is not equivalent to discouraging people from bringing their best selves to interactions with the dying, or to using whatever insights the theory provides. But I must reject the contention that the stage theory of dying is so important and useful that research can wait. It is precisely because the experiences of the dying person and all those around him are so important that we ought not to base our work indefinitely upon an untested theory. If the theory is substantially correct, then we should use it for all that it is worth; if it has decided limitations or inaccuracies, then we should move without delay to find alternatives.

3. Factors Insufficiently Considered by the Stage Theory of Dying It is here suggested that Kübler-Ross's theory suffers from what could be described either as overreliance upon one component of the total situation or underappreciation of the total context. In this regard, the theory perhaps is suffering a flaw common to most stage theories. Mentioned in the following paragraphs are several other sources of variance that are neglected by the emphasis upon the five hypothesized stages of individual adaptation to terminal illness.

Nature of the Disease   There have always been physicians who maintain that a person "dies the death of his disease." In other words, the patterning of the pathology dominates all else. This contention, like those of the stage theory of dying, has yet to be tested critically. But it is evident that the nature-of-the-disease process can greatly affect pain, mobility, trajectory of dying, and the social stimulus value of the dying person, to mention just some of the dimensions involved. Within the realm of cancer alone, for example, the person with head or neck cancer looks and feels different from the person with leukemia. The person with emphysema, subject to terrifying attacks in which each breath of air requires a struggle, experiences his situation differently from the person with advanced renal failure, or with a cardiovascular trajectory. Although Kübler-Ross's theory directs welcome attention to the universal psychosocial aspects of terminal illness, we also lose much sensitivity if the disease process itself is not fully respected.

Sex Differences   Do men and women experience terminal illness identically, even if both are afflicted by the same condition? Clinical experience suggests that the sexes differ with respect to the type of discomfort, impairment, and limitations of function that are of greatest concern. Some of our research in progress further suggests that pain, dependency, and loss of occupational role rank very high for men, while women are more distressed by the impact of their illness and death upon others. It is possible, then, that sex-role attitudes may be a significant source of variance in adaptation to terminal illness.

Ethnicity   Is it legitimate to die in a hospital or other public institution? How is pain to be experienced and expressed? Is it most important to keep up the strong front or the family name? Does the death event signify triumph and release or dismal failure? For some people, the answers to these questions may be found most clearly in their ethnic identity. The total interpersonal situation that surrounds a terminally ill person as well as his own responses can differ radically depending upon the ethnic patterns involved—as thousands of nurses can testify.

Personality or Cognitive Style   Whatever makes a person the particular person he is has much to do with the nature of his terminal phase of life. No single personality or cognitive style is invariably adaptive; in fact, any of a number of cognitive style variables might be equally adequate. The point is that we approach our death to some extent as the type of person we have always been—reflective or impulsive, warm or aloof, whatever. A view of the dying process that excludes personality as such must also exclude much of reality.

Developmental Level The meaning of dying and death differs for the infant who has known little of life and for the aged man or woman who has known much. Additionally, whatever merit there is in classifying people according to developmental level applies as well to appreciating their experiences in the terminal phase of life. People come to death as more or less mature organisms, and with very different positions along with their own potential life cycles. In other words, the person's general developmental situation must be taken into account as well as any modes of development that are specific to the dying process itself.

Sociophysical Milieu What is the nature of the environment in which the person is dying? Is it an efficient, professionalized world of strangers? A slow-paced nursing home? A room in the house where the person was born many years before? Is the environment over- or underprotective? Does it value expression or suppression of feelings? Is this an environment in which there are clear, conflicting, or no expectations of the dying person himself? However we may choose to analyze the sociophysical milieu, it is obviously a major source of variance in influencing what the dying person says and does, and perhaps also what he feels.

Formulations of the dying process could be derived from each of the areas sketched earlier. Some appear as promising or more promising than a stage theory, some less promising. Useful theories of dying could be grounded, for example, in the sociophysical milieu. The work of Glaser and Strauss (1965) moves in this direction. The milieu also has the advantage of being somewhat amenable to change. A formulation that incorporates two or more sources of variation could be even more powerful (e.g., the developmental and the sociophysical). There is no compelling reason to limit our thinking to any single realm.

Even if Kübler-Ross's theory could be supported as an accurate representation of adaptive strategies on the part of the dying person, it would still tell us little that we need to know about the interaction with disease process, ethnicity, personality style, and so on. Were less claimed for her theory, more could be granted to it. Hastily accepted as *the* account of the dying process. Kübler-Ross's theory emphasizes one possible set of dynamics to the virtual exclusion of all others.

One of the consequences is establishment of the image of *the* dying person moving through the universal five stages. Yet it is always a specific person dying in a specific environment that has its own social and physical dynamics, and the person approaches death through one or more specific disease modalities, responding in terms of the idiosyncratic integration of personality, ethnic, sex-role, and developmental resources. Viewed in this light, each death is individual. The five stages, if they do exist, are found within the context of the situation but do not necessarily dominate it.

4. Other Problems with the Stage Theory of Dying In keeping with most developmental theories, the stage theory of dying assumes a single primary path of movement. We grow up one way. We die one way. Variations are acknowledged, but are seen as deviations from a central mode of progression. This approach is objectionable in the stage theory of dying as well as other forms of developmental theory—objectionable because the uncritical perpetuation of the one-path conception (a) impedes the appreciation and discovery of alternate approaches and (b) has the effect of stereotyping uncommon or idiosyncratic patterns as deviant.

Both the stage theory of dying and developmental theories in general sometimes fail to distinguish adequately between what usually happens and what *should* happen. The problem may, however, be more severe in the present use of the stage theory of dying, where conception and application are closely linked, and both under intense emotional pressure. Kübler-Ross herself has cautioned that people should not be rushed through the stages. Yet the theory implies that there is a valued destination to be reached, and that one should keep moving toward acceptance, if at his or her own pace. Less a problem of the theory itself than of some of its applications, there is nevertheless a disturbing tendency for description to be converted imperceptibly into prescription. In general, the relationships between fact and surmise, surmise and theory, and theory and value orientation remain obscure and vulnerable in the stage theory of dying.

Clinical research concerning the dying process by other investigators does not clearly support the existence of the five stages or of any universal form of staging. A recent review of the literature, scant as it is, finds no evidence for five predictable stages of psychological adaptation. Other investigators' data "show the process of dying to be less rigid and even stageless. There is some consensus among all researchers that terminal patients are depressed shortly before they die, but there is not consistent evidence that other affect dimensions characterize the dying patient [Schulz & Alderman, 1974]." We must add that this negative conclusion is based upon studies conducted by various clinical investigators with equally various populations, techniques, and objectives, none of which were to make critical tests of stage theory. Nevertheless, the fact that available data do not make a strong case for the stage theory of dying obviously must be kept in mind.

D. Concluding Note on the Stage Theory of Dying

Although this has been perhaps the most systematic exploration yet made of the stage theory of dying, much remains to be learned and discussed. It is possible that the theory, either in its present or a revised form, might eventually become established as a faithful representation of central facts in the dying process and a dependable guide to education and action. For the moment, however, what we have is the early social history of a simple formulation about some vital aspects of human existence. This theory fills various individual and social needs; it is illuminated by the experience and insight of its author; and it can be appealing to those who are avid collectors of stage theories. We hope to have suggested that the application of stage theory to significant—literally life-and-death—experience should be accompanied by the critical and self-correcting perspective of science, no matter how we might want to believe that the truth is at hand. Those who have taken up the theory only to abandon it after clinical trials might also find it useful to examine their own reasons for both acceptance and rejection. What was expected or demanded of the theory? Were these expectations appropriate? What can we require realistically of any formulation of the dying process, and what must we require directly of ourselves? No matter what base of external knowledge or what theoretical perspective we bring to the dying situation, there is no substitute for confronting and in some manner accommodating ourselves to the prospect of our own deaths—a central theme in the work of Kübler-Ross and most other pioneers in this field.

REFERENCES

Feifel, H., ed. *The meaning of death*. New York: McGraw-Hill, 1959.
Glaser, B.G., and Strauss, A. *Awareness of dying*. Chicago: Aldine Publishing, 1965.
Kübler-Ross, E. *On death and dying*. New York: Macmillan, 1969.
Schulz, R. and Alderman, D. Clinical research and the "stages of dying." *Omega* 5: 137-144, 1974.

DYLAN THOMAS

Do Not Go Gentle into that Good Night

The foregoing readings have necessarily generalized patterns in the dying process, but as the following poem makes clear, the style of dying is a highly individual choice. Writing about the death of his father, Dylan Thomas calls for a powerful resistance to death as a way of affirming all that has been valuable in life.

Do not go gentle into that good night
Old age should burn and rave at close of day;
Rage, rage against the dying of the light.

Though wise men at their end know dark is right,
Because their words have forked no lightning they
Do not go gentle into that good night.

Good men, the last wave by, crying how bright
Their frail deeds might have danced in a green bay,
Rage, rage against the dying of the light.

Wild men who caught and sang the sun in flight,
And learn, too late, they grieved it on its way,
Do not go gentle into that good night.

Grave men, near death, who see with blinding sight
Blind eyes could blaze like meteors and be gay,
Rage, rage against the dying of the light.

And you, my father, there on the sad height,
Curse, bless, me now with your fierce tears, I pray.
Do not go gentle into that good night.
Rage, rage against the dying of the light.

Source: *The Poems of Dylan Thomas.* Copyright ©1952 by Dylan Thomas. Reprinted by permission of New Directions Publishing Corporation.

WILLIAM CARLOS WILLIAMS

To Waken an Old Lady

Though it is always a mistake to attribute the thoughts of a single writer to an age or a culture, individual thoughts do serve as windows to attitudes. Literary studies of death are often studies of life as well, with symbolic elements conveying much of the meaning. William Carlos Williams develops a vignette that contrasts sharply in tone with Thomas's poem.

Old age is
a flight of small
cheeping birds
skimming
bare trees
above a snow glaze.
Gaining and failing
they are buffeted
by a dark wind—
But what?
On harsh weedstalks
the flock has rested,
the snow
is covered with broken
seedhusks
and the wind tempered
by a shrill
piping of plenty.

Source: William Carlos Williams, *Collected Earlier Poems.* Copyright ©1938 by New Directions Publishing Corporation. Reprinted by permission of publisher.

HARVEY BLUESTONE and
CARL L. McGAHEE

Reaction to Extreme Stress: Impending Death by Execution

There are many ways to die, and there are many ways of facing death. Terminal illness is not the only condition in which one knows that one's death is imminent. Capital punishment sets the individual the same task of preparing to die, but in an ignominious way. Unlike the case of the patient, there is no question of keeping the face of impending death from the prisoner and little or no social support to help him rationalize the fact of death. In a series of brief case histories, Bluestone and McGahee describe the development of characteristic coping mechanisms which serve to protect the prisoners from experiencing overwhelming anxiety or depression. Denial, projection, and obsessional concerns may have a specific content here, but the process of adjustment to stress is a familiar one.

We conventionally think of death as "the worst thing" that can happen to us. Knowing, as we all do, that we will die in some vague future does not impose any great stress. The man in the grip of a relentlessly fatal disease has to cope with much more severe stress. But mercifully, his death date is not fixed and he can always hope to see tomorrow's sun rise. Presumably, the greatest of stresses would be imposed on the man who knows he is going to be put to death—and knows just when that will be.

We have studied 18 men and one woman in the Sing Sing death house. Because of the inmates' utilizing opportunities for appeals for clemency or commutation there is adequate time for repeated psychiatric interviews and psychologic examinations.

These men are housed in an area detached from the rest of the prison. They have few visitors, though the authorities impose no restrictions on visiting. One might expect them to show severe depression and devastating anxiety, yet neither symptom

Source: Bluestone, H. and McGahee, C.L. "Reaction to Extreme Stress: Impending Death by Execution." *American Journal of Psychiatry*, vol. 119, pp. 393–396, 1962. Copyright ©1962, the American Psychiatric Association. Reprinted by permission.

was conspicuous among these 19 doomed persons. By what mechanisms did they avoid these expected reactions to such overwhelming stress? Do their emotional patterns change during a year or two in a death cell? And, do these defenses function to the moment of execution—or do they crumble toward the end?

The 19 histories had certain features in common. All had come from deprived backgrounds. All but one came from homes where the father was missing (deserted, dead, unknown, or separated) during the childhood or adolescence. Practically all had been brought up (during their growing years) in institutions or foster homes. Not one had an education better than that of tenth grade. Some were illiterate. Their intelligence varied from an IQ of 60 to one with an IQ of 140. All had been convicted of murder. None of the murders was long planned: they were impulsive. Many were committed in connection with a felony. The world appeared as a hostile, dangerous, and menacing place, and they had reacted in their way—by aggression, suspiciousness and cynicism.

The following are brief summaries of the reaction of some of these men to their imprisonment in the death house. (For collective data, see chart to follow.)

1. **Age range of death house prisoners**
   - 18 or younger 1
   - 19 or 20 2
   - 21 through 25 5
   - 26 through 30 3
   - 30 to 35 5
   - over 35 3

2. **Family background**
   - Parents together during most of childhood 1
   - Father unknown or deserted 7
   - Father divorced or separated 10
   - Father and mother unknown 1

3. **Highest school grade reached**
   - Fourth or lower 4
   - Fifth or sixth 8
   - Seventh or eighth 2
   - Ninth or tenth 5

4. **Intelligence quotient**
   - 60 through 69 2
   - 70 through 79 5
   - 80 through 89 7
   - 90 through 119 4
   - 120 through 140 1

5. **Family status of prisoner as adult**
   - Never married, but had common-law spouse 5
   - Never married, no regular consortium 11
   - Married, but separated 2
   - Living with wife 1

6.   **Psychological defense mechanisms used**
     (Totals more than 19; some used more than once)
     Denial by isolation of affect 7
     Denial by minimizing the predicament 4
     Denial by delusion formation 1
     Denial by living only in the present 4
     Projection 7
     Obsessive rumination in connection with appeals 3
     Obsessive preoccupation with religion 2
     Obsessive preoccupation with intellectual or
        philosophical matters 5

1.   This man has the longest residence in the death house of those in this study, approximately two years. An overt confirmed homosexual, he maintained a calm conviction that he would be ultimately pardoned. This belief remained bolstered throughout by an unchanging contention that he had been framed by the legal and medical authorities involved in his prosecution. Psychological testing showed a man of average intelligence with considerable withdrawal from real emotional interaction with others. Defense mechanisms of denial and projection were effective in warding off anxiety and depression despite prolonged incarceration in the death house.

2.   This inmate is the only woman in this series. She is of dull intelligence, acts in a playful and flirtatious manner. She was usually euphoric, but became transiently depressed when she thought her case was going badly. She frequently complained of insomnia and restlessness. These symptoms quickly disappeared when she was visited by a psychiatrist whom she enjoyed seeing and talking to in a self-justifying and self-pitying manner. Psychological tests showed pervasive feelings of insecurity, repressive defenses, and an inability to handle angry and aggressive feelings in an effectual manner.

3.   This inmate is a withdrawn, sullen, uncommunicative individual. When visited in the death house he would elaborately and slowly wash his clothes ignoring examiners. He spends much of his time reading profound philosophical works which are beyond his comprehension. His intelligence is dull-normal. He has become progressively more suspicious and grandiose during his death house stay.

4.   This man gives a long history of delinquent behavior. He is a litigiously minded individual who states that he can appeal his case for years. He is obsessed with his own power and is convinced that a law suit against the district attorney for lost automobile tools kept that official from being reelected. He has become progressively more angry and abusive ultimately necessitating his physical isolation from other inmates. His IQ is 134. Projective tests show a chronically cold, withdrawn, narcissistically invested personality. Withdrawal, projection and denial are prominent defense mechanisms.

5.   This man is at all times euphoric. He has shown little anxiety during the full year he has spent in the death house. He has led a hedonistic life and has never been able to make future plans. His inability to see beyond the day seems quite effective in enabling him to avoid anxiety and depression.

6.   This inmate showed during his early months of incarceration a contemptuous indifference toward the authorities and his own plight. Gradually, however, depression appeared and became progressively more intense. This was rather dramatically reversed when the inmate presented an apparent religious conversion, which seemed to both

occupy his mind and also elevate him above the authorities and his situation. However, this defense was only partially successful for this individual who had a life-long history of discharging all tensions by immediate impulsive acting-out. Psychological testing showed dull-normal intelligence and a primitive, self-absorbed, hostility-ridden personality.

8. This inmate related to examiners in an open and direct manner. He is mentally dull and preoccupied with thoughts of voodoo spells. His primary defense mechanism is denial of the possibility of being executed. This works poorly and he is chronically anxious and periodically depressed. His anger at his accomplice, who he is convinced is the cause of his difficulties, seems to relieve him of some of his unpleasant feelings. He amuses himself in working on a taunting poem which he proposes to recite when his accomplice is executed. This mechanism, too, is ineffectual and he reverts from these thoughts of revenge to a contemplation of his own plight.

9. This man is a moody individual who feels he is the victim of a Jewish plot since the judge, district attorney, and his own court-appointed lawyer are Jewish. He denied his guilt repeatedly during his early days in the death house, but became progressively more confused and a few days before his scheduled execution asked the examiner for truth serum so that he would know whether or not he committed the crime. He showed alternating use of introjection and projection. He would become depressed when news of his appeal was bad, and when a stay of execution was granted he became paranoid and grandiose. He managed in some obscure way to identify his impending death with that of Lumumba, who had recently been killed in the Congo, and felt that his own execution would make him a martyr in the cause of anti-imperialism.

10. This man stands out in the series as being the one who most successfully employed intellectualization as a means of defending against anxiety and depression. He elaborated a philosophy of life and values in which his own criminal career became not only justifiable, but even respectable. He rationalized his crimes by emphasizing the hypocrisy and perfidy of society on the one hand and by comparing himself with policemen and soldiers and others who live honorably ''by the gun'' on the other. This system was so effective for him that even when execution appeared imminent he maintained his hero's martyr role and disdained to request executive clemency.

11. This inmate is an illiterate, inadequate individual who was convicted as an accomplice to a robbery-murder. He has an overall IQ of 51. He showed primarily depression, withdrawal, and obsessive rumination over the details of the crime and conviction.

He eventually evolved a poorly elaborated paranoid system whereby he supposedly was betrayed and framed by his girlfriend and one of the co-defendants. Despite the looseness of his persecutory thinking, it was accompanied by a clear-cut elevation in his mood and reduction of anxiety.

12. This inmate, also an accomplice to a robbery-murder, showed one of the most florid pictures of any in this series. Both grandiose and persecutory themes were prominent, but the latter predominated. He maintained that his arrest and conviction were malicious frauds, and he meticulously and obsessively combed through the court record to substantiate his contentions. His arguments were labored and illogical, hinging on such points as the use of words like ''who'' and ''whom.'' The paranoid mechanisms seemed to mitigate, but not completely defend him against depression.

13. He is one of the two inmates in this series who uses religious preoccupation as his major defense mechanism. He repeatedly, in an almost word for word way, stated his

Editor's Note: Number 7 was omitted in the original article and has been exactly reprinted here.

situation as follows. "No one can understand how I feel unless it happened to you. Christ came to me and I know He died for my sins. It doesn't matter if I am electrocuted or not. I am going to another world after this and I am prepared for it." As his stay progresses he becomes increasingly more hostile and antagonistic, and his behavior progressively out of keeping with his professed religious ideas. In addition to obsessive rumination, projection and withdrawal are employed to ward off feelings of anxiety and depression.

DISCUSSION

Faced with certain and ignominious death, a person would presumably be overwhelmed with anxiety or plunge into the depths of depression. Yet this does not happen. What defense does the human mind set up against intense anxiety or a paralyzing depression? We suggest, on the basis of our 19 case studies, that the defenses are of mainly three types—denial, projection and obsessive rumination. The commonest form of *denial* is isolation of affect. "So, they'll kill me; and that's that"—this said with a shrug of the shoulders suggests that the affect appropriate to the thought has somehow been isolated. A second common form of denial is to minimize the gravity of the present situation and to take for granted that an appeal will be successful. The third and most extreme manifestation of denial, used by only one individual, was to delusionally believe that a pardon had been granted. Denial is also commonly used by persons dying of disease.

There is another phenomenon which deserves further explanation, since it may easily be confused with denial. Several cases impressed the examiners as being so immersed in the present moment as to virtually be insulated from any significant emotional relatedness with their own past or future. Thus, they do not have to deny anxiety since they do not experience it. This, incidentally, is the traditional profile of the "psychopath" who reacts only to present stimuli.

Projection is an obvious and not uncommon mechanism. Typically, it takes the form of persecutory delusions. At least three of our prisoners considered themselves persecuted by specific groups in the community. This mechanism converts dissolute criminals into martyrs. It is a comforting delusion. While it does not deny that death is just around the corner, it tries to lend it dignity and meaning. In some men there seems to be an almost quantitative reciprocal relationship between the use of projection and introjection so that they are either overly paranoid or depressed.

A third way of coping with painful affects is to *think furiously* about something else. Thus, the depressing thought is elbowed out of consciousness by the crowd of other ideas. We see this in a morbid obsessional concern about the preparing of appeals or pleas for clemency. One prisoner spoke to us for an hour about whether a pronoun in the appeal transcript should be "who" or "whom." To be sure, a meticulous concern with the appeal brief is rational; in these cases, however, the concern is obsessional, ruminative and ineffective. Another type of obsession (two of the men showed this) is preoccupation with religon to the exclusion of everything else. The prisoners who developed this syndrome had involved their confederates in death sentences too, though neither accomplice had killed anyone. Presumably, this religious conversion served to blunt guilt feelings about involving the accomplices. This activity served two other purposes: it distracted them from anxiety, and it offered a route to a happy life in the hereafter. The third type of obsessive rumination is the intellectual: a dipping into philosophical thought by a man whose life had hitherto been devoted to hedonistic pursuits.

Some try desperately to mould a respectable image of themselves. This is certainly one sluiceway for draining out anxiety—as illustrated, for example, in the way in which one of the prisoners identified himself with Lumumba and the world-shaking events in the Congo.

The group support these men receive from fellow inmates is variable. Some are quite appealing and receive considerable emotional and even material support in terms of cigarettes and help with their correspondence. Others manage quickly to antagonize their fellows and are in turn ridiculed and tormented by them in a direct and sadistic manner. This is often true when a man gets the reputation of being a malingerer. The inmates are quite antagonistic to anyone they feel is falsifying religious beliefs or feigning mental symptoms.

CONCLUSION

Traditional ego defense mechanisms alleviate distress. They also mitigate anxiety and depression which would otherwise overwhelm the prisoner in a death cell. Some psychiatrists allege that the death fear (whether on the battlefield or in the death house) serves as an irrational surrogate for some other fear—such as castration. This oversimplified explanation does scant justice to the inescapable certainty shared by all, but anticipated only by man.

ANSELM L. STRAUSS and
BARNEY G. GLASER

Awareness of Dying

The relationship between the individual's awareness of his own dying and the institutional response, as examined in the previous article for the atypical setting of a prison,
is pursued by Strauss and Glaser for the more typical occurrence of hospital death.
When dying occurs in a hospital, as is most often the case in North America, not only
the family but also the hospital staff enter into a complex interaction with the dying
person often to maintain the fiction of nonterminal illness. In the following article,
the authors describe the organizational strategies used to avoid confrontation with
the patient and his death. The work of Strauss and Glaser has played a part in bringing about major change in institutional response toward dying patients, but the
situations they identify still occur with some frequency.

Americans are characteristically unwilling to talk openly about the process of dying
and death and are prone to avoid telling a dying person his prognosis. This is, in part,
a moral attitude: life is preferable to whatever may follow it, and one should not look
forward to death unless in great pain.

This moral attitude appears to be shared by the professional people who work
with or near the patients who die in our hospitals. Although trained to give specialized
medical or nursing care to terminal patients, much of their behavior toward the dying
resembles the layman's. The training that physicians and nurses receive equips them
principally for the technical aspects of patient care; their teachers deal only briefly or
not at all with the management of the emotional response of patients to illness and
death.

Similarly, students at schools of nursing are taught how to give nursing care to
terminal patients, as well as how to give "post-mortem care," but only recently have

Source: Anselm L. Strauss and Barney G. Glaser, "Awareness of Dying," in *Loss and Grief: Psychological Management in Medical
Practice.* Edited by Bernard Schoenberg, Arthur C. Carr, David Peretz, and Austin H. Kutscher, New York: Columbia University Press,
1970, 298–309.

the psychological aspects of nursing care been included in the nurses' training. Few teachers talk about such matters, and they generally confine themselves to a lecture or two near the end of the course, sometimes calling in a psychiatrist to give a kind of "expert testimony."[1]

Beyond the medical education experience, management of the dying patient in the hospital setting is quite naturally only in strictly technical medical and nursing terms. Staff members are not required to report to each other or to their superiors what they have talked about with dying patients; they are "accountable" only for the technical aspects of their work with the dying.[2]

Medical and nursing personnel commonly recognize that working with dying patients is upsetting and sometimes traumatic. Consequently, some physicians purposely specialize in branches of medicine that will minimize their chances of encountering dying patients; many nurses frankly admit a preference for those wards or fields of nursing in which death is infrequently encountered. Those who bear the brunt of caring for terminal patients understandably develop both standardized and idiosyncratic modes of coping with the inherent threats. The most standard mode is a tendency to avoid contact with those patients who, as yet unaware of impending death, are inclined to question staff members about their increasing debilitation. Also avoided are those patients who have not "accepted" their approaching deaths, and those whose deaths are accompanied by great pain. Staff members' efforts to cope with death often have undesirable effects on both the social and psychological aspects of patient care and their own comfort. Personnel in contact with terminal patients are always somewhat disturbed by their own ineptness in handling the dying.

The social and psychological problems involved in dying are perhaps most acute when the dying person knows that he is dying. For this reason, among others, American physicians are quite reluctant to disclose impending death to their patients, and nurses are expected not to disclose it without the consent of the responsible physicians. At the same time, personnel generally agree that a patient will usually discover the truth without being told explicitly. Some physicians maneuver conversations with patients so that disclosure is made indirectly. In any event, the demeanor and actions of a patient who knows or suspects that he is dying differ from those of a patient who is not aware of dying. The problem of "awareness" is crucial to what happens both to the dying patient and to the people who give him medical and nursing care.

From one point of view the problem of awareness is a technical one: Should the patient be told he is dying, and what exactly is to be said if he knows, does not know, or only suspects? But the problem is also a moral one. Is it really proper to deny a dying person the opportunity to make his peace with his conscience and with his God, to settle his affairs and provide for the future of his family, and to determine his style of dying, much as he determined his style of living? Does anyone, the physician included, have the right to withhold such information? And on whose shoulders should this responsibility of disclosure fall—the physician, the family, or the patient?

Both the human and the technical aspects of the awareness problem are becoming increasingly momentous. One reason for this is that most Americans no longer die at home. Fifty-three percent of all deaths in the United States in 1967 occurred in hospitals, and many more in nursing homes.[3] These people, then, pass through the dying process surrounded for the most part by strangers. Dying away from home is compounded by a noticeable and important medical trend—because medical technology has vastly improved, fewer people are dying from acute diseases and more from chronic diseases. Moreover, the usual duration of most chronic diseases has increased.

The public has become increasingly sophisticated regarding the implications of physical signs and symptoms and will not be put off by evasive or oversimplified answers to their questions. Inevitably, they will understand the truth. Therefore, it is predictable that the problem of awareness will become more and more central to what happens as people pass from life to death in American hospitals.

AWARENESS CONTEXTS

There are specific "awareness contexts" revolving around the confrontation of patient and hospital personnel: for example, a patient may not recognize his impending death even though everyone else does, or he may also suspect what everyone else knows for certain. On the other hand, both patient and others may know that death is imminent yet pretend this is not so. Or they may all act on such awareness relatively openly. We shall refer to these situations as the following types of awareness: *closed awareness, suspected awareness, mutual pretense awareness,* and *open awareness.* The impact of each type of awareness context upon the interplay between patients and personnel is profound, for people guide their talk and actions according to who knows what and with what certainty. As talk, action, and the accompanying cues unfold, certain awareness contexts tend to evolve into other contexts.

Closed Awareness and Suspected Awareness

There are at least five important structural conditions which contribute to the existence and maintenance of the closed awareness context:

First, most patients have had little or no experience in recognizing the signs of impending death.

A second structural condition is that American physicians ordinarily do not tell patients outright that death is probable or inevitable. As a number of studies have shown, physicians proffer medical justifications for not disclosing the fatal prognosis to their patients.[4] For instance, one investigator[5] found that many physicians maintain that when one announces terminality to a patient, he is likely to "go to pieces"; one must therefore carefully judge whether or not to tell after sizing up the individual patient. In actual fact, this investigator notes, the "clinical experience" is not genuinely grounded experience but a species of personal mythology. The judgement was found to be based on one or two unfortunate incidents or even incidents recounted by colleagues.

Many physicians believe that patients really do not wish to know whether they are dying; if they did, then they would find out anyhow, so there is no sense telling them directly. Presumably some patients do not wish to know their fates, but there is no really good evidence that all wish to remain in blissful ignorance. There is, in fact, good evidence that they do wish to know.[6]

A third structural condition is that families tend to guard the secret, thereby confirming what the physician has announced. An interesting contrast is the practice in Asian countries, where the extended kin gather around the hospital death bed two or more days before death is expected, openly indicating to the patient that they are there to keep him company during his passage to death.

A fourth structural condition is that of the organization of hospitals and the commitments of personnel who work within them by which medical information is concealed from patients. Records are kept out of reach. Staff is skilled at withholding information. Medical talk about patients generally occurs in far-removed places, and if it occurs nearby it is couched in medical jargon. Staff members are trained to discuss with patients only the surface aspects of their illnesses, and, as we shall see, they are accustomed to acting collusively around patients so as not to disclose medical secrets.

A fifth structural condition, perhaps somewhat less apparent, is that ordinarily the patient has no allies who reveal or help him discover the fact of his impending death. Not only his family but other patients (if they know) withhold that information.

In her book, *Experiment Perilous,* Renée Fox has described a small research hospital whose patients recognized their own inevitable terminality.[7] Death was an open and everyday occurrence. Patients could talk familiarly to each other as well as to the staff members about their respective fatal conditions. Various consequences flowed from this *open* situation: patients could give each other support, and the staff could support the patients. Patients could even raise the flagging spirits of the staff! From their deathbeds, patients could thank the physicians for their unstinting efforts and wish them luck in solving their research problems in time to save other patients. They could close their lives with rituals such as letter writing and praying. They could review their lives and plan realistically for their families' futures. These consequences are, of course, not available to patients in the closed awareness situation. Instead, other consequences emerge. Since the unaware patient believes he will recover, he acts on that supposition. Thus he may convert his sick room into a temporary work-place, writing his unfinished book, telephoning his business partners, and in other ways carrying on his work somewhat "as usual." He carries on his family life and friendships with only the interruption necessitated by temporary illness. He plans as if life stretched before him. On the other hand, he may work less feverishly on his unfinished book than if he knew time was short and so fail to finish it. He may set plans into operation that in reality are useless and the plans will have to be undone after his death. The unaware patient may unwittingly shorten his life because he does not realize that special care is necessary to extend it, he may not understand the necessity for certain treatments and refuse them.

It is in some ways easier for the family to face a patient who does not know of his terminality, especially if he is the kind of person who is likely to die "gracelessly." And if an unaware person is suddenly stricken and dies, sometimes his family is grateful that "he died without knowing." On the other hand, when the kin must participate in a lengthy nondisclosure drama, they shoulder a tremendous burden. They suffer because they cannot express their grief openly to the dying person; this is especially true of husbands and wives who have always shared fully with each other.

> A dying man's wife had been informed of the prognosis by the doctor and had shared this information with friends, whose daughter told the patient's young son. The son developed a strong distrust for the doctor, and felt disinherited by his father since they had not (nor could they have) discussed the responsibilities that would fall to him in the future.

The closed context instituted by the physician permits him to avoid the potentially distressing scene that may follow an announcement to his patient, but such a closed context only subjects nurses to strain, for it is they who must spend the most time with the unaware patient, guarding constantly against disclosure. Nurses may sometimes actually be relieved when the patient talks openly about his demise and they no longer have to guard against disclosure. On the other hand, under certain conditions nurses prefer the closed context. Some do not care to talk about death with a patient, especially a patient who does not accept it with fortitude. An unaware person is sometimes easier to handle because he has not "given up." The closed awareness situation prevents staff members from enjoying certain advantages that accompany a patient's resigned—or joyous—meeting with death.

Important consequences of closed awareness also hold for the staff as a whole. Unaware patients who die quickly represent simply routine work for the staff. In contrast, the patient who moves explosively and resentfully from an unaware to a highly suspicious or fully aware state is disruptive.

The most crucial institutional consequence has already been mentioned: because American physicians generally choose not to tell patients of their terminal status, this burden falls squarely and persistently upon the nursing personnel. This considerable burden is built into the organization of the hospital services that deal with terminal patients. Another social structure condition intrinsic to the functioning of American hospitals also increases the nurse's burden, namely, the nurse's commitment to work relatively closely with and around patients. This structural condition can be better appreciated when seen in contrast to conditions in Asian hospitals, where the family clusters thickly and persistently around the dying patient, thus permitting the nursing personnel to remain at a relatively greater emotional distance from, and spend relatively little time with the patient. In addition, the enormously high patient-to-personnel ratio increases the probability of great distance and little contact.

Mutual Pretense Awareness and Open Awareness

The mutual pretense awareness context is perhaps less visible, even to its participants, than the closed, open, and suspicion contexts. A prime structural condition of this context is that unless the patient initiates conversation about his impending death, no staff member is required to talk about it with him. The patient may wish to initiate such conversation, but surely neither hospital rules nor common convention urges it upon him. Consequently, unless either the aware patient or a staff member breaks the silence by words or gestures, a mutual pretense rather than an open awareness context will exist.

The patient, of course, is more likely than the staff members to refer openly to his death, thereby inviting them, explicitly or implicitly, to respond in kind. If they seem unwilling, he may decide they do not wish to confront openly the fact of his death, and then he may, out of tact or genuine empathy for their embarrassment or distress, keep his silence.

Staff members, in turn, may give him opportunities to speak of his death without a direct or obvious reference. But if he does not care to act or talk as if he were dying, then they will support his pretense. In doing so, they have, in effect, accepted a complementary assignment of status—they will act with pretense toward his pretense.

Staff members may rationalize pretense by maintaining that if the patient wishes to pretend, it may well be best for his health. A second rationale is that perhaps they can give him better medical and nursing care if they do not have to face him so openly. A third rationale is that this sort of action is most tactful.

During the pretense episodes both sides naturally assume certain implicit rules of behavior. One rule is that dangerous topics should generally be avoided—the most obvious being the patient's death; another, the events that will happen afterward.

Talk about dangerous topics is permissible as long as neither party breaks down. The patient and the nurses may discuss daily events—such as treatments—as if they had implications for a real future, when the patient will have recovered from his illness. Some of the patient's brave, or foolhardy activities (as when he bathes himself or insists on tottering to the toilet by himself) may signify a brave show of pretense. The staff, in turn, permits his activity.

It is customary, then, that patient and staff focus determinedly on appropriately safe topics—daily routines of eating and sleeping; complaints and their management; minor personal confidences; events on the ward, and news events. Talk about the fatal illness is safe enough if confined to the symptoms themselves.

When something happens or is said that threatens to expose the fiction that both parties are attempting to sustain, then each must pretend that nothing has gone awry. Thus, a nurse may take special pains to announce herself before entering a patient's room so as not to surprise him at his crying. If she finds him crying, she may ignore it or convert it into an innocuous event with a skillful comment or gesture. A patient who cannot control a sudden expression of great pain will verbally discount its significance, while the nurse in turn goes along with his pretense. Clearly then, each party to the ritual pretense shares responsibility for maintaining it.

A mutual pretense context that is not sustained can only change to an open awareness context. The change may be sudden, temporary, or permanent. Or the change may be gradual: nurses, and relatives, too, are familiar with patients who admit to terminality more openly on some days than they do on other days, when pretense is dominant, until finally pretense vanishes altogether. Sometimes the physician skillfully paces his interaction with a patient, leading the patient finally to refer openly to his terminality and to leave behind the earlier phase of pretense.

Pretense generally collapses when certain conditions make its maintenance increasingly difficult, for example, when the patient cannot keep from expressing his increasing pain, or his suffering grows to the point that he must be kept under heavy sedation.

The pretense context can provide the patient with a measure of dignity and considerable privacy, although it may deny him the close relationship with his family that is created when he allows them to participate in his open acceptance of death. For the family—especially more distant kin—the pretense context can minimize embarrassment and other interactional strains; but for closer kin, openness may have many advantages. Oscillation between contexts of open awareness and mutual pretense is in itself a source of stress.

But whether staff or patient initiates the ritual of pretense, maintaining it creates a charcteristic mood of cautious serenity throughout the ward. Even one such patient can set such an atmosphere. Denial in the patients of a cancer hospital (buttressed by staff silence), all of whom know the nature of the hospital, can be so strong that few patients talk openly about anyone's condition.

A persistent context of pretense profoundly affects the more permanent aspects of hospital organization as well. When closed awareness generally prevails, the personnel must guard against disclosure, but they need not organize themselves as a team to handle continued pretense and its sometimes stressful breakdown. Also a chief organizational consequence of the mutual pretense context is that it eliminates any possibility that staff members might "work with" patients psychologically on a professional basis. It is also entirely possible that a ward mood of tension can be set when a number of elderly dying patients continually communicate to each other their willingness to die, but the staff members persistently insist on the pretense that the patients are going to recover. On the other hand, the prevailing ward mood accompanying mutual pretense tends to be more serene—or at least less obviously tense—than when suspected awareness is dominant.

The context of open awareness does not eliminate complexity, and, in fact, certain ambiguities associated with two properties of the open awareness context are inevitable. Even when he recognizes and acknowledges the fact of terminality, the patient's awareness is frequently qualified by his ignorance or suspicion about other aspects of his dying. Thus, a patient who knows that he is dying may be convinced that death is still some months away. Staff members may then conceal their own knowledge of the time that death is expected to occur, even though they may refer openly to the fact that it is expected. Similarly, they may keep secret their expectation that the patient is going to deteriorate badly, so long as he is unaware of this contingency.

Of course, certain patients (such as physicians) may, as a matter of course, be aware of these subsidiary aspects of impending death. Patients who have the same disease are often kept together, so that each may observe a kind of rehearsal of his own fate by watching others who are closer to death.

The second ambiguous element of the open awareness context is the divergence in expectations about "appropriate" ways of dying which reflects in part the common tendency for staff and patients to come from different class and ethnic backgrounds.

It also reflects deeply inculcated professional and institutional norms which differ from those of patients.

Once a patient has indicated his awareness of dying, he becomes responsible for his acts as a *dying* person. He knows now that he is not merely sick but dying. He must face that fact. Sociologically, facing an impending death means that the patient will be judged, and will judge himself, according to certain standards of proper conduct concerning his behavior during his final days and hours. At the same time, hospital personnel will be judged and will judge themselves in their responses to dying patients.

At first glance, the medical personnel's obligation to a dying patient seems obvious enough. If possible, they must save him; if not, then they must give proper medical and nursing care until he dies. But ethical and social, in addition to medical, judgments enter into questions such as when to try to save a patient and when to cease trying, whether to prolong life when death is certain or the patient is already comatose, and so on. These judgments, as well as less dramatic ones such as administering ''better'' care, depend in many instances, not on objective, but subjective criteria such as the ''deserving'' character of the patient.

Patients defined as less deserving risk the additional judgment that they are acting with purpose. If they know that they are dying, their improper behavior cannot be interpreted as a consequence of ignorance. Patients known to be aware of death have two kinds of obligation: first, they should not act to bring about their own death; second, there are certain positive obligations one has as a dying patient. There are no clear rules of behavior provided for the dying nor are there clear expectations on the part of the staff regarding his behavior.

Nevertheless, staff members do judge the conduct of dying patients by certain implicit standards. These standards are related to the work that hospital personnel do, as well as to some rather general American notions about courageous and decent behavior. A partial list of implicit canons includes the following: the patient should maintain relative composure and cheerfulness; at the very least, he should face death with dignity; he should not cut himself off from the world, turning his back upon the living, but should continue to be a good family member, and be ''nice'' to other patients; if he can, he should participate in the ward social life; he should cooperate with the staff members who care for him, and if possible he should avoid distressing or embarrassing them. A patient who does most of these things will be respected.

What the staff defines as unacceptable behavior in aware dying patients is readily illustrated. For instance, physicians usually honor requests for confirmatory consultations with other physicians but object to ''shopping around'' for impossible cures. Some patients do not face dying with fortitude but become noisy or hysterical. Other patients make excessive demands. Some patients wail, cry out in terror, complain, accuse the staff of doing nothing, or refuse to cooperate in their medical or nursing care. Perhaps the most unnerving are the patients who become apathetic or hostile and reproachful.

In general, then, the staff appreciates patients who exit with courage and grace, not merely because they create fewer scenes and cause less emotional stress, but because they evoke genuine admiration and sympathy, as well as feelings of professional usefulness. It is difficult to admire a patient who behaves improperly even though one can sympathize with his terrible situation. People cannot help judging him, even if by diverse and not altogether explicit standards. Occasionally a patient provides such a model of courage and fortitude that the staff remembers him with admiration long after his death. The reactions of staff members include not only respect for a great human being but also gratitude for being allowed to participate in the near-perfect drama of his dying.

A few points about the consequences of open awareness are worth emphasizing here. Awareness of impending death gives the patient an opportunity to close his life in the manner he chooses. He may finish important work, establish reconciliations, make satisfying farewells, give gifts to his friends, and leave detailed plans for his family and estate.

But open awareness has disadvantages for the patient, too. Other people may not approve of the patient's way of managing his death, and may attempt to change or subvert his management. A patient may not be able to close his life usefully and with dignity because he cannot face the dying process and death. An aware patient, therefore, may be unable to face death with equanimity, dying with more anguish and less dignity than he might if he were unaware of his terminality. For some patients there is the added stress of deciding whether to accept imminent death or to perhaps prolong life through surgery.

A patient who meets death with equanimity at the same time also makes this possible for his family. They will be able to share his satisfaction and they will treasure their experience for the remainder of their lives.

NOTES

1. J.C. Quint and A.L. Strauss, "Nursing Students, Assignments, and Dying Patients," *Nursing Outlook* 12 (January 1964): 24.
2. A.L. Strauss, B.G. Glaser, and J.C. Quint, "The Nonaccountability of Terminal Care," *Hospitals* 38 (January 16, 1964): 73.
3. R. Fulton, "Death and Self," *Journal of Religion and Health* 3 (July 1964): 364.
4. H. Feifel, "Death," in *Taboo Topics,* ed. N.L. Farberow (New York: Atherton Press, 1963).
5. D. Oken, "What to Tell Cancer Patients: A Study of Medical Attitudes," *Journal of the American Medical Association* 175 (April 1, 1961): 1120.
6. Eighty-two percent of Feifel's sample of sixty patients wanted to be informed about their condition.
7. Renée Fox, *Experiment Perilous* (New York: The Free Press, 1959).

Questions

1. Define the following terms and give examples of each where appropriate. Terms marked with an asterisk are psychological, sociological, or medical terms the authors of the selections expect readers to know. If you are not familiar with their meanings, consult a dictionary, a medical dictionary, or an abnormal psychology textbook.

   *defense mechanism
   psychological crisis
   *denial
   bargaining
   *depression
   *preparatory grief
   acceptance
   resignation
   living–dying interval
   *crisis
   *anxiety
   *coping mechanism
   integrity vs despair
   *regression
   *ego function
   *hemodialysis

   *diagnosis
   *prognosis
   *developmental level
   *cognitive style
   awareness context
   closed awareness
   mutual pretense awareness
   open awareness
   socio-physical milieu
   structural conditions
   ritual pretense
   *projection
   stage theory
   thanatos
   *interrater reliability procedures
   awareness of terminality

2. Pattison defines the period between *knowledge of death* and *actual death* as the "living–dying period." What support does he suggest that the patient needs during this time? Using other selections in the chapter, list some of the factors that might make it difficult for the family to give the needed support.

3. a. Death-related research began with the study of relatively long-term illnesses with a terminal prognosis. How well do Pattison's "crisis model" and Kübler-Ross's stages fit the death row prisoners described by Bluestone and McGahee? To what extent do you think the concepts would apply to patients with a "suspended sentence," e.g., chronic hemodialysis, chronic cardiac disease, or emphysema?
    b. How might the stages of dying discussed by Kübler-Ross differ with family structure? Religious beliefs? Ethnic background? Type of illness?

4. Denial is a complex concept, more complex than this chapter indicates. Kübler-Ross has described denial as a result of interpersonal dynamics, but Glaser and Strauss have shown that it may be part of the social interaction process as well. What would you, as a helper, look for in deciding whether a patient's "denial" represented a serious inability to deal with significant facts of his illness, or an attempt to cope with what the patient perceived as others' inability to do so? What might you want to take into account in deciding whether, and how, to intervene?

5. Suppose the father in "Do Not Go Gentle into That Good Night" was admitted to a nursing home. What psychological supports would Pattison and Kübler-Ross recommend for the father? For the speaker in the poem?

6. Does final acceptance require that a patient work through all of the other attitudes? What is the difference between the acceptance of death and the resignation to death? Do you agree that acceptance as described by Kübler-Ross is a natural and desirable goal for all dying patients? Why or why not? How does age or "engrossment" in life as described by Kastenbaum affect potential acceptance?

7. Kübler-Ross and Pattison are writing about processes that occur in a person who is aware that he is dying. Having read these selections, would you recommend withholding terminal diagnosis from a dying person? If so, under what circumstances? Survey the class on the following two questions:
    a. If you had a terminal illness, would you want to be told?
    b. If your mother (or father) had a terminal illness, would you want her (or him) to be told?
    Using Strauss and Glaser, discuss your reasons for your answers. Consider both advantages and disadvantages of withholding the information from the point of view of the patient, of the hospital staff, and of the family.

8. a. In a way, the death row prisoner and the terminal cancer patient are both awaiting the execution of a death sentence. Compare and contrast the two situations, considering the origin of the death

sentence, the amount of control held by various individuals in the setting, the psychological and social meaning of the "sentence," the relative determinancy of the "sentence," and the rationalizations available to the individual.

b. Considering cultural assumptions in North America, is it possible for death by execution to be considered an appropriate death? Under what conditions?

Projects for Further Study

1. Psychiatrist Raymond Moody has reported in *Life After Life* (1975) accounts of "return from the dead." Using Moody's accounts and others (see for example, R. Noyes, Jr., and D.J. Slymen, "The Subjective Response to Life-threatening Danger, *Omega*, 9 (1978-79): 313-321, respond to the following questions:
    a. What features do the accounts have in common?
    b. What discrepancies are there in the "typical" features reported by the authors?
    c. Do you believe that such reports are evidence for "life after death," as some have claimed? If not, what do they tell us about phenomena of clinical death?
    d. What role do cultural factors play in the content of the reports?
    e. How do cultural variations in content affect the apparent validity of the reports in your mind?

2. Leo Tolstoy's novella *The Death of Ivan Illych* is often used by contemporary humanists to illustrate the needs of the dying and the failures of family, friends, and society to meet them. Read the short novel and identify situations that seem to fit the ideas presented in this chapter: the fears of the dying patient (Pattison), the stages/reactions of dying (Kübler-Ross), and the awareness context (Glaser and Strauss). In addition, it would be interesting to compare Ivan's transcendental experience with experiences reported by survivors of clinical death and cancer patients undergoing LSD therapy for pain reduction and conflict resolution.

3. Literature surrounding the concept of appropriate death has in recent years often been exaggerated to the point where it depicts romanticized notions of "the happy death." Indulge in hyperbole to write a brief script of the idealized "happy death." Remember the ability to parody well is a test of objectivity.

Structured Exercises

Before beginning these exercises, please read "Note to the Instructor" on page xiii. To help students recognize their own attitudes to the experience of dying, have them respond to the following situations.

1. List six problems that you think would be most likely to trouble you if everything in your life were as it is now except that yesterday you were told you have an inoperable advanced cancer. Then, on a separate sheet of paper, rank order the six problems from 1 (most important to you) to 6 (least important to you). Show your original (unranked) list to someone else (this can be done pairwise or by randomly redistributing the lists among the class) and have that person rank the list of problems according to their importance to him. Then compare the rankings together, discussing your reasons for agreeing or disagreeing with each other.

   As a further attempt to understand others' perspectives on terminal illness, you could consider how the original list would change if:
   a. you were 20 years older or younger
   b. you were the other sex
   c. you were on welfare
   d. you had just learned that your two-year old son was mentally retarded
   e. your same-sexed parent had died of the same illness
   f. you were recently married
   Adapted from R. Koenig, "Counseling in Catastrophic Illness: A Self-Instructional Unit," *Omega*, 6, (1975): 227–241.

2. Try to look ahead to the time when you will actually die. Envision the ideal scene of your dying in some detail. Consider the following questions about how you would like your dying to be.
   a. How old would you be?

139

b. Where would you be?
c. What time of day would it be?
d. What special objects would you see as you looked around you?
e. What music would be playing in the background?
f. What would you have been doing with your life just prior to this time?
g. Who would be with you?
h. What would you want to tell them?

In order to share the experience, the class could:

a. Write the answers to these questions on a sheets of paper numbered from 1 to 8 and then, holding the sheets of paper in front of them, chest high, the students could walk around the room reading each other's comments. The reading should take place without conversation and involve only eye contact or other nonverbal communication. Once everyone has finished reading, class discussion of reactions can take place.
b. Each person can draw what he has imagined instead of writing it down. The drawings can be signed or left anonymous. They can be taped up around the room, the class can browse among them, and the group can discuss them.

3. Suppose you learned that a casual acquaintance had developed a terminal illness and was hospitalized. Would you visit the person? Why or why not?
    a. Assume you did visit the person. What would you hope to accomplish with your visit? What hopes and fears would you confront as you anticipated the visit?
    b. Assume now that you are hospitalized with a terminal illness and that you are expecting a visit from a casual acquaintance? What are your hopes and fears? What would you hope to accomplish during the visit?

For Further Reading

The following books provide in-depth coverage of the topics introduced in this chapter.

Brim, O.G., Freeman, H.E., Levine, S., and Scotch, N.A., eds. *The Dying Patient*. New York: Russell Sage Foundation, 1970.

Charmaz, C. *The Social Reality of Death*. Reading, Mass.: Addison-Wesley, 1980.

Garfield, C.A. *Psychosocial Care of the Dying Patient*. New York: McGraw-Hill, 1978.

Glaser, B.G., and Strauss, A.L. *Awareness of Dying*. Chicago: Aldine, 1965.

————. *Time for Dying*. Chicago: Aldine, 1968.

Kübler-Ross, E. *On Death and Dying*. New York: Macmillan, 1969.

Lamerton, R. *Care of the Dying*. Westport, Conn: Technomic Publishing Co., 1976.

Levy, N.B., ed. *Living or Dying: Adaptations to Hemodialysis.* Springfield: Charles C. Thomas, 1974.

Moody, R.A., Jr. *Life After Life*. Covington, Ky.: Mockingbird Press, 1975.

Pattison, E.M. *The Experience of Dying.* Englewood Cliffs, N.J.: Prentice-Hall, 1977.

Prichard, E.R., Collard, J., Orcutt, B.A., Kutscher, A.H., Seeland, I., and Lefkowitz, N., eds. *Social Work with the Dying Patient and the Family*. New York: Columbia University Press, 1977.

Quint, Jeanne. *The Nurse and the Dying Patient*. New York: Macmillan, 1967.

Shepard, M. *Someone You Love Is Dying*. New York: Harmony Books, 1975.

Chapter Three

Grief, Mourning, and Social Functions

At the same time the contemporary person has been deprived of his own death, he has been similarly deprived of the right to mourn the dead. Philippe Ariès, surveying the reversal in social obligations attending death and mourning, has charged that "modern society deprives man of his own death, and . . . it allows him this privilege only if he does not use it to upset the living. In a reciprocal way, society forbids the living to appear moved by the death of others; it does not allow them either to weep for the deceased or to seem to miss them."

Psychiatry, however, has long recognized that grief is a natural and necessary—albeit complex—reaction accompanied by a range of contradictory emotions and apparently aberrant behaviors. Unpleasant and irrational as it may appear to many, the grief process cannot be safely bypassed. Freud recognized this in his key paper, "Mourning and Melancholia," which provides a theoretical framework for understanding reactions to loss, a framework that still underlies our conception of mourning today.

The Freudian model has led to the study of both the normal "symptomatology" of grief reactions and the pathological consequences of distorted grief. The condition of bereavement itself has been related to depression, suicide, psychosomatic disorders, and even to death from "natural" causes.

143

STYLES OF GRIEF

The understanding and consequent acceptance of grief results in the recognition of varied styles of mourning: the dynamics of grief will vary with the nature of the death. One mourns differently for a child than for an aged parent; the aftermath of a loved one's suicide differs from the aftermath of death in wartime. As the state of extended dying becomes common, anticipatory grief must be given more prominence. Preparatory mourning shared by the dying person with his family in a state of open awareness can attenuate the experience of grief by providing mutual support and an opportunity for gradual separation *during* the dying rather than after it.

COMMUNITY

The shift from *intervention* to *prevention* in mental health care has been greatly influenced by the study of grief and bereavement. Now informal grief counseling, educational seminars on psychological and practical aspects of bereavement, and crisis intervention programs are often sponsored by churches, hospitals, and schools. Model programs such as "Widow to Widow," begun by Phyllis Silverman at the Harvard Laboratory of Community Psychiatry, and its West Coast counterpart, "Journey's End," at the University of Southern California have given rise to community support groups throughout the country. Such groups seek to provide not only emotional support during the crisis of bereavement, but also to offer practical information to aid the bereaved in the social readjustment to life as a single person.

APPROPRIATE GRIEF

The development of "preventive" psychiatry emphasizes the relationship between personal pathology and pathological social structures that have failed to meet the individual's needs. If society's prohibition of mourning has caused repression of grief, then society must now develop new cultural forms to handle grief adequately. Ariès has emphasized the role that ritual has played historically in guiding mourning, both supporting the individual and maintaining the identity of the group when death occurs. Ritual makes sense of death by placing it in the context of a world view; by requiring individuals to return to their group identity, ritual publicly reminds them of their shared beliefs. As the distance from one's own death increases and the right to mourn is taken away, the ability to "make sense" of death breaks down and there is growing dissatisfaction with the ritual that supports that rationalization. Criticism is often directed at the funeral industry and religious liturgies for being "exploitative," "insensitive," or simply "irrelevant." This criticism may be symptomatic of dissatisfaction with the social prescriptions for mourning, a dissatisfaction that is also creative in that it reflects an expanded awareness of mourning and a recognition of the benefits both to the mourner and to society when grief is publicly accepted.

OVERVIEW OF THE CHAPTER

The readings in Chapter Three begin by examining the nature and distortions of grief; they then turn to the rituals and social institutions which inform the experience of mourning. In "Symptomatology and Management of Acute Grief," psychiatrist Erich Lindemann outlines the dynamics of grief, distinguishing between normal manifestations of acute grief and pathological consequences of the refusal to mourn. Establishing that the manifestations of acute grief are often so overwhelming that a mourner needs reassurance of their validity, Lindemann then describes the forms that pathological grief may assume. The special grief reactions of a survivor of suicide are taken up by Albert Cain, also a psychiatrist, in *"Survivors of Suicide."* Next, in the poem "Daddy," Sylvia Plath, master poet of the twentieth century, weaves an expression of acute grief together with the theme of communal loss in a symbolic fabric that stands as an artistic counterpart to the preceding analytic readings.

As "Daddy" illustrates, the holocaust of World War II remains a powerful metaphor for the outrage of death. Writing from the experience of World War I, Sigmund Freud assessed the impact of war itself on the modern concept of death. His "Thoughts for the Times on War and Death: Our Attitudes Toward Death" remains a classic statement of the challenge the violence of war makes to the individual sense of immortality.

With the ambivalence toward death made clear by Freud's treatment of the impact of war, the relationship of bereavement to culture in general is addressed in the next three readings. In "Bereavement and Mental Health," psychiatrist Edmund Volkhart, in collaboration with Stanley Michael, distinguishes between the private experience of grief and the observable condition of bereavement. The two urge a scrutiny of the intervening concepts (for example, social institutions, status, roles) that link culture and individual behavior. Inquiry into the cultural orientations will, they hold, help realign the disjunction between personal experience and expected behavior. In the excerpt taken from *Group Behavior at Funeral Gatherings*, sociologist Leroy Bowman sketches the traditional background of American funeral practices. Then, in "Death and Bereavement: The Role of the Black Church," Jean Masamba, a Black African clergyman and pastoral psychologist, collaborates with Richard A. Kalish in a discussion of the factors (religious, psychological, social) that influence the behavior of the bereaved. Using spirituals as reflections of beliefs about death, they demonstrate how Black funeral practices facilitate grief work as they re-incorporate the bereaved into the community.

In the last reading of the chapter, psychohistorian Robert J. Lifton moves the discussion from funeral rituals to symbolic systems in general, noting that the death of a significant other assaults one's own sense of continued existence. In "The Struggle for Cultural Rebirth," Lifton extends the concept of immortality from its traditional theological context into additional symbolic modes—biological, psychological, social, and transcendental.

Conceptions of symbolic immortality are vital to a community, but, as the following Encounter demonstrates, they do not dull the edge of fresh loss.

Encounter

THE EXPERIENCE OF GRIEF

I knew Martin was dead, but somehow it took a long time for the reality to seep in, become part of me. I would go to the supermarket and think, "Oh, they have endive today. I'd better get some. Martin likes it so much." I would pick out an avocado for him, a fruit I've never really liked. Then I would realize, "My God! He is dead!" and put the avocado back as if it were burning me.

When something funny happened, I'd say to myself "Oh, wait until I tell Martin about this tonight! He'll never believe it." There were times in my office when I would stretch out my hand to the telephone to call him, to chat. Reality always intervened before I dialed that disconnected number. . . .

One day when I was on the Fifth Avenue bus I spotted a man who looked like Martin. I pulled the cord and plunged after him. I knew it wasn't Martin, but I tried desperately to catch up with him. I couldn't. I lost sight of him and it made me very depressed, as if Martin had rejected me.

And I had dreams. I would dream that I heard the door open while I was in the kitchen getting the ice for our evening drink. It was Martin, home from work. I would be so happy to hear him come in. But I always woke up before I saw him.

I had a sense of Martin, of some quality of Martin that had filtered into me. A very real feeling that part of me was Martin.

1. Lynn Caine reports a disturbing but frequent and natural reaction to a recent death. Can you recall similar experiences following personal loss such as the death of a loved one, a divorce, or a separation? Describe three reactions to that loss.

2. Caine viewed the episodes in which Martin's presence continued to influence her behavior as part of her "crazy period." Have you ever tried to retain elements of a lost relationship in your own life? Is doing so necessarily dysfunctional?

Source: Lynn Caine, *Widow*. New York: Morrow, 1974.

ERICH LINDEMANN

Symptomatology and Management of Acute Grief

The work of mourning is more complicated and more time consuming than most people expect or can easily accept. In the following article, Erich Lindemann places the anecdotal Encounter in a context for analysis. He defines grief as a "definite syndrome with psychological and somatic symptomatology." Presenting the sometimes distressing responses to recent death as natural and necessary, Lindemann emphasizes the need to mourn: denial of grief is a predisposing factor in both psychopathology and physical illness. Lindemann's model of bereavement as a crisis period of increased vulnerability is one of the classic works in preventive community psychiatry.

INTRODUCTION

At first glance, acute grief would not seem to be a medical or psychiatric disorder in the strict sense of the word but rather a normal reaction to a distressing situation. However, the understanding of reactions to traumatic experiences whether or not they represent clear-cut neuroses has become of ever-increasing importance to the psychiatrist. Bereavement or the sudden cessation of social interaction seems to be of special interest because it is often cited among the alleged psychosomatic disorders. The enormous increase in grief reactions due to war casualties, furthermore, demands an evaluation of their probable effect on the mental and physical health of our population.

The points to be made in this paper are as follows:

1. Acute grief is a definite syndrome with psychological and somatic symptomatology.
2. This syndrome may appear immediately after a crisis; it may be delayed; it may be exaggerated or apparently absent.

Source: Erich Lindemann. "Symptomatology and Management of Acute Grief." *American Journal of Psychiatry*, CI (1944), 141–148. (Vol. 101)

3. In place of the typical syndrome there may appear distorted pictures, each of which represents one special aspect of the grief syndrome.
4. By appropriate techniques these distorted pictures can be successfully transformed into a normal grief reaction with resolution.

Our observations comprise 101 patients. Included are psychoneurotic patients who lost a relative during the course of treatment, relatives of patients who died in the hospital, bereaved disaster victims (Cocoanut Grove Fire) and their close relatives, and relatives of members of the armed forces.

The investigation consisted of a series of psychiatric interviews. Both the timing and the content of the discussions were recorded. These records were subsequently analyzed in terms of the symptoms reported and of the changes in mental status observed progressively through a series of interviews. The psychiatrist avoided all suggestions and interpretations until the picture of symptomatology and spontaneous reaction tendencies of the patients had become clear from the records. The somatic complaints offered important leads for objective study. Careful laboratory work on spirograms, g.–i. functions, and metabolic studies is in progress and will be reported separately. At present we wish to present only our psychobiological observations.

SYMPTOMATOLOGY OF NORMAL GRIEF

The picture shown by persons in acute grief is remarkably uniform. Common to all is the following syndrome: sensations of somatic distress occurring in waves lasting from twenty minutes to an hour at a time, a feeling of tightness in the throat, choking with shortness of breath, need for sighing, and an empty feeling in the abdomen, lack of muscular power, and an intense subjective distress described as tension or mental pain. The patient soon learns that these waves of discomfort can be precipitated by visits, by mentioning the deceased, and by receiving sympathy. There is a tendency to avoid the syndrome at any cost, to refuse visits lest they should precipitate the reaction, and to keep deliberately from thought all references to the deceased.

The striking features are the marked tendency to sighing respiration; this respiratory disturbance was most conspicuous when the patient was made to discuss his grief. The complaint about lack of strength and exhaustion is universal and is described as follows: "It is almost impossible to climb up a stairway." "Everything I lift seems so heavy." "The slightest effort makes me feel exhausted." "I can't walk to the corner without feeling exhausted." Digestive symptoms are described as follows: "The food tastes like sand." "I have no appetite at all." "I stuff the food down because I have to eat." "My saliva won't flow." "My abdomen feels hollow." "Everything seems slowed up in my stomach."

The sensorium is generally somewhat altered. There is commonly a slight sense of unreality, a feeling of increased emotional distance from other people (sometimes they appear shadowy or small), and there is intense preoccupation with the image of the deceased. A patient who lost his daughter in the Cocoanut Grove disaster visualized his girl in the telephone booth calling for him and was much troubled by the loudness with which his name was called by her and was so vividly preoccupied with the scene that he became oblivious of his surroundings. A young navy pilot lost a close friend; he remained a vivid part of his imagery, not in terms of a religious survival but in terms of an imaginary companion. He ate with him and talked over problems with him, for instance, discussing with him his plan of joining the Air Corps. Up to the time of the study, six months later, he denied the fact that the boy was no longer with him. Some patients are much concerned about this aspect of their grief reaction because they feel it indicates approaching insanity.

Another strong preoccupation is with feelings of guilt. The bereaved searches the time before the death for evidence of failure to do right by the lost one. He accuses himself of negligence and exaggerates minor omissions. After the fire disaster the central topic of discussion for a young married woman was the fact that her husband died after he left her following a quarrel, and of a young man whose wife died that he fainted too soon to save her.

In addition, there is often a disconcerting loss of warmth in relationship to other people, a tendency to respond with irritability and anger, a wish not to be bothered by others at a time when friends and relatives make a special effort to keep up friendly relationships.

These feelings of hostility, surprising and quite inexplicable to the patients, disturbed them and again were often taken as signs of approaching insanity. Great efforts are made to handle them, and the result is often a formalized, stiff manner of social interaction.

The activity throughout the day of the severely bereaved person shows remarkable changes. There is no retardation of action and speech; quite to the contrary, there is a push of speech, especially when talking about the deceased. There is restlessness, inability to sit still, moving about in an aimless fashion, continually searching for something to do. There is, however, at the same time, a painful lack of capacity to initiate and maintain organized patterns of activity. What is done is done with lack of zest, as though one were going through the motions. The bereaved clings to the daily routine of prescribed activities; but these activities do not proceed in the automatic, self-sustaining fashion which characterizes normal work but have to be carried on with effort, as though each fragment of the activity became a special task. The bereaved is surprised to find how large a part of his customary activity was done in some meaningful relationship to the deceased and has now lost its significance. Especially the habits of social interaction—meeting friends, making conversation, sharing enterprises with others—seem to have been lost. This loss leads to a strong dependency on anyone who will stimulate the bereaved to activity and serve as the initiating agent.

These five points—(1) somatic distress, (2) preoccupation with the image of the deceased, (3) guilt, (4) hostile reactions, and (5) loss of patterns of conduct—seem to be pathognomonic for grief. There may be added a sixth characteristic, shown by patients who border on pathological reactions, which is not so conspicuous as the others but nevertheless often striking enough to color the whole picture. This is the appearance of traits of the deceased in the behavior of the bereaved, especially symptoms shown during the last illness, or behavior which may have been shown at the time of the tragedy. A bereaved person is observed or finds himself walking in the manner of his deceased father. He looks in the mirror and believes that his face appears just like that of the deceased. He may show a change of interests in the direction of the former activities of the deceased and may start enterprises entirely different from his former pursuits. A wife who lost her husband, an insurance agent, found herself writing to many insurance companies offering her services with somewhat exaggerated schemes. It seemed a regular observation in these patients that the painful preoccupation with the image of the deceased described above was transformed into preoccupation with symptoms or personality traits of the lost person, but now displaced to their own bodies and activities by identification.

COURSE OF NORMAL GRIEF REACTIONS

The duration of a grief reaction seems to depend upon the success with which a person does the *grief work,* namely, emancipation from the bondage to the deceased, readjustment to the environment in which the deceased is missing, and the formation of new relationships. One of the big obstacles to this work seems to be the fact that many patients try to avoid the intense distress connected with the grief experience and to avoid the expression of emotion necessary for it. The men victims after the Cocoanut Grove fire appeared in the early psychiatric interviews to be in a state of tension with tightened facial musculature, unable to relax for fear they might "break down." It required considerable persuasion to yield to the grief process before they were willing to accept the discomfort of bereavement. One assumed a hostile attitude toward the psychiatrist, refusing to allow any references to the deceased and rather rudely asking him to leave. This attitude remained throughout his stay on the ward, and the prognosis for his condition is not good in the light of other observations. Hostility of this sort was encountered on only occasional visits with the other patients. They became willing to accept the grief process and to embark on a program of dealing in memory with the deceased person. As soon as this became possible there seemed to be a rapid relief of tension and the subsequent interviews were rather animated conversations in which the deceased was idealized and in which misgivings about the future adjustments were worked through.

Examples of the psychiatrist's role in assisting patients in their readjustment after bereavement are contained in the following case histories. The first shows a very successful readjustment.

> A woman, aged 40, lost her husband in the fire. She had a history of good adjustment previously. One child, ten years old. When she heard about her husband's death she was extremely depressed, cried bitterly, did not want to live, and for three days showed a state of utter dejection.
>
> When seen by the psychiatrist, she was glad to have assistance and described her painful preoccupation with the memories of her husband and her fear that she might lose her mind. She had a vivid visual image of his presence, picturing him as going to work in the

morning and herself as wondering whether he would return in the evening, whether she could stand his not returning, then, describing to herself how he does return, plays with the dog, receives his child, and gradually tried to accept the fact that he is not there any more. It was only after ten days that she succeeded in accepting his loss and then only after having described in detail the remarkable qualities of her husband, the tragedy of his having to stop his activities at the pinnacle of his success, and his deep devotion to her.

In the subsequent interviews she explained with some distress that she had become very much attached to the examiner and that she waited for the hour of his coming. This reaction she considered disloyal to her husband but at the same time she could accept the fact that it was a hopeful sign of her ability to fill the gap he had left in her life. She then showed a marked drive for activity, making plans for supporting herself and her little girl, mapping out the preliminary steps for resuming her old profession as secretary, and making efforts to secure help from the occupational therapy department in reviewing her knowledge of French.

Her convalescence, both emotional and somatic, progressed smoothly, and she had a good adjustment immediately on her return home.

A man of 52, successful in business, lost his wife, with whom he had lived in a happy marriage. The information given him about his wife's death confirmed his suspicions of several days. He responded with a severe grief reaction, with which he was unable to cope. He did not want to see visitors, was ashamed of breaking down, and asked to be permitted to stay in the hospital on the psychiatric service, when his physical condition would have permitted his discharge, because he wanted further assistance. Any mention of his wife produced a severe wave of depressive reaction, but with psychiatric assistance he gradually became willing to go through this painful process, and after three days on the psychiatric service he seemed well enough to go home.

He showed a high rate of verbal activity, was restless, needed to be occupied continually, and felt that the experience had whipped him into a state of restless overactivity.

As soon as he returned home he took an active part in his business, assuming a post in which he had a great many telephone calls. He also took over the role of amateur psychiatrist to another bereaved person, spending time with him and comforting him for his loss. In his eagerness to start anew, he developed a plan to sell all his former holdings, including his house, his furniture, and giving away anything which could remind him of his wife. Only after considerable discussion was he able to see that this would mean avoiding immediate grief at the price of an act of poor judgment. Again he had to be encouraged to deal with his grief reactions in a more direct manner. He has made a good adjustment.

With eight to ten interviews in which the psychiatrist shares the grief work, and with a period of from four to six weeks, it was ordinarily possible to settle an uncomplicated and undistorted grief reaction. This was the case in all but one of the 13 Cocoanut Grove fire victims.

MORBID GRIEF REACTIONS

Morbid grief reactions represent distortions of normal grief. The conditions mentioned here were transformed into "normal reactions" and then found their resolution.

Delay of Reaction

The most striking and most frequent reaction of this sort is *delay* or *post-ponement*. If the bereavement occurs at a time when the patient is confronted with important tasks and when there is necessity for maintaining the morale of others, he may show little or no reaction for weeks or even much longer. A brief delay is described in the following example.

> A girl of 17 lost both parents and her boy friend in the fire and was herself burned severely, with marked involvement of the lungs. Throughout her stay in the hospital her attitude was that of cheerful acceptance without any sign of adequate distress. When she was discharged at the end of three weeks she appeared cheerful, talked rapidly, with a considerable flow of ideas, seemed eager to return home and to assume the role of parent for her two younger siblings. Except for slight feelings of "lonesomeness" she complained of no distress.
>
> This period of griefless acceptance continued for the next two months, even when the household was dispersed and her younger siblings were placed in other homes. Not until the end of the tenth week did she begin to show a true state of grief with marked feelings of depression, intestinal emptiness, tightness in her throat, frequent crying, and vivid preoccupation with her deceased parents.

That this delay may involve years became obvious first by the fact that patients in acute bereavement about a recent death may soon upon exploration be found preoccupied with grief about a person who died many years ago. In this manner a woman of 38, whose mother had died recently and who had responded to the mother's death with a surprisingly severe reaction, was found to be but mildly concerned with her mother's death but deeply engrossed with unhappy and perplexing fantasies concerning the death of her brother, who died twenty years ago under dramatic circumstances from metastasizing carcinoma after amputation of his arm had been postponed too long. The discovery that a former unresolved grief reaction may be precipitated in the course of the discussion of another recent event was soon demonstrated in psychiatric interviews by patients who showed all the traits of a true grief reaction when the topic of a former loss arose.

The precipitating factor for the delayed reaction may be a deliberate recall of circumstances surrounding the death or may be a spontaneous occurrence in the patient's life. A peculiar form of this is the circumstance that a patient develops the grief reaction at the time when he himself is as old as the person who died. For instance, a railroad worker, aged 42, appeared in the psychiatric clinic with a picture which was undoubtedly a grief reaction for which he had no explanation. It turned out that when he was 22, his mother, then 42, had committed suicide.

Distorted Reactions

The delayed reactions may occur after an interval which was not marked by any abnormal behavior or distress, but in which there developed an *alteration* in the patient's *conduct* perhaps not conspicuous or serious enough to lead him to a psychiatrist. These alterations may be considered as the surface manifestations of an unresolved grief reaction, which may respond to fairly simple and quick psychiatric management if recognized. They may be classified as follows: (1) *overactivity without a sense of loss,* rather with a sense of wellbeing and zest, the activities being of an expansive and adventurous nature and bearing semblance to the activities formerly carried out by the deceased, as described above; (2) *the acquisition of symptoms belonging to the last illness of the deceased.* This type of patient appears in medical clinics and is often labelled hypochondriasis or hysteria. To what extent actual alterations of physiological functions occur under these circumstances will have to be a field of further careful inquiry. I owe to Dr. Chester Jones a report about a patient whose electrocardiogram showed a definite change during a period of three weeks, which started two weeks after the time her father died of heart disease.

While this sort of symptom formation "by identification" may still be considered as conversion symptoms such as we know from hysteria, there is another type of disorder doubtlessly presenting (3) a recognized *medical disease,* namely, a group of psychosomatic conditions, predominantly ulcerative colitis, rheumatoid arthritis, and asthma. Extensive studies in ulcerative colitis have produced evidence that 33 out of 41 patients with ulcerative colitis developed their disease in close time relationship to the loss of an important person. Indeed, it was this observation which first gave the impetus for the present detailed study of grief. Two of the patients developed bloody diarrhea at funerals. In the others it developed within a few weeks after the loss. The course of the ulcerative colitis was strikingly benefited when this grief reaction was resolved by psychiatric technique.

At the level of social adjustment there often occurs a conspicuous (4) *alteration in relationship to friends and relatives.* The patient feels irritable, does not want to be bothered, avoids former social activities, and is afraid he might antagonize his friends by his lack of interest and his critical attitudes. Progressive social isolation follows, and the patient needs considerable encouragement in re-establishing his social relationships.

While overflowing hostility appears to be spread out over all relationships, it may also occur as (5) *furious hostility against specific persons;* the doctor or the surgeon is accused bitterly for neglect of duty and the patient may assume that foul play has led to the death. It is characteristic that while patients talk a good deal about their suspicions and their bitter feelings, they are not likely to take any action against the accused, as a truly paranoid person might do.

(6) Many bereaved persons struggled with much effort against these feelings of hostility, which to them seem absurd, representing a vicious change in their characters and to be hidden as much as possible. Some patients succeed in hiding their hostility but become wooden and formal, with affectivity and conduct *resembling schizophrenic pictures.* A typical report is this, "I go through all the motions of living. I look after my children. I do my errands. I go to social functions, but it is like being in a play; it doesn't really concern me. I can't have any warm feelings. If I were to have any feelings at all I would be angry with everybody." This patient's reaction to

therapy was characterized by growing hostility against the therapist, and it required considerable skill to make her continue interviews in spite of the disconcerting hostility which she had been fighting so much. The absence of emotional display in this patient's face and actions was quite striking. Her face had a mask-like appearance, her movements were formal, stilted, robot-like, without the fine play of emotional expression.

(7) Closely related to this picture is a *lasting loss of patterns of social interaction.* The patient cannot initiate any activity, is full of eagerness to be active—restless, can't sleep—but throughout the day he will not start any activity unless "primed" by somebody else. He will be grateful at sharing activities with others but will not be able to make up his mind to do anything alone. The picture is one of lack of decision and initiative. Organized activities along social lines occur only if a friend takes the patient along and shares the activity with him. Nothing seems to promise reward; only the ordinary activities of the day are carried on, and these in a routine manner, falling apart into small steps, each of which has to be carried out with much effort and without zest.

(8) There is, in addition, a picture in which a patient is active but in which most of his activities attain a coloring which is *detrimental to his own social and economic existence.* Such patients, with uncalled for generosity, give away their belongings, are easily lured into foolish economic dealings, lose their friends and professional standing by a series of "stupid acts," and find themselves finally without family, friends, social status or money. This protracted self-punitive behavior seems to take place without any awareness of excessive feelings of guilt. It is a particularly distressing grief picture because it is likely to hurt other members of the family and drag down friends and business associates.

(9) This leads finally to the picture in which the grief reaction takes the form of a straight *agitated depression* with tension, agitation, insomnia, feelings of worthlessness, bitter self-accusation, and obvious need for punishment. Such patients may be dangerously suicidal.

> A young man aged 32 had received only minor burns and left the hospital apparently well on the road to recovery just before the psychiatric survey of the disaster victims took place. On the fifth day he had learned that his wife had died. He seemed somewhat relieved of his worry about her fate; impressed the surgeon as being unusually well controlled during the following short period of his stay in the hospital.
>
> On January 1st he was returned to the hospital by his family. Shortly after his return home he had become restless, did not want to stay at home, had taken a trip to relatives trying to find rest, had not succeeded, and had returned home in a state of marked agitation, appearing preoccupied, frightened, and unable to concentrate on any organized activity. The mental status presented a somewhat unusual picture. He was restless, could not sit still or participate in any activity in the ward. He would try to read, drop it after a few minutes, or try to play pingpong, give it up after a short time. He would try to start conversations, break them off abruptly, and then fall into repeated murmured utterances: "Nobody can help me. When is it going to happen? I am doomed, am I not?" With great effort it was possible to establish enough rapport to

carry on interviews. He complained about his feeling of extreme tension, inability to breathe, generalized weakness and exhaustion, and his frantic fear that something terrible was going to happen. "I'm destined to live in insanity or I must die. I know that it is God's will. I have this awful feeling of guilt." With intense morbid guilt feelings, he reviewed incessantly the events of the fire. His wife had stayed behind. When he tried to pull her out, she had fainted and was shoved out by the crowd. She was burned while he was saved. "I should have saved her or I should have died too." He complained about being filled with an incredible violence and did not know what to do about it. The rapport established with him lasted for only brief periods of time. He then would fall back into his state of intense agitation and muttering. He slept poorly even with large sedation. In the course of four days he became somewhat more composed, had longer periods of contact with the psychiatrist, and seemed to feel that he was being understood and might be able to cope with his morbid feelings of guilt and violent impulses. On the sixth day of his hospital stay, however, after skillfully distracting the attention of his special nurse he jumped through a closed window to a violent death.

If the patient is not conspicuously suicidal, it may nevertheless be true that he has a strong desire for painful experiences, and such patients are likely to desire shock treatment of some sort, which they picture as a cruel experience, such as electrocution might be.

A 21-year-old woman, whose 20-month-old son was accidentally smothered, developed a state of severe agitated depression with self-accusation, inability to enjoy anything, hopelessness about the future, overflow of hostility against the husband and his parents, also with excessive hostility against the psychiatrist. She insisted upon electric-shock treatment and was finally referred to another physician who treated her. She responded to the shock treatments very well and felt relieved of her sense of guilt.

It is remarkable that agitated depressions of this sort represent only a small fraction of the pictures of grief in our series.

PROGNOSTIC EVALUATION

Our observations indicate that to a certain extent the type and severity of the grief reaction can be predicted. Patients with obsessive personality make-up and with a history of former depressions are likely to develop an agitated depression. Severe reactions seem to occur in mothers who have lost young children. The intensity of interaction with the deceased before his death seems to be significant. It is important to realize that such interaction does not have to be of the affectionate type; on the contrary, the death of a person who invited much hostility, especially hostility which could not well be expressed because of his status and claim to loyalty, may be followed by a severe grief reaction in which hostile impulses are the most conspicuous feature. Not infrequently the person who passed away represented a key person in a social system, his death being followed by disintegration of this social system and by a profound alteration of the living and social conditions for the bereaved. In such cases readjustment presents a severe task quite apart from the reaction to the loss incurred. All these factors seem to be more important than a tendency to react with neurotic symptoms in previous life. In this way the most conspicuous forms of morbid identification were found in persons who had no former history of a tendency to psychoneurotic reactions.

MANAGEMENT

Proper psychiatric management of grief reactions may prevent prolonged and serious alterations in the patient's social adjustment, as well as potential medical disease. The essential task facing the psychiatrist is that of sharing the patient's grief work, namely, his efforts at extricating himself from the bondage to the deceased and at finding new patterns of rewarding interaction. It is of the greatest importance to notice that not only over-reaction but under-reaction of the bereaved must be given attention because delayed responses may occur at unpredictable moments and the dangerous distortions of the grief reaction, not conspicuous at first, be quite destructive later and these may be prevented.

Religious agencies have led in dealing with the bereaved. They have provided comfort by giving the backing of dogma to the patient's wish for continued interaction with the deceased, have developed rituals which maintain the patient's interaction with others, and have counteracted the morbid guilt feelings of the patient by Divine Grace and by promising an opportunity for "making up" to the deceased at the time of a later reunion. While these measures have helped countless mourners, comfort alone does not provide adequate assistance in the patient's grief work. He has to accept the pain of the bereavement. He has to review his relationships with the deceased, and has to become acquainted with the alterations in his own modes of emotional reaction. His fear of insanity, his fear of accepting the surprising changes in his feelings, especially the overflow of hostility, have to be worked through. He will have to express his sorrow and sense of loss. He will have to find an acceptable formulation of his future relationship to the deceased. He will have to visualize his feelings of guilt, and he will have to find persons around him whom he can use as "primers" for the acquisition of new patterns of conduct. All this can be done in eight to ten interviews.

Special techniques are needed if hostility is the most marked feature of the grief reaction. The hostility may be directed against the psychiatrist, and the patient will have such guilt over his hostility that he will avoid further interviews. The help of a social worker or a minister, or if these are not available, a member of the family, to urge the patient to continue coming to see the psychiatrist may be indispensable. If the tension and the depressive features are too great, a combination of benzedrine sulphate, 5–10 mgm. b.i.d., and sodium amytal, 3 gr. before retiring, may be useful in first reducing emotional distress to a tolerable degree. Severe agitated depressive reactions may defy all efforts of psychotherapy and may respond well to shock treatment.

Since it is obvious that not all bereaved persons, especially those suffering because of war casualties, can have the benefit of expert psychiatric help, much of this knowledge will have to be passed on to auxiliary workers. Social workers and ministers will have to be on the look-out for the more ominous pictures, referring these to the psychiatrist while assisting the more normal reactions themselves.

ANTICIPATORY GRIEF REACTIONS

While our studies were at first limited to reactions to actual death, it must be understood that grief reactions are just one form of separation reactions. Separation by death is characterized by its irreversibility and finality. Separation may, of course, occur for other reasons. We were at first surprised to find genuine grief reactions in patients who had not experienced a bereavement but who had experienced separation, for instance with the departure of a member of the family into the armed forces. Separation in this case is not due to death but is under the threat of death. A common picture hitherto not appreciated is a syndrome which we have designated *anticipatory grief*. The patient is so concerned with her adjustment after the potential death of father or son that she goes through all the phases of grief-depression, heightened preoccupation with the departed, a review of all the forms of death which might befall him, and anticipation of the modes of readjustment which might be necessitated by it. While this reaction may well form a safeguard against the impact of a sudden death notice, it can turn out to be of a disadvantage at the occasion of reunion. Several instances of this sort came to our attention when a soldier just returned from the battlefront complained that his wife did not love him anymore and demanded immediate divorce. In such situations apparently the grief work had been done so effectively that the patient has emancipated herself and the readjustment must now be directed towards new interaction. It is important to know this because many family disasters of this sort may be avoided through prophylactic measures.

NOTES

Many of the observations are, of course, not entirely new. Delayed reactions were described by Helene Deutsch (1). Shock treatment in agitated depressions due to bereavement has recently been advocated by Myerson (2). Morbid identification has been stressed at many points in the psychoanalytic literature and recently by H.A. Murray (3). The relation of mourning and depressive psychoses has been discussed by Freud (4), Melanie Klein (5), and Abraham (6). Bereavement reactions in wartime were discussed by Wilson (7). The reactions after the Cocoanut Grove fire were described in some detail in a chapter of the monograph on this civilian disaster (8). The effect of wartime separations was reported by Rosenbaum (9). The incidence of grief reactions among the psychogenic factors in asthma and rheumatoid arthritis has been mentioned by Cobb, et al., (10, 11).

1. Helene Deutsch, "Absence of Grief," *Psychoanalyt. Quart.* 6 (1937):12.
2. Abraham Myerson, "The Use of Shock Therapy in Prolonged Grief Reactions," *New England J. Med.* 230 (Mar. 2, 1944):9.
3. H.A. Murray, "Visual Manifestations of Personality," *Jr. Abn. & Social Psychol.* 32 (1937):161–184.

4. Sigmund Freud, "Mourning and Melancholia," *Collected Papers*, IV, 288–317; 152–170.
5. Melanie Klein, "Mourning and Its Relation to Manic-Depressive States," *Internat. J. Psychoan.* 21 (1940):125–153.
6. C. Abraham, "Notes on the Psycho-analytical Investigation and Treatment of the Libido, Viewed in the Light of Mental Disorder." Selected Papers.
7. A.T.M. Wilson, "Reactive Emotional Disorders," *Practitioner* 146:254–258.
8. S. Cobb and E. Lindemann, "Neuropsychiatric Observations after the Cocoanut Grove Fire," *Ann. Surg.,* June 1943.
9. Milton Rosenbaum, "Emotional Aspects of Wartime Separations," *Family* 24 (1944):337–341.
10. S. Cobb, W. Bauer, and I. Whitney, "Environmental Factors in Rheumatoid Arthritis," *J.A.M.A.* 113 (1939):668–670.
11. N. McDermott and S. Cobb, "Psychogenic Factors in Asthma," *Psychosom. Med.* 1 (1939):204–341.
12. Erich Lindemann, "Psychiatric Factors in the Treatment of Ulcerative Colitis," *Archives of Neurology and Psychiatry* 49 (1943):323–324.

ALBERT C.CAIN

Survivors of Suicide

Complex as the symptomatology of normal grief is, the mourning process for a survivor of suicide is infinitely more so. Albert Cain emphasizes the psychological vulnerability of the survivor, who is often tormented by feelings of personal responsibility in addition to the normal grief reactions of pain, anger, and guilt. Society offers no explanation or absolution for the death; rather it stigmatizes the mourner, depriving him of support.

The papers included in this book speak of and for the survivors of suicide, of their torment and their desperate need for psychological assistance. Seen at varying ages, individually or as a family, in different settings, at widely varying intervals following the suicide, in highly divergent forms of study or intervention, the survivors of suicides nevertheless spoke a story with many major convergences: The authors of these papers underline that there are qualitative and quantitative features in the stresses impinging upon the family survivors of suicide that range significantly beyond those typical of bereavement per se. They are struck by the severity of psychopathology found in the survivors, and by the intrinsic vulnerability of suicide survivors. They are not only aware of, but quick to insist upon the *multiplicity* of *pre-suicide* and *post-suicide* determinants of the survivor's personality and psychopathology. They are emphatic in balancing discussions of the obvious direct pathogenic impact of suicide itself with references to *preexisting* profoundly pathogenic influences (grossly evidenced, for instance, in the effects upon the family members of an eventual suicide's prior alcoholism, repeated desertions, acting out, borderline psychosis, depression, raw marital strife, and such—conditions often reported in the pre-suicide behavior of those who eventually commit suicide). So too do they spell out many powerful *post-suicide* secondary and tertiary pathogenic forces.[1] From these reports there evolves, frame by frame, a picture of the legacy of suicide that is simultaneously cognitive and affective, that captures the complex individual intrapsychic sequelae, placing these in

Source: Albert C. Cain. *Survivors of Suicide*. Edited by Albert C. Cain. Springfield, Illinois: Charles C. Thomas, 1972. Copyright© by Charles C. Thomas. Used by permission.

turn within a powerful interpersonal and familial field of forces, and using a wide angle lens, within the larger social milieu of clan, neighbors and society.

The reactions portrayed, complex and individual as they are, can perhaps be clustered and capsuled as follows:

1. *Reality distortion*—massive, insistent use of denial and repression; tangled webs of evasions, contradictory beliefs, deliberate lies; concealment and anxiety-clouded confusion of memory, fantasy, and "imposed" redefinitions of reality . . . often elaborated into family myths, misconceptions, and varying disorders of reality linkage (feelings of unreality, derealization, weakened capacity for or commitment to reality testing, marked ego-splitting).

2. *Tortured object-relations*—desperate lonely neediness; disillusioned and doubt-filled distrust of human relationships; a hunger for, yet fear of closeness; a repetitive need to reenact separations, drive loved objects away, replay experiences of estrangement and reunion (or conversely, within the same dynamic configuration, ferocious determination to maintain crucial object-relations at any and all costs).

3. *Guilt*—visible quite directly, or in blaming and accusations, or in more symptomatic form; utterly irrational or painfully appropriate; focused variously on general anger and death wishes, specific acts, feelings that one could or should have prevented the suicide, a pervasive sense of complicity, or a sense of having been blamed by the suicidal individual for his despair; guilt variously fused with, displaced to or serving as screen guilt for other earlier guilts from myriad developmental sources.

4. *Disturbed self-concept*—compounded of a sense of shame, dishonor, and stigma; of having been cast away, abandoned, unwanted; of being worthless, unlovable if not bad or rotten; of being helpless, vulnerable; of being eternally unsure of self or others.

5. *Impotent rage*—intense yet admitting of little socially acceptable discharge; multiplied by the frequent sense of rejection and deliberate desertion, with its core narcissistic insult; fed by the social "branding" and at times ostracism, the intense frustration of ongoing needs, and the enforced facing of old and huge new burdens alone.

6. *Identification with the suicide*—often the result of a commingling of archaic introjective mechanisms and interpersonal tugs and pulls toward redefinition of self and family role;[2] masked or overt, accepted or fiercely defended against; the identification variously focusing upon personality features of the suicide, the threatening of suicide, the bodily sensations of the suicidal act, the committing of suicide—even the specific act of suicide itself in like manner, setting, or anniversary date.

7. *Depression and self-destructiveness*—bred of the guilt, shame, rage, unmet yearning and unresolved grief delineated above, depression in its many faces is paramount: in active self-hatred, in states of hollow emptiness and deadness; in apathy, withdrawal, and immobilization; in sadness and despair; these depressive processes, exacerbated by the identification processes noted, are visible in

implacably self-destructive ways of life and a remarkable incidence of direct suicidal behavior—suicidal impulses, fantasies, threats, preoccupation,[3] repeated suicidal attempts and completed suicides.

8. *Search for meaning*—driven, endless repetitions and reconstructions of different versions of the events preceding the suicide, and a groping quest for the "meaning" of the suicide. Spared temporarily for some by avoidance, suppression, flights into activity, spared for others by rigid, abrupt foreclosure of all but one unthreatening interpretation or construction; for many a struggle, too often alone, for a fixed sense of the specific suicidal events, the why of it, and the fit of the experience itself with the larger order of life. For too many this floundering search to construct a meaning, an interpretation of suicide, of *the* suicide, provides too few answers not colored with guilt, with perceived responsibility, with despair beyond redefinition or reparation.

9. *Incomplete mourning*—given the potent factors of denial, concealment, and evasion in the face of suicide, the shame and guilt-engendered avoidance of communication, and the mutual withdrawal of and from friends, neighbors and relatives (with consequent lack of opportunity for reassurance, reality testing, catharsis, shared grieving, and social support), the gradual working through of mourning is severely hampered if not made impossible; thus the survivor of suicide is peculiarly vulnerable to the crippling effects of unresolved mourning so richly described initially outside the realm of suicide (Bowlby, 1961, 1963; Lindemann, 1944).

It is also apparent from the studies presented here that these psychological processes neither originate nor evolve in an interpersonal vacuum.[4] Quite the contrary. They are often shaped by and amidst family interactions contorted by individuals too deeply preoccupied with their own grief to be helpful to each other, brimming with needs to blame and externalize, contending with newly erupted affects and problem behavior in themselves and each other, abruptly forced into significantly restructuring delicately intertwined family roles and sometimes required to learn utterly new roles and skills, caught between divergent if not conflicting patterns or pace of grief reactions among family members, urgently pressed to replace previous highly cathected modes of interpersonal relationship and sources of need-gratifications, buffeted as well by major practical problems which weigh toward further dissolution of the already harshly rent family structure.

These family processes are seen as still further contextually influenced by and infused with the prevalent values, constructions, taboos, and orientations toward suicide of a society whose proffered meanings of suicide tend to be at best ambiguous and fertile with the seeds of blame; a society whose attitudes toward suicide are basically punitive; a society which affords virtually no institutions or mechanisms for relieving the unique burdens bequeathed the suicide's bereaved. And ultimately a social milieu is portrayed which surrounds suicide and its survivors with the mark of *stigma*; stigma whose familiar accompaniments of shame, disgrace, social avoidance, and cloaked communication (if not forthright malignant blaming and ostracism) multiply the intrinsically formidable tasks of mourning and coping with the suicide death of a family member.

NOTES

1. One can no more suggest that the substantial psychopathology seen is *purely* the product of, for example, parent suicide than one could claim that Oedipus' fall, torment, and commitment to self-destruction was purely or primarily the product of Jocasta's self-hanging!

2. Most vividly seen with the young children of suicides, whose surviving parent suddenly imposes identification—"mis-identification" in John Benjamin's fortunate term—with the dead parent upon them.

3. Reference here to suicidal preoccupation is not only to preoccupation with one's own suicide, but a pervasive interest in and often effort to involve oneself with suicidal individuals (evident in the number of survivors of suicide—family suicides or those of other intimates—who volunteer and often helpfully serve as lay staff in suicide prevention agencies).

4. It has been suggested that accumulating evidence of psychopathology in survivors of suicide attests to the validity of the concept that a primary motive of suicide is to damage others—blame them, accuse them, cause sorrow, regret and trouble. This concept is, of course, key to Adlerian approaches to suicidal behavior (Ansbacher, 1970). "Revenge suicides" are well known and have been a normal social mechanism in a number of societies (Westermarck, 1906; Jeffreys, 1952; Murphy, 1954; Noyes, 1968). There are dramatic clinical cases of openly hostile, vengeful suicides on record, and many instances in which such motives and fantasies are not difficult to discern. In many others, however, no such motivation is apparent. But more to the point, it must be emphasized here that the "survivor" materials presented in this volume provide *no direct evidence* whatsoever as to the nature and meaning of the prior suicides per se. To infer from the effects on survivors simply and linearly to the suicides' *intention* is *a distortion of clinical inference and a misuse of survivor data.*

SYLVIA PLATH

Daddy

Responses to a person's death are as intricate as the relationship with the individual was in life. Anger and guilt, as well as sorrow, must find a place in any mourning process. But the mourner's expression of anger and guilt is often difficult for others to accept. On occasion, the mourner may find a vehicle for the expression of his feelings (whether socially acceptable or not) and a means of resolving the irrational contradictions of emotions through writing. In her poetry, Sylvia Plath often explored the chaotic emotions surrounding death—her own and that of others. In "Daddy," a mourning poem of a sort, the speaker gives vent to strong feelings of anger and merges the response to a particular death symbolically with the holocaust experience of the Jews in World War II.

You do not do, you do not do
Any more, black shoe
In which I have lived like a foot
For thirty years, poor and white,
Scarcely daring to breathe or Achoo.

Daddy, I have had to kill you.
You died before I had time—
Marble-heavy, a bag full of God,
Ghastly statue with one grey toe
Big as a Frisco seal

And a head in the freakish Atlantic
Where it pours bean green over blue
In the waters off beautiful Nauset.
I used to pray to recover you.
Ach, du.

In the German tongue, in the Polish
      town
Scraped flat by the roller
Of wars, wars, wars.
But the name of the town is common.
My Polack friend.

Says there are a dozen or two.
So I could never tell where you
Put your foot, your root,
I never could talk to you.
The tongue stuck in my jaw.

It stuck in a barb wire snare.
Ich, ich, ich, ich.

I could hardly speak.
I thought every German was you.
And the language obscene

An engine, an engine
Chuffing me off like a Jew.
A Jew to Dachau, Auschwitz, Belsen.
I began to talk like a Jew.
I think I may well be a Jew.

The snows of the Tyrol, the
   clear beer of Vienna
Are not very pure or true.
With my gypsy ancestress and
   my weird luck
And my Taroc pack and my Taroc
   pack
I may be a bit of a Jew.

I have always been scared of *you,*
With your Luftwaffe, your
   gobbledygoo.
And your neat moustache
And your Aryan eye, bright blue.
Panzer-man, panzer-man, O You—

Not God but a swastika
So black no sky could squeak
   through.
Every woman adores a Fascist,
The boot in the face, the brute
Brute heart of a brute like you.

You stand at the blackboard, daddy,
In the picture I have of you,
A cleft in your chin instead of your
   foot
But no less a devil for that, no not
Any less the black man who

Bit my pretty red heart in two.
I was ten when they buried you.
At twenty I tried to die
And get back, back, back to you.
I thought even the bones would do.

But they pulled me out of the sack,
And they stuck me together with glue.
And then I knew what to do.
I made a model of you,
A man in black with a Meinkampf
   look

And a love of the rack and the screw.
And I said I do, I do.
So daddy, I'm finally through.
The black telephone's off at the root,
The voices just can't worm through.

If I've killed one man, I've killed
   two—
The vampire who said he was you
And drank my blood for a year,
Seven years, if you want to know
Daddy, you can lie back now.

There's a stake in your fat black heart
And the villagers never liked you.
They are dancing and stamping on
   you.
They always *knew* it was you.
Daddy, daddy, you bastard, I'm
   through.

SIGMUND FREUD

Thoughts for the Times
on War and Death:
Our Attitude toward Death

Extraordinary death by war, suicide, or holocaust defies reason and challenges a community's feelings of personal immortality. Writing shortly after World War I, Freud explores two factors responsible for mental distress among noncombatants: the first part of his discussion (not reprinted here) centers on the disillusionment caused by the war; the second part, printed below, examines altered attitudes toward death. Freud likens the unconscious mind of modern man to primeval man, who did not believe in his own death. Both primeval and modern man may desire the death of enemies, but it is the dilemma of modern man, Freud explains, to encounter ambivalent feelings in contemplating the death of another. In time of war, when the sanction against killing is removed, the balance among unconscious tensions is upset. Because the absence of war is an idealistic impossibility, Freud argues for a recognition of unsanctioned instincts.

A factor to which I attribute our present sense of estrangement in this once lovely and congenial world is the disturbance that has taken place in the attitude which we have hitherto adopted toward death.

That attitude was far from straightforward. To anyone who listened to us we were of course prepared to maintain that death was the necessary outcome of life, that everyone owes nature a death[1] and must expect to pay the debt—in short, that death was natural, undeniable and unavoidable. In reality, however, we were accustomed to behave as if it were otherwise. We showed an unmistakable tendency to put death on

Source: Chapter II, "Our Attitudes Toward Death," from Paper XVII, "Thoughts for the Times on War and Death," in Volume 4, *Collected Papers*, by Sigmund Freud, edited by Ernest Jones, M.D., authorized translation under the supervision of Joan Riviere, published by Basic Books, Inc. by arrangement with The Hogarth Press Ltd. and the Institute of Psycho-Analysis, London. For permission to reprint for the United States. For Great Britain and Canada, permission to reprint from "Thoughts for the Times on War and Death" in Volume XIV of *The Standard Edition of the Complete Psychological Works of Sigmund Freud*, revised and edited by James Strachey, with permission from Sigmund Freud Copyrights Ltd., The Institute of Psychoanalysis and The Hogarth Press Ltd.

one side, to eliminate it from life. We tried to hush it up; indeed we even have a saying (in German): to think of something as though it were death.[2] That is, as though it were our own death, of course. It is indeed impossible to imagine our own death; and whenever we attempt to do so we can perceive that we are in fact still present as spectators. Hence the psychoanalytic school could venture on the assertion that at bottom no one believes in his own death, or, to put the same thing in another way, that in the unconscious every one of us is convinced of his own immortality.

When it comes to someone else's death, the civilized man will carefully avoid speaking of such a possibility in the hearing of the person under sentence. Children alone disregard this restriction; they unashamedly threaten one another with the possibility of dying, and even go so far as to do the same thing to someone whom they love, as, for instance: "Dear Mummy, when you're dead I'll do this or that." The civilized adult can hardly even entertain the thought of another person's death without seeming to himself hard-hearted or wicked: unless, of course, as a doctor or lawyer or something of the kind, he has to deal with death professionally. Least of all will he allow himself to think of the other person's death if some gain to himself in freedom, property or position is bound up with it. This sensitiveness of ours does not, of course, prevent the occurrence of deaths; when one does happen, we are always deeply affected, and it is as though we were badly shaken in our expectations. Our habit is to lay stress on the fortuitous causation of the death—accident, disease, infection, advanced age: in this way we betray an effort to reduce death from a necessity to a chance event. A number of simultaneous deaths strikes us as something extemely terrible. Toward the actual person who has died we adopt a special attitude—something almost like admiration for someone who has accomplished a very difficult task. We suspend criticism of him, overlook his possible misdeeds, declare that *de mortuis nil nisi bonum*, and think it justifiable to set out all that is most favorable to his memory in the funeral oration and upon the tombstone. Consideration for the dead, who, after all, no longer need it, is more important to us than the truth, and certainly, for most of us, than consideration for the living.

The complement to this cultural and conventional attitude toward death is provided by our complete collapse when death has struck down someone whom we love—a parent or a partner in marriage, a brother or sister, a child or a close friend. Our hopes, our desires and our pleasures lie in the grave with him, we will not be consoled, we will not fill the lost one's place. We behave as if we were a kind of Asra, who die when those they love die.[3]

But this attitude of ours toward death has a powerful effect on our lives. Life is impoverished, it loses in interest, when the highest stake in the game of living, life itself, may not be risked. It becomes as shallow and empty as, let us say, an American flirtation, in which it is understood from the first that nothing is to happen, as contrasted with a Continental love-affair in which both partners must constantly bear its serious consequences in mind. Our emotional ties, the unbearable intensity of our grief, make us disinclined to court danger for ourselves and for those who belong to us. We dare not contemplate a great many undertakings which are dangerous but in fact indispensable, such as attempts at artificial flight, expeditions to distant countries or experiments with explosive substances. We are paralysed by the thought of who is to take the son's place with his mother, the husband's with his wife, the father's with his children, if a disaster should occur. Thus the tendency to exclude death from our calculations in life brings in its train many other renunciations and exclusions. Yet the motto of the Hanseatic League ran: *Navigare necesse est, vivere non necesse* (It is necessary to sail the seas, it is not necessary to live.)

It is an inevitable result of all this that we should seek in the world of fiction, in literature and in the theatre compensation for what has been lost in life. There we still find people who know how to die—who, indeed, even manage to kill someone else. There alone too the condition can be fulfilled which makes it possible for us to reconcile ourselves with death: namely, that behind all the vicissitudes of life we should still be able to preserve a life intact. For it is really too sad that in life it should be as it is in chess, where one false move may force us to resign the game, but with the difference that we can start no second game, no return-match. In the realm of fiction we find the plurality of lives which we need. We die with the hero with whom we have identified ourselves; yet we survive him, and are ready to die again just as safely with another hero.

It is evident that war is bound to sweep away this conventional treatment of death. Death will no longer be denied; we are forced to believe in it. People really die; and no longer one by one, but many, often tens of thousands, in a single day. And death is no longer a chance event. To be sure, it still seems a matter of chance whether a bullet hits this man or that; but a second bullet may well hit the survivor; and the accumulation of deaths puts an end to the impression of chance. Life has, indeed, become interesting again; it has recovered its full content.

Here a distinction should be made between two groups—those who themselves risk their lives in battle, and those who have stayed at home and have only to wait for the loss of one of their dear ones by wounds, disease or infection. It would be most interesting, no doubt, to study the changes in the psychology of the combatants, but I know too little about it. We must restrict ourselves to the second group, to which we ourselves belong. I have said already that in my opinion the bewilderment and the paralysis of capacity, from which we suffer, are essentially determined among other things by the circumstance that we are unable to maintain our former attitude toward death, and have not yet found a new one. It may assist us to do this if we direct our psychological enquiry toward two other relations to death—the one which we may ascribe to primeval, prehistoric men, and the one which still exists in every one of us, but which conceals itself, invisible to consciousness, in the deeper strata of our mental life.

What the attitude of prehistoric man was toward death is, of course, only known to us by inferences and constructions, but I believe that these methods have furnished us with fairly trustworthy conclusions.

Primeval man took up a very remarkable attitude toward death. It was far from consistent; it was indeed most contradictory. On the one hand, he took death seriously, recognized it as the termination of life and made use of it in that sense; on the other hand, he also denied death and reduced it to nothing. This contradiction arose from the fact that he took up radically different attitudes toward death of other people, of strangers, of enemies, and towards his own. He had no objection to someone else's death; it meant the annihilation of someone he hated, and primitive man had no scruples against bringing it about. He was no doubt a very passionate creature and more cruel and more malignant than other animals. He liked to kill, and killed as a matter of course. The instinct which is said to restrain other animals from killing and devouring their own species need not be attributed to him.

Hence the primeval history of mankind is filled with murder. Even today, the history of the world which our children learn at school is essentially a series of murders of peoples. The obscure sense of guilt to which mankind has been subject since prehistoric times, and which in some religions has been condensed into the doctrine of primal guilt, of original sin, is probably the outcome of a blood-guilt, incurred by prehistoric man. In my book *Totem and Taboo* (1912-13) I have, following clues given by Robertson Smith, Atkinson and Charles Darwin, tried to guess the nature of this primal guilt, and I believe, too, that the Christian doctrine of today enables us to deduce it. If the Son of God was obliged to sacrifice his life to redeem mankind from original sin, then by the law of talion, the requital of like by like, that sin must have been a killing, a murder. Nothing else could call for the sacrifice of a life for its expiation. And the original sin was an offence against God the Father, the primal crime of mankind must have been a parricide, the killing of the primal father of the primitive human horde, whose mnemic image was later transfigured into a deity.[4]

His own death was certainly just as unimaginable and unreal for primeval man as it is for any one of us today. But there was for him one case in which the two opposite attitudes toward death collided and came into conflict with each other; and this case became highly important and productive of far-reaching consequences. It occurred when primeval man saw someone who belonged to him die—his wife, his child, his friend—whom he undoubtedly loved as we love ours, for love cannot be much younger than the lust to kill. Then, in his pain, he was forced to learn that one can die, too, oneself, and his whole being revolted against the admission; for each of these loved ones was, after all, a part of his own beloved self. But, on the other hand, deaths such as these pleased him as well, since in each of the loved persons there was also something of the stranger. The law of ambivalence of feeling, which to this day governs our emotional relations with those whom we love most, certainly had a very much wider validity in primaeval times. Thus these beloved dead had also been enemies and strangers who had aroused in him some degree of hostile feeling.[5]

Philosophers have declared that the intellectual enigma presented to primeval man by the picture of death forced him to reflection, and thus became the starting-point of all speculation. I believe that here the philosophers are thinking too philosophically, and giving too little consideration to the motives that were primarily operative. I should like therefore to limit and correct their assertion. In my view, primeval man must have triumphed beside the body of his slain enemy, without being led to rack his brains about the enigma of life and death. What released the spirit of enquiry in man was not the intellectual enigma, and not every death, but the conflict of feeling at the death of loved yet alien and hated persons. Of this conflict of feeling psychology was the first offspring. Man could no longer keep death at a distance, for he had tasted it in his pain about the dead; but he was nevertheless unwilling to acknowledge it, for he could not conceive of himself as dead. So he devised a compromise: he conceded the fact of his own death as well, but denied it the significance of annihilation—a significance which he had had no motive for denying where the death of his enemy was concerned. It was beside the dead body of someone he loved that he invented spirits, and his sense of guilt at the satisfaction mingled with his sorrow turned these new-born spirits into evil demons that had to be dreaded. The (physical) changes brought about by death suggested to him the division of the individual into a body and a soul—originally several souls. In this way his train of thought ran parallel with the process of disintegration which sets in with death. His persisting memory of the dead became the basis for assuming other forms of existence and gave him the conception of a life continuing after apparent death.

These subsequent existences were at first no more than appendages to the existence which death had brought to a close—shadowy, empty of content, and valued at little until later times; they still bore the character of wretched makeshifts. We may recall the answer made to Odysseus by the soul of Achilles:

> For of old, when thou wast alive, we Argives honoured thee even as the gods, and now that thou art here, thou rulest mightily over the dead. Wherefore grieve not at all that thou art dead, Achilles.
> So I spoke, and he straightway made answer and said: ''Nay, seek not to speak soothingly to me of death, glorious Odysseus. I should choose, so I might live on earth, to serve as the hireling of another, of some portionless man whose livelihood was but small, rather than to be lord over all the dead that have perished.''[6]

Or in Heine's powerful and bitter parody:

> Der kleinste lebendige Philister
> Zu Stuckert am Neckar
> Viel glucklicher ist er
> Als ich, der Pelide, der tote Held,
> Der Schattenfurst in der Unterwelt.[7]

It was only later that religions succeeded in representing this after-life as the more desirable, the truly valid one, and in reducing the life which is ended by death to a mere preparation. After this, it was no more than consistent to extend life backwards into the past, to form the notion of earlier existences, of the transmigration of souls and of reincarnation, all with the purpose of depriving death of its meaning as the termination of life. So early did the denial of death, which we have described as a ''conventional and cultural attitude,'' have its origin.

 What came into existence beside the dead body of the loved one was not only the doctrine of the soul, the belief in immortality and a powerful source of man's sense of guilt, but also the earliest ethical commandments. The first and most important prohibition made by the awakening conscience was "Thou shalt not kill." It was acquired in relation to dead people who were loved, as a reaction against the satisfaction of the hatred hidden behind the grief for them; and it was gradually extended to strangers who were not loved, and finally even to enemies.

This final extension of the commandment is no longer experienced by civilized man. When the furious struggle of the present war has been decided, each one of the victorious fighters will return home joyfully to his wife and children, unchecked and undisturbed by thoughts of the enemies he has killed whether at close quarters or at long range. It is worthy of note that the primitive races which still survive in the world, and are undoubtedly closer than we are to primeval man, act differently in this respect, or did until they came under the influence of our civilization. Savages—Australians, Bushmen, Tierra del Fuegans—are far from being remorseless murderers; when they return victorious from the war-path they may not set foot in their villages or touch their wives till they have atoned for the murders they committed in war by penances which are often long and tedious. It is easy, of course, to attribute this to their superstition: the savage still goes in fear of the avenging spirits of the slain. But the spirits of his slain enemy are nothing but the expression of his bad conscience about his blood-guilt; behind this superstition there lies concealed a view of ethical sensitiveness which has been lost by us civilized men.[8]

Pious souls, no doubt, who would like to believe that our nature is remote from any contact with what is evil and base, will not fail to use the early appearance and the urgency of the prohibition against murder as the basis for gratifying conclusions as to the strength of the ethical impulses which must have been implanted in us. Unfortunately this argument proves even more for the opposite view. So powerful a prohibition can only be directed against an equally powerful impulse. What no human soul desires stands in no need of prohibition;[9] it is excluded automatically. The very emphasis laid on the commandment "Thou shalt not kill" makes it certain that we spring from an endless series of generations of murderers, who had the lust for killing in their blood, as, perhaps, we ourselves have today. Mankind's ethical strivings, whose strength and significance we need not in the least depreciate, were acquired in the course of man's history; since then they have become, though unfortunately only in a very variable amount, the inherited property of contemporary men.

Let us now leave primeval man, and turn to the unconscious in our own mental life. Here we depend entirely upon the psychoanalytic method of investigation, the only one which reaches to such depths. What, we ask, is the attitude of our unconscious toward the problem of death? The answer must be: almost exactly the same as that of primeval man. In this respect, as in many others, the man of prehistoric times survives unchanged in our unconscious. Our unconscious, then, does not believe in its own death; it behaves as if it were immortal. What we call our "unconscious"—the deepest strata of our minds, made up of instinctual impulses—knows nothing that is negative, and no negation; in it contradictories coincide. For that reason it does not know its own death, for to that we can give only a negative content. Thus there is nothing instinctual in us which responds to a belief in death. This may even be the secret of heroism. The rational grounds for heroism rest on a judgment that the subject's own life cannot be so precious as certain abstract and general goods. But more frequent, in my view, is the instinctive and impulsive herosim which knows no such reasons, and flouts danger in the spirit of Anzengruber's *Steinklopferhans:* "Nothing can happen to *me!*"[10] Or else those reasons only serve to clear away the hesitations which might hold back the heroic reaction that corresponds to the unconscious. The fear of death, which dominates us oftener than we know, is on the other hand something secondary, and is ususally the outcome of a sense of guilt.[11]

On the other hand, for strangers and for enemies we do acknowledge death, and consign them to it quite as readily and unhesitatingly as did primeval man. There is, it is true, a distinction here which will be pronounced decisive so far as real life is concerned. Our unconscious does not carry out the killing; it merely thinks it and wishes it. But it would be wrong so completely to undervalue this psychical reality as compared with factual reality. It is significant and momentous enough. In our unconscious impulses we daily and hourly get rid of anyone who stands in our way, of anyone what has offended or injured us. The expression "Devil take him!" which so often comes to people's lips in joking anger and which really means "Death take him!" is in our unconscious a serious and powerful death-wish. Indeed, our unconscious will murder even for trifles; like the ancient Athenian code of Draco, it knows no other punishment for crime than death. And this has a certain consistency, for every injury to our almightly and autocratic ego is at bottom a crime of *lèse-majesté*.

And so, if we are to be judged by our unconscious wishful impulses, we ourselves are, like primeval man, a gang of murderers. It is fortunate that all these wishes do not possess the potency that was attributed to them in primeval times;[12] in the cross-fire of mutual curses mankind would long since have perished, the best and wisest of men and the loveliest and fairest of women with the rest.

Psychoanalysis finds as a rule no credence among laymen for assertions such as these. They reject them as calumnies which are confuted by conscious experience, and they adroitly overlook the faint indications by which even the unconscious is apt to betray itself to consciousness. It is therefore relevant to point out that many thinkers who could not have been influenced by psychoanalysis have quite definitely accused our unspoken thoughts of being ready, heedless of the prohibition against murder, to get rid of anything which stands in our way. From many examples of this I will choose one that has become famous:

In *Le Père Goriot*, Balzac alludes to a passage in the works of J.J. Rousseau where that author asks the reader what he would do if—without leaving Paris and of course without being discovered—he could kill, with great profit to himself, an old mandarin in Peking by a mere act of will. Rousseau implies that he would not give much for the life of that dignitary. "*Tuer son mandarin*" has become a proverbial phrase for this secret readiness, present even in modern man.

There are also a whole number of cynical jokes and anecdotes which reveal the same tendency—such, for instance, as the words attributed to a husband: "If one of us two dies, I shall move to Paris.''[13] Such cynical jokes would not be possible unless they contained an unacknowledged truth which could not be admitted if it were expressed seriously and without disguise. In jest—it is well known—one may even tell the truth.

Just as for primeval man, so also for our unconscious, there is one case in which the two opposing attitudes towards death, the one which acknowledges it as the annihilation of life and the other which denies it as unreal, collide and come into conflict. This case is the same as in primal ages: the death, or the risk of death, of someone we love, a parent or a partner in marriage, a brother or sister, a child or a dear friend. These loved ones are on the one hand an inner possession, components of our own ego; but on the other hand they are partly strangers, even enemies. With the exception of only a very few situations, there adheres to the tenderest and most intimate of our love-relations a small portion of hostility which can excite an unconsious death-wish. But this conflict due to ambivalence does not now, as it did then, lead to the doctrine of the soul and to ethics, but to neurosis, which affords us deep insight into normal mental life as well. How often have physicians who practice psychoanalysis had to deal with the symptom of an exaggerated worry over the well-being of relatives, or with entirely unfounded self-reproaches after the death of a loved person. The study of such phenomena has left them in no doubt about the extent and importance of unconscious death-wishes.

The layman feels an extraordinary horror at the possibility of such feelings, and takes this aversion as a legitimate ground for disbelief in the assertions of psychoanalysis. Mistakenly, I think. No depreciation of feelings of love is intended, and there is in fact none. It is indeed foreign to our intelligence as well as to our feelings thus to couple love and hate; but Nature, by making use of this pair of opposites, contrives to keep love ever vigilant and fresh, so as to guard it against the hate which lurks behind it. It might be said that we owe the fairest flowerings of our love to the reaction against the hostile impulse which we sense within us.

To sum up: our unconscious is just as inaccessible to the idea of our own death, just as murderously inclined toward strangers, just as divided (that is, ambivalent) towards those we love, as was primeval man. But how far we have moved from this primal state in our conventional and cultural attitude toward death!

It is easy to see how war impinges on this dichotomy. It strips us of the later accretions of civilization, and lays bare the primal man in each of us. It compels us once more to be heroes who cannot believe in their own death; it stamps strangers as enemies, whose death is to be brought about or desired; it tells us to disregard the death of those we love. But war cannot be abolished; so long as the conditions of existence among nations are so different and their mutual repulsion so violent, there are bound to be wars. The question then arises: Is it not we who should give in, who should adapt ourselves to war? Should we not confess that in our civilized attitude toward death we are once again living psychologically beyond our means, and should we not rather turn back and recognize the truth? Would it not be better to give death the place in reality and in our thoughts which is its due, and to give a little more prominence to the unconscious attitude toward death which we have hitherto so carefully suppressed? This hardly seems an advance to higher achievement, but rather in some respects a backward step—a regression; but it has the advantage of taking the truth more into account, and of making life more tolerable for us once again. To tolerate life remains, after all, the first duty of all living beings. Illusion becomes valueless if it makes this harder for us.

We recall the old saying: *Si vis pacem, para bellum.* If you want to preserve peace, arm for war.

It would be in keeping with the times to alter it: *Si vis vitam, para mortem.* If you want to endure life, prepare yourself for death.

NOTES

1. A reminiscence of Prince Hal's remark to Falstaff in *I, Henry IV*, v.1: "Thou owest God a death." This was a favorite misquotation of Freud's. See, for instance, *The Interpretation of Dreams*, Standard Ed., 4, 205, and a letter to Fliess of February 6, 1899 (Feud, 1950a, Letter 104), in which he explicitly attributes it to Shakespeare.
2. To think something unlikely or incredible.
3. The Asra in Heine's poem ("Der Asra," in *Romanzero*, based on a passage in Stendhal's *De l'amour*) were a tribe of Arabs who "die when they love."
4. Freud, *Totem and Taboo*, Essay IV, Standard Ed., *13*, 146 ff.
5. Ibid., Essay II, Standard Ed., *13*, 60 ff.
6. *Odyssey* XI, 484-91, Trans., A.T. Murray.
7. Literally: "The smallest living Philistine at Stuckert-am-Neckar is far happier than I, the son of Peleus, the dead hero, the shadow-prince in the underworld." The closing lines of "Der Scheidende," one of the very last of Heine's poems.
8. Freud, op cit., Standard Ed., *13*, 66 ff.
9. Cf. Frazer's brilliant argument quoted in *Totem and Taboo*, Standard Ed., *13*, 123.
10. "Hans the Stone-Breaker"—a character in a comedy by the Viennese dramatist Ludwig Anzengruber (1839-89).
11. Fuller discussions of the fear of death will be found in the closing paragraphs of *The Ego and the Id* (1923b) and at the end of Chapter VII of *Inhibitions, Symptoms and Anxieties* (1926d).
12. Freud, op. cit., Essay IV, Standard Ed., *13*, 85 f, S.F. XIV—U.
13. This is also quoted in Freud's *The Interpretation of Dreams* (1900a), Standard Ed., *5*, 485.

EDMUND H. VOLKHART
with the collaboration of
STANLEY T. MICHAEL

Bereavement and Mental Health

Societies vary in their patterns of dealing with death. In the following cross-cultural study, Volkhart and Michael explore individual vulnerability to pathological grief reactions as a function of the cultural assumptions surrounding death. They conclude that the more significance a family structure places on a few individuals, the greater the impact of the loss of one of those individuals. In addition, the authors point out that conflict arises when personal reactions are at variance with social expectations.

CULTURAL PERSPECTIVES

A convenient place to begin is with the concept of culture, which is often regarded as the most important single concept in the social sciences. Although it may be defined technically in different words and used in slightly different ways, culture refers basically to the ideas, norms, values, practices, and beliefs which are historically shared by the members of an organized group or society. Each society has its own distinctive culture; and whereas at one level of abstraction there are certain universals common to all cultures, the specific contents of various cultures are amazingly diverse.[1,2]

The concept of culture is significant in the present connection in that each individual is born into and develops within specific cultural context. By example, precept, reward, and punishment he learns most of the culture to which he is exposed.[3]

Any sociocultural system may be envisaged as being composed of a series of organized groups, of what are sometimes termed "social institutions."[4] At one level

Source: Edmund H. Volkhart and Stanley T. Michael. "Bereavement and Mental Health." *Explorations in Social Psychiatry*. Edited by A.H. Leighton, J.A. Clausen, and R.N. Wilson. New York: Basic Books, 1957.

of analysis these are specific and local—i.e., *a* family, *a* school, *a* church, and so on; at another level of analysis the specific units are combined into "type" institutions—i.e., *the* family, *the* school, *the* church, and so on, indicating a particular emphasis on the typical features of each.

Each such group, or institutional unit, in turn may be regarded as an organization of "positions" or "statuses." A family, for example, is composed of husband, wife, parents, children, brothers and sisters; each status being identified by its relation to another (i.e., husband-wife, parent-child, brother-sister, etc.). These positions are, of course, occupied by particular persons, but the behavior of the persons in their relation to each other is channeled by the structure of the relationship itself. Mutual expectations arise, and the statuses of the relationships come to involve certain "roles" or role behaviors vis-à-vis each other. All of the principal social relationships, in any culture, may be regarded as interlocking roles.[5-7]

As soon as an individual is born, he begins to be a part of a social relationship (parent-child), in the setting of a particular situation (the family), which is composed, at least in part, of persons who have already been culturally trained. In their behavior toward the newcomer, much of their cultural learning will be manifest; and this is important because individual *self* will develop primarily in interaction with family members.[8,9] The individual self, in brief, is a social self, including the "reflected appraisals of others," such roles as have been internalized, and "the residue" of an individual's experiences within his institutional and cultural framework.[10,11]

From the standpoint of a given individual, his culture is experienced by the way in which his interactions are channeled in social relationships, within institutional settings, and by the various pressures, demands, responses, and expectations of others which make themselves felt in countless life situations. Thus each individual, consciously or unconsciously, comes to adopt most of the prevailing ideas, practices, norms, values and beliefs which parents, peers, and nonfamilial adults introduce to him. In this way he has available, for practically every life-situation, a culturally determined solution.

Thus far, then, culture has been shown to be linked to individual behavior[12] by means of a series of intervening concepts: social institutions, positions and statuses, roles, and the self. At this point some general implications of the concept of culture may be suggested.

In the first place, human death is a universal and recurring event. Every culture has its own values, ideas, beliefs, and practices concerning it. An individual learns the orientations of his culture toward death; and thus when he is faced with bereavement, one factor involved is his conception of the meaning of death. In this connection many, if not most, societies throughout the world do not regard the event of death as being an inevitable fact of life; rather, it is often construed as being the result of an accident, of negligence, or of malice on the part of magicians or sorcerers.[13] Similarly, the cultural orientation of many peoples toward death is that it represents a gain for the deceased, an improvement in his prospects and status, and that mourning for his loss of life is inappropriate.[14,15] These are in marked contrast to our own prevailing beliefs, for with us death is inevitable, and the fate of the deceased is by no means as clear and as certain as it may once have been in the Christian tradition.

If, then, we assume that beliefs can influence self-perceptions and self-reactions, the kinds of beliefs that are accepted and internalized will condition bereavement reactions. By the same token, the emotional displays of bereaved persons may also be learned responses and may have nothing to do with necessary and inherent feelings of grief. Conventional bereavement behavior varies widely from culture to culture, and whether it is genuine, "natural" emotional expression or mere ritual performance is in given cases often open to question.[16-18] In some cultures, for example, our conventional sign of grief—weeping—either is not manifest by the bereaved or is manifest in circumstances that we should regard as strange or is mingled with laughter as we understand it.

All of this raises the question, of course, as to whether the self is entirely social or whether it shares some deep-seated, indestructible fragments of humanity in general. Social scientist tend to hold the former view, whereas some branches of psychiatry tend to hold the latter. The issue cannot now be resolved, but it should be apparent that cross-cultural data can at least provide fresh perspectives on bereavement reactions and present viewpoints concerning them.

Moreover, it may not be amiss to note that cultural considerations may influence any attempt scientifically to analyze bereavement problems. Those who are familiar with, and sensitive to, cultural influences on behavior should first be wary of themselves and their work—i.e., the way in which they perceive, categorize, and explain behavioral events. For various implicit and explicit assumptions, biases, terminology and evaluations, all derived from the culture, can easily intrude upon the task at hand; they cannot all be erased, but they should at least be recognized for what they are: a curious blend of folk knowledge, rationalizations, beliefs, and ignorance. It may even be that some mental health problems we attribute to bereavement, by reason of proximity in time, have other and quite different sources.

The phenomena which we label "bereavement" and "grief" are embedded in a cultural frame of reference. Just as other peoples have their interpretation of death, and appropriate reactions to it, so, too, do we in Western civilizations; but our own implicit interpretation is not easy for us to recognize and make explicit as a cultural rather than scientific orientation simply because we have absorbed that orientation and perceive events accordingly.

Thus, as a cultural norm and idea we tend to define a given death as a "loss" to someone, especially to close members of the family of the deceased. Almost any behavior that they then manifest is regarded as "grief"; thus the term "grief" functions, culturally, both as a descriptive label and as a satisfying interpretation based on a presumably known "cause." Moreover, we tend to regard such "grief" not only as natural but also as desirable. A bereaved person *ought* to show grief, both as a token of respect for the dead and for the sake of his own mental health—expression of grief gets it "out of the system."

It is simply generally assumed that a bereaved person[19] will be grief-stricken; but whether these displays of grief stem from internal compulsions or external demands is not usually a matter of concern. Indeed, the very source of the behavior and the imputed feelings is assumed to lie in what were satisfactory relationships with the deceased other, even though it is often well known that a given relationship, husband-wife or parent-child, fell far short of being satisfactory to one or both partners. At least in our culture there is a tendency to idealize the relationship which has been severed by death—and this, too, is culturally encouraged. "Don't speak ill of the dead."

In short, the behavioral phenomena characterized by the words "bereavement" and "grief" are heavily saturated with cultural assumptions. Moreover, any analyst, be he psychiatrist or social scientist, has absorbed many of these premises long before he has professed to be a scientist; to the extent that he has accepted and internalized them, his perceptions of events have therefore been previously structured, thus preconditioning the analysis through the uncritical use of conventional categories.

The point here, of course, is not the validity of the prevailing cultural interpretation of bereavement and grief, which may be correct in part or in whole, as other folk interpretations of event have been correct in the past. The point is that the cultural orientation is a matter for inquiry and verification rather than a priori, and often unwitting, acceptance.

Caution is therefore indicated. At best, words are slippery instruments of thought and expression, and this is especially true when familiar, and perhaps value-laden, terms are used.

Bereavement can be defined with sufficient precision to be useful. "Grief" on the other hand presents difficulties: the total reaction pattern of a bereaved person may be only partially an expression of grief (in the sense of felt loss), and the amount of grief anyone possesses is always inferential anyway. For these reasons, the phenomena that we usually label as "grief," "sorrow," and "mourning" will here be designated by the more colorless phrases "bereavement behavior" or "bereavement reactions." Such usage will not alter any of the distress of the experience or its poignancy, but it will remind us, perhaps, that more elements than sorrow or grief are involved, and it will also facilitate cross-cultural comparisons. "Behavior" can be observed and recorded, "grief" cannot. And it is essential that as much cross-cultural perspective as possible be gained, else the purported analysis may prove to be nothing more than a technical restatement of prevailing cultural premises.[20,21]

BEREAVEMENT, FAMILY STRUCTURE, AND THE SELF

Of all the social institutions, the family and kinship systems are of the greatest importance insofar as the study of bereavement is concerned. Indeed, their structure and the manner in which they emphasize some relationships rather than others supply initial reference points for the concept of bereavement itself. Always and everywhere some persons rather than others are considered to have a special interest in a given death; but who they are, and in what relationship they stand to the deceased, are matters of cultural variability.

In our society, for example, when a married adult dies, the prevailing definition of bereaved persons includes his parents and siblings (i.e., members of his family of orientation) and his spouse and their children (i.e., members of his family of procreation). The emphasis is placed on members of the immediate nuclear families as having suffered the main loss;[22-24] and if collateral relatives, such as cousins or aunts or uncles or "in-laws" are included, it is by special relationship rather than as part of the system. They are family members nominally, not functionally.[25]

By way of contrast, the Trobriand Islanders have a quite different scheme of family relationships and a correspondingly different concept of who constitute the bereaved.[26] Their emphasis is placed on persons related to the deceased through his mother—that is, his maternal kin of all kinds are considered to have been "closest" to the deceased and to have more of an interest in the event than any of the paternal relatives or even the spouse. A wife, for example, may "grieve" at the death of her husband, but this is usually ceremonial and obligatory rather than spontaneous, and she is not considered by others to be bereaved in the same sense as are the maternal kin.

These brief, contrasting examples of family systems indicate that, regardless of cultural variability, bereavement is an observable condition; it is not inferential; its definition, in cultural terms, can be determined. Further, bereavement is a formal status in which individuals either have or have not legitimate occupancy. It derives from family and kinship structures which place persons in necessary or preferred positions vis-à-vis each other. Thus, in some places a maternal aunt or a paternal uncle may be more important to the individual, socially and psychologically, than are his own biological or sociological parents. When they die bereavement is thrust upon him by the system.

Such considerations are important not only for purposes of initial orientation toward phenomena but also because they bear upon the development of the self in terms of to whom the individual will attach himself and in what manner. That is, although different family systems may have the same positions or statuses in the abstract (i.e., mothers, fathers, aunts, siblings, etc.) the psychological value of such positions in interpersonal relations is by no means always equivalent. Some positions may be singled out according to cultural principles of descent as more important than others; and their interpersonal value will also be influenced by the size of the family unit, together with the degree to which intrafamily relations are based on different ideas of authority, punishment, need satisfaction, and so on.

Thus, since the development of the self takes place primarily within the family context, that process will be influenced by the range, frequency, intimacy, and quality of the interactions provided by the family system. The number of "targets" for emotional attachment will vary accordingly, as will the particular statuses that will become targets. Such factors, in turn, will affect the number and kinds of identifications the self will make, the degree of dependency on others, and the general mode and strength of affective ties.[27]

If, then, the amount of self-involvement with another is a major variable in bereavement behavior, its sources must lie at least in part in the familial conditions of self-development. And if this is true, we should expect typically different bereavement behaviors in societies with different systems. There is some evidence for this interpretation, as the following examples will illustrate.

In his study of the Ifaluk people, Spiro[28] was puzzled by some features of bereavement there. When a family died, the immediate survivors displayed considerable pain and distress, which behavior was in accordance with local custom. However, as soon as the funeral was over, the bereaved were able to laugh, smile, and behave in general as if they had suffered no loss or injury at all. Their "grief" seemed to disappear as if by magic, and this too was approved by custom.

Several hypotheses might be offered to account for these events which contrast sharply with those we would expect. At one extreme, it might plausibly be argued that the brief, but intense, mourning period was sufficient to discharge all the implicated emotions (such as hostility, loss, guilt, etc.) and thus provided rapid reintegration of the self. This would assume object-relationships of a kind familiar to us but would not particularly account for the efficiency and timing of the observed behavior. At the other extreme,[29] it might be said that the displays were mere conventions, rituals, and, having little to do with emotional experience, could be turned off and on as learned. Or it might be suggested that the grief actually represented intense subjective feelings and that these persisted privately after the funeral but in a manner not easily detected by an observer.

Spiro's analysis, based on his knowledge of the total culture, is along the following lines, which involve the family system and socialization practices that prevail among the Ifaluk. There the developing child forms no exclusive emotional attachments to other family members. Child-rearing is not conducted solely in the home by parents and siblings but involves many other persons who are as important in an individual's life as are family members. The growing child and the mature adult have, therefore, diffused and dispersed their emotional ties among many persons rather than focused them on a few. Accordingly, the psychological significance of any single family member to any other family member is muted rather than intensified.

In terms of the thesis being developed here, the bereavement behavior of the Ifaluk suggest that their family system is such as to develop selves which are initially less vulnerable in bereavement than are the selves we are accustomed to. This can be explained by a consideration of how both social and psychological forces interact.

If we assume that any social relationship, mediated by physical and symbolic interaction, inevitably produces in the partners the feelings and conditions of love, ambivalence, hostility, identification, and dependence, then the Ifaluk develop selves in which these are relatively weak insofar as any given other person is concerned. The family relationships which impinged on self-development are such as to minimize personal dependence on any one person, to make a person's identifications multiple rather than exclusive, and to enable him to distribute his feelings of love and hostility more widely.

Another way of stating this is that in self-other relations among the Ifaluk, the other is not valued by the self as a unique and necessary personality. Functionally speaking, not only are the roles of others dispersed, but the roles themselves are more important psychologically than are the particular persons who play the roles vis-à-vis the self. Multiple and interchangeable personnel performing the same functions for the individual provide the individual with many psychological anchors in his social environment; the death of any one person leaves the others and thus diminishes loss.

In American society, of course, it is not so easy to describe *the* family system, for there are many sub-group variations. Nevertheless, some sociologists have discerned a trend toward the "small family system," particularly among middle-class urban populations.[30-33] To relate this system to the present problem involves considerable overgeneralization, yet for heuristic purposes it may be contrasted with the Ifaluk system.

The American small family system has several dimensions. In contrast to the extended family, it is one in which there are relatively few members and these few live together under one roof and somewhat apart from relatives and neighbors.

In terms of self-development, the small family system means a number of things. During a person's early years the range of his interactions is largely confined to his mother, father, and siblings, if any, and especially to his mother. Frequency and intimacy of contact are thereby channeled among the same few persons who become the only (and repetitive) targets for identification and dependency. Moreover, these same few sources provide the person with his most intense gratifications and frustrations, a condition that tends to maximize ambivalence as well as repressed hostility.[34] Guilt feelings are easily aroused in connection with authority figures—especially since the person knows that he is supposed to love them, yet cannot do so all the time because they punish and frustrate him.

In these circumstances, it is likely that the self develops strong emotional attachments to the family figures and has considerable affective investment in them. These self-feelings are, however, quite complicated. To the extent that one loves his family members (and this is inculcated as a cultural value), he may feel a corresponding loss when they die—a sentiment which is reinforced by the fact that, as a cultural norm, the death of a family member is socially defined as a loss. But, in addition to the love elements and those of dependency and identification, there are intertwined with them the self-feelings of ambivalence and hostility. In bereavement the self, therefore, faces not only the problem of replacing the loss but also the one of managing these feelings of guilt and hostility.

Moreover, the small family system tends to breed overidentification and overdependence. That is to say, intrafamily experiences are such as to make it difficult for the person to separate the parental activities toward him from the particular individuals who engage in those activities. The maternal role, for example, which aunts, older sisters, or other female adults could occupy and enact, is occupied continuously by the same woman, for in the small family system there are no other persons to act as substitutes and thus disperse the emotional investment. Emotional attachments to particular persons are thereby fostered, and the person becomes dependent on their unique personalities in addition to their roles.

Furthermore, other cultural values operate in the development of the self to influence the process similarly. Not only does the child experience the same persons in the roles of father and mother, but he is taught that he can have only one father and mother—that it, the particular persons who are thus labeled. Cultural training and actual experience thus reinforce each other in such a way that specific persons continually appear to be irreplaceable, and no one is psychologically prepared to accept substitutes.

By way of contrast, it is reported of the Murngin[35] that the death of a father creates few psychological problems for his children. All their lives they have called their paternal uncles "father," and their relationships with these uncles have not differed very much from their relationships with their father. When the self develops in such a system, there is less likelihood that it will become closely attached to a particular figure; thus the sense of loss is lessened and the relationship with that figure can be more readily transferred to substitute figures.

The inference to be drawn from all this is that familial systems, by their influence on the development of the self, can enhance or reduce the initial vulnerability of persons in bereavement. This vulnerability is increased to the extent that self-involvements with others are diffuse, thus minimizing the psychological significance of any one other.

In this connection, one further feature of the small family system should be noted. Typically, a married adult belongs to two families, the one of orientation and the one of procreation. In a sense this dual membership involves a dispersion of affect and self-involvement, for the person simply has more relationships: in addition to being son or daughter, brother or sister, he is now also husband and parent. His roles have multiplied.

But, although membership in the family of orientation is officially retained, residence in a separate household usually diminishes his opportunities for interaction and continued emotional investment in parents and siblings. There simply is not so much intimate association with them as there was when he lived under the same roof. He tends, therefore, to gain some release from whatever self-feelings he had toward them by increasing his physical, social, and psychological distance from them. Thus his vulnerability vis-à-vis these family members tends to be reduced.

At the same time, through marriage, children, and a separate residence, he is again enmeshed in a small family system, but with new personnel. Now his self-involvements tend to be directed toward spouse and children, and, because of the way his self developed in the small family of orientation, his relationships with these "new" persons tend to be of the same order as were the old—i.e., exclusive attachments.

In brief, membership in the two small families does not necessarily have the same psychological effect as continued residence in an extended family may have. Dispersion of affect need not occur. Rather, it is much more likely that one's emotional investments are merely redirected from one set of figures to another; and as vulnerability to bereavement in the family of orientation diminishes, vulnerability to deaths in the family of procreation may increase.

The preceding pages have attempted to sketch some of the ideal-typical relationships between family structure, self-development, and vulnerability in bereavement. From the two polar-type family systems that were used for illustrative purposes it is suggested that the meaning of bereavement to the persons involved can be modified. In one case the degree of self-involvement with others, and therefore vulnerability in bereavement, was minimal; in the other the degree of self-involvement with others, and therefore vulnerability in bereavement, was maximal.

High vulnerability in interpersonal relationships does not, however, mean the inevitable presence of mental health problems in bereavement. Psychic stresses and strains may be multiplied, to be sure, but if these have been fostered by some social and cultural conditions, there may be other social and cultural conditions which can help to ease them.[36,37] In brief, the course and outcome of high vulnerability in bereavement may be a function not only of itself but also of the requirements and taboos that exist within the bereavement situation. This can best be indicated by considering the importance and utility of the concept of "social role" as this is applicable to bereavement reactions.

BEREAVEMENT AND SOCIAL ROLES

It has previously been indicated that the category of bereaved persons, at a given death, is culturally defined. Some relationships in the family and kinship system are included and some are not, and the inclusions and exclusions vary from culture to culture; but whenever a death evokes that category, the persons in it come to occupy a formal, legitimate status in the eyes of others as well as in their own eyes. And as is the case with other statuses, the persons in it have a new social role to play—the social role of the bereaved person.

In cross-cultural terms, the specific content of the role varies widely: weeping, personal preparation of the corpse for burial, gashing one's body with knives or sharp sticks, protracted seclusion, fasting, wreaking vengeance on those responsible for the death, special religious obligations of prayer or sacrifice, sharp and humiliating alterations in dress and appearance, and so on.

In a given culture, some of these role behaviors may apply to all persons in the bereavement status, whereas others apply only to persons in specified relation to the deceased. For example, the widow may have some obligations which apply only to her, such as not to remarry or not to remarry within certain periods of time; or it may be that she is obliged to remarry with her next partner being culturally prescribed—e.g., a brother or cousin of the deceased husband.

Although there are great variations in the specific content of the social role of the bereaved person, one point is clear: whatever the obligations, proscriptions, or injunctions may be, they exist from his standpoint in the form of expectations, demands, and pressures from others. They are *social* obligations, immediate and potent, yet to fulfill them in a way that is both psychologically and socially satisfactory is by no means as obvious or as easy as is frequently assumed. Often the role requirements are painful in themselves, and it is also a difficult role to learn because it is not encountered frequently in the course of life and opportunities for rehearsal are scarce.

The import of this is to suggest that the conception of the bereaved person as having a social role to perform provides another perspective from which to examine mental health problems in bereavement. Such problems may be socially induced as well as psychologically induced—i.e., they may have their source in role deficiencies and difficulties as well as in the self-other relationship itself. Such a formulation suggests a number of possibilities that psychiatrists and social scientists might further explore.

The formulation, for example, opens up the possibility that some bereavement problems may be occasioned not by severe loss but by an awareness of one's inability to play the bereaved role properly.[38] If we assume that one of the role obligations is to express grief and loss and that these sentiments are imputed to the bereaved by others, the bereaved person who lacks these sentiments may be in a painfully dangerous situation as the result of guilty fear.

A hypothetical reconstruction, in terms of the present analysis, may illustrate the problem. A given role (husband, wife, mother, etc.) is culturally defined as involving considerable emotional investment in the partner who occupies the complementary role in the relationship. The role, in its ideal sense, is internalized by an individual, but his experience in the relationship contradicts the role. Inappropriate sentiments are developed—e.g., more hostility than love. Fearing the reactions of others, he remains in the relationship which, on the surface, does not deviate too far from the typical; but the hostility must be repressed and guilt over failure to meet the ideal is increased. Then, in bereavement, this individual is supposed to feel loss, and the social role he is expected to enact deals almost entirely with this imputed sentiment. He is expected to express grief. Such expectations and imputations are not congruent with his own self-feelings, and awareness of the discrepancy between self and role[39] increases guilt. There are also no socially sanctioned avenues for the release or displacement of the hostility. There is, in short, an accumulation of pressures which come to a climax in bereavement. In such a case, which is probably quite atypical, the bereavement experience, including the incompatible role that is imposed, precipitates and crystallizes mental health problems that were already incipient. Such a case can indicate the significance of situational pressures to adopt the proper role.

In American culture, it is difficult to consider the social role of the bereaved person in other than very general terms, but it appears to center around ideas of loss and the desirability of expressing that loss and grief. The language makes "bereavement" and "loss" interchangeable terms. Individuals learn to regard bereavement as meaning loss, and this sentiment is attributed to them by others when the bereavement situation actually occurs. Thus, to the extent that this evaluation of the event has been internalized, and to the extent that the self-other relationship as personally experienced makes it possible, the psychological sense of loss will be enhanced. When this happens, the bereaved person can more or less adequately play his required role—i.e., to have some sort of episodic breakdown, express his grief conventionally, and thus behave "normally."

However, this type of role, with its emphasis on loss, grief, and expression of them, may not always be psychologically functional. And here several possibilities appear.

For example, this particular type of role of the bereaved person may conflict with other roles he has—e.g., sex roles. In our society, females are generally permitted and encouraged to be more "emotional" than males in various life situations. To the extent that women internalize this segment of their sex role, it should be easier for them to meet the requirements of "expressing grief" in their social role of the bereaved person; it simply requires a reapplication of a lifelong pattern.

Men, on the other hand, are expected and encouraged to be more stoical and restrained than women in any life emergency.[40] The role of male in our culture does not encourage emotional displays. Thus, in bereavement males may experience a conflict between their life-long training in their sex role and the immediate situational demand for emotional expression as a bereaved person.[41] It may be, therefore, that when bereaved males exhibit signs of psychic stress, in the form of intensities and distortions beyond expected levels, they are reflecting this conflict in addition to, or even instead of, the sense of loss and grief.

Our cultural emphasis on loss in bereavement, with its social role preoccupied with grief expression, provides still other problems. The social role, by concentrating on the feeling and expression of loss, thereby neglects to provide for other emotions and the needs they create. This can be formulated as follows: The emotions of a bereaved person, vis-à-vis the deceased other, consist of various degrees and intensities of the sense of loss, hostility, guilt, and the like. When these are minimal in strength, the bereaved person has a very low initial vulnerability to any mental health problems. When these are maximal and complicated, the person (unless he has a correspondingly high ego strength) has a high initial vulnerability to mental health problems in bereavement, for the stronger and more complex these self-feelings are, the greater is their tendency to create new personality needs. If a strong sense of loss is involved, there is a need for replacement; if there is much latent hostility, there is need for discharge; if guilt is strong, there is need for release or displacement. If all are present, as our family and cultural system tends to make probable, then the bereaved person is vulnerable unless his social role as a bereaved person adequately meets these needs.

In other words, the character of the self-other relationship conditions the level of initial vulnerability in bereavement. When this level is high, and new personality needs are therewith generated, the social role of the bereaved person may either lessen that vulnerability by meeting the needs or exacerbate it by failing to meet them.

From this standpoint, our preoccupation with loss and grief in bereavement may create special kinds of mental health problems of which we are only dimly aware. For example, as has been previously suggested, the significant other in our culture is significant in terms of his unique personality in addition to, or instead of, the functions he performs vis-à-vis the self. Thus, in bereavement, one loses not merely a role in his whole system of interaction but a particular person in the role. Thus, whereas we stress the sense of loss and recognize the need for replacement,[42] basically the culture creates conditions in which the deceased is irreplaceable because he cannot ever really be duplicated. The social role cannot contain a provision for "automatic replacement" because all our patterns of interpersonal relationships militate against such replacement.

In order for replacements to be accepted and acceptable, the role of the deceased must be regarded, culturally and personally, as at least equal in importance to the person who plays it. Other societies have handled this problem of replacement by the devices of obligatory remarriage[43,44] or adoption. Such arrangements, though, are not merely *ad hoc,* set up to take care of bereavement problems alone. Rather, they are basic ingredients of the way in which the sociocultural system operates, of the way in which interpersonal relations are perceived, valued, and practiced. Since the expectations of the partners in the social relationship do not come to include the absorption of the self in the other, it is possible for the social role of the bereaved person (i.e., as widow, widower, orphan, etc.) to include replacement of the other without particular psychic stress.

The fact that the social role of the bereaved person in our culture may not easily cope with the problem of replacement is, therefore, a local one. It is bound up in our system of interpersonal relations, the kind of selves we tend to develop, and is exaggerated by our cultural emphasis on loss. In this way the bereaved person has no automatic solution to the problem of replacement.

In the same manner, the social role of the bereaved person in our culture makes no real provision for the other emotions and the personality needs they create—i.e., hostility and guilt and their release, discharge, or displacement. At least, there are no obvious segments of the role which include socially approved devices for handling those residues of guilt, hostility, and ambivalence. With the person left on his own, so to speak, to handle them as best he can, it is not surprising that these feelings and the unmet needs they create appear in cases of "acute" or "distorted" grief in our society.

In many cultures prevailing mourning customs may be interpreted as providing role requirements which do meet some of these emotional needs. Opler,[45] for example, has shown how the ambivalence toward relatives, which is induced by the social structure of the Apache, finds socially sanctioned displacement in mourning rites and customs. Warner[46] indicates how the obligation of the bereaved to avenge the death of the deceased provides sanctioned means of ridding guilt feelings and hostility among the Murngin. And in anthropological literature there are many examples of the bereaved being required to inflict pain and disfigurement on their bodies—obligations which may be regarded as attempts to fasten the attention of the bereaved upon himself and therefore to hasten his emancipation from the deceased.

Such considerations lend some weight to the hypothesis that different cultures will select, from among all the possible involvements the self may have with the other, one or a few which will be dealt with in the social role of the bereaved person. Thus, if the bereavement problems of a given culture are adequately perceived, functionally adequate social roles for the bereaved may be devised which can blunt such vulnerability to breakdown as may appear. But to the extent that social and cultural conditions encourage interpersonal relationships in which overidentification, overdependence, sense of loss, hostility, guilt, and ambivalence are bred in profusion, and to the extent that the social role of the bereaved person does not take account of these feelings and the needs they inspire—to that extent bereaved persons may often be unintended victims of their sociocultural system. In our case, the sense of loss may be handled satisfactorily by the role which encourages expression of loss and grief; but the role does not, and cannot, adequately provide for replacement when this need is strong, and the added burdens of accumulated and unrelieved guilt, hostility, and ambivalence, when they are strong, can only increase vulnerability to psychic breakdown.

NOTES

1. C. Kluckhohn, "Culture and Behavior," in *Handbook of Social Psychology,* ed. G. Lindsey (Reading, Mass.: Addison-Wesley, 1954), p. 922.

2. ———, Universal Categories of Culture," in *Anthropology Today,* ed. A.L. Kroeber (Chicago: University of Chicago Press, 1953).

3. Strictly speaking, "learning" and "internalizing" should not be used as equivalents. One may "learn" a given idea or act, or how to act, without being impelled to so behave; he may simply learn that such is proper under certain circumstances. When something is "internalized," on the other hand, the implication is that the range of alternatives has been at least drastically restricted, if not eliminated. In other words, learning can be more superficial than internalization.

4. D.N. Mitra, "Mourning customs and modern life in Bengal," *Am. J. Sociol.* 52 (1947): 309–311.

5. L.S. Cottrell, Jr.; "The adjustment of the individual to his age and sex roles," *Am Sociol. Rev.* 7 (1942): 618–625.

6. T. Parsons, *The Social System* (New York: The Free Press, 1951).

7. T.R. Sarbin, "Role Theory," in *Handbook of Social Psychology,* ed. G. Lindsey (Reading, Mass.: Addison-Wesley, 1952), Chap. 6.

8. G.H. Mead, *Mind, Self and Society,* ed. C.W. Morris (Chicago: University of Chicago Press, 1934).

9. H.S. Sullivan, *The Interpersonal Theory of Psychiatry.* (New York: Norton, 1953).

10. C. Kluckhohn, "Culture and Behavior," in *Handbook of Social Psychology,* ed. G. Lindsey (Reading, Mass.: Addison-Wesley, 1954), p. 922.

11. T.R. Sarbin, "Role Theory," in *Handbook of Social Psychology,* p. 224.

12. In a sense this can never be completely achieved to the satisfaction of psychology or psychiatry. Sapir's observations on this point are relevant: "problems of social science differ from problems of individual behavior in degree of specificity, not in kind. Every statement about behavior which throws the emphasis . . . on the actual integral experiences of defined personalities or types of personalities is a datum of psychology or psychiatry rather than of social science. Every statement about behavior which aims, not to be accurate about the behavior of an actual individual or individuals or about the expected behavior of a physically and psychologically defined type of individual, but which abstracts from such behavior in order to bring out in clear relief certain expectancies with regard to those aspects of individual behavior which various people share, as an interpersonal or 'social' pattern, is a datum . . . of social science." E. Sapir, "Why Cultural Anthropology Needs the Psychiatrist," *Psychiatry* 1 (1938):12.

13. L.W. Simmons, *The Role of the Aged in Primitive Society* (New Haven: Yale University Press, 1945), pp. 217–220.

14. Ibid., pp. 223–224.

15. W.G. Sumner and A.C. Keller, *The Science of Society,* 3 Vols (New Haven: Yale University Press, 1927), 2, pp. 943 ff.

16. Durkheim went so far as to write: "Mourning is not a natural movement of private feelings wounded by cruel loss; it is a duty imposed by the group. One weeps, not simply because he is sad, but because he is forced to weep. It is a ritual attitude which he is forced to adopt . . . but which is, in a large measure, independent of his affective state."

17. H. Gerth and C.W. Mills, *Character and Social Structure* (New York: Harcourt Brace, Jovanovich, 1953), p. 20 and pp. 48 ff.

18. E.L. Hartley and R.E. Hartley, *Fundamentals of Social Psychology* (New York: Knopf, 1952), p. 210.

19. In one sense "bereavement" and "grief" can be defined in terms of each other, i.e., not one without the other. As will be indicated, however, clarity is gained if they are viewed independently.

20. C. Kluckhohn, "Culture and Behavior," in *Handbook of Social Psychology,* ed. G. Lindsey (Reading, Mass.: Addison-Wesley, 1954), p. 922.

21. E. Stainbrook, "A Cross-cultural Evaluation of Depressive Reactions," in *Depression,* ed. Hoch and Zubin (New York: Grune & Stratton, 1954).

22. T.D. Eliot, "The Adjustive Behavior of Bereaved Families: A New Field for Research," *Social Forces* 8 (1930): 543–549.

23. ———, "The Bereaved Family." *Ann. Am. Acad. Pol. and Soc. Sci.,* March 1932, pp. 1–7.

24. W. Waller and R. Hill, *The Family* (Dryden, 1951), Chap. 22.

25. T. Parsons, "The Kinship System of the Contemporary United States." *Am. Anthropologist.*

26. B. Malinowski, *Crime and Custom in Savage Society* (Atlantic Highlands, N.J.: Humanities Press, 1926), p. 26.

27. In a smaller vein, Sarbin writes that "we would expect different kinds of self-concepts in persons whose early socializing interactions were limited to one or two parent figures from those whose early socializing interactions were more extensive."

28. M.E. Spiro, "Ifaluk: a South Sea Culture," unpublished ms., submitted as a final report, Coordinated Investigation of Micronesian Anthropology, Pacific Science Board, National Research Council. Human Relations Area Files, Yale University, 1949.

29. E. Durkheim, *The Elementary Forms of Religious Life* (New York: The Free Press, 1947), p. 397.

30. J.H.S. Bossard, *Parent and Child*. (Philadelphia: University of Pennsylvania Press, 1953).

31. A.W. Green, "The Middle Class Male Child and Neurosis," *Am. Sociol. Rev.* 11 (1946):31–41.

32. T. Parsons, "Certain Primary Sources and Patterns of Agression in the Social Structure of the Western World," in P. Mullahy, ed., *A Study of Interpersonal Relations*. Nelson, 1949, pp. 269–296.

33. ———, "The kinship system of the contemporary United States." *Am. Anthropologist.*

34. ———, "Certain Primary Sources and Patterns of Agression in the Social Structure of the Western World," in P. Mullahy, ed., *A Study of Interpersonal Relations*. Nelson, 1949, pp. 269–296.

35. W.L. Warner, *A Black Civilization*. Harper, 1937.

36 L.W. Simmons, *The Role of the Aged in Primitive Society*. Yale Univ. Press, 1945, pp. 217–220.

37. M.E. Spiro, "A psychotic personality in the South Seas." *Psychiat.*, 13:189–204, 1950, pp. 202–203.

38. This touches upon a problem raised by Rado.

39. This is in line with Sarbin's comment that "the self is what the person 'is,' the role is what the person 'does.'"

40. J.E. Anderson, "Changes in Emotional Responses with Age," in Martin L. Reymert, ed., *Feelings and Emotions*. McGraw-Hill, 1952, pp. 424–425.

41. Thus Lindemann observed men patients who, in bereavement, appeared unable to express their grief for fear they might "break down."

42. E. Lindemann, "Modifications in the course of ulcerative colitis in relationship to changes in life situations and reaction patterns." In *Life Stress and Bodily Disease*. Williams and Wilkins. pp. 708–710.

43. As an illustration: "The heartbroken widow would be an object of curiosity; the widow mourns her husband in the prescribed manner with, it may be, genuine but very transient grief, and takes up life against just where she left it, but in the home of her next husband." A.T. and G.M. Culwick, *Ubena of the Rivers* (London: Allen & Unwin, 1936), p. 366.

     Also: "In three deaths which I observed, the widows were married by levirate husbands on the third day after mortuary rites. In two of these the widows passed to the deceased's oldest brother; in the third, to his parallel cousin." A. R. Holmberg, *Nomads of the Long Bow*. Publications of the Institute of Social Anthropology, No. 10, Smithsonian Institute (Washington: Government Printing Office, 1950), p. 88.

44. W.G. Sumner and A. C. Keller, *The Science of Society*. 3 Vols. Yale Univ. Press, 1927. Vol. 3, pp. 1841–1884.

45. M.E. Opler, "An interpretation of ambivalence in two American Indian tribes." *J. Soc. Psychol.*, 7:82–116, 1936.

46. W.L. Warner, *A Black Civilization*. Harper, 1937, pp. 414–415.

LEROY BOWMAN

selection from
Group Behavior
at Funeral Gatherings

As Volkhart and Michael pointed out, when social role expectations no longer fit social realities, a new form of ritual must emerge. Whatever their form, funeral rituals traditionally serve the following functions: disposal of the body; provision for the spiritual well-being of the deceased; comfort of the mourners; reestablishment of the sense of solidarity among the living; and affirmation of shared beliefs about life and death. In the following selection, Leroy Bowman gives a dispassionate account of the traditional funeral. Bowman's objective analysis of formal and informal practices provides an opportunity to examine the form and function of American funerals.

THE RITUAL SERVICE

The funeral service is the third stage of the funeral proceedings, following the preparations in the home, and the wake. It is different from the wake in almost all particulars. For one thing it is a brief ceremony as compared with the sessions of the preceding stage. It is formal in content and procedure, in the church setting in which it is held, and even in the attire of those attending. At the wake, friends and relatives are inclined to lighten the spirit of the occasion and often to avoid the mournful aspects of the death; at the funeral service the most serious of death's meanings are confronted. Except in very rare instances the service is intended to be a serious and sobering experience.

The funeral service is a ritual lying traditionally in the province of the church. Even among non-church members, the majority of persons look upon the church as

Source: Leroy Bowman. "Group Behavior at Funeral Gatherings." *The American Funeral: A Study in Guilt, Extravagence, and Sublimity.* Washington, D.C.: Public Affairs Press, 1959.

189

the place for the holding of the service, or on a clergyman, bringing the message of the church to the funeral parlor, as the appropriate individual to officiate. There are exceptions, as in the case of brief ceremonies of the family and friends at home or in funeral parlors, in which there is no clerical leadership but rather that of the elder member, friend, or organization official. The relation of the funeral to the essential activities of the church varies among denominations and among churches within one denomination. In some instances it is strictly a church affair and the members are all expected to put in an appearance. In others, it may be peripheral in its relation to the congregational aspect of the church, or regarded as a matter of chief concern only to the clergyman and the bereaved family.

On the whole, fewer persons attend the church service than come at one time or another to the wake. In metropolitan areas the funeral service of a prominent leader in a minority group is often the occasion for a mass demonstration of solidarity that fills the largest church and throngs the street on which it stands.

At the service emphasis is put on the seating arrangements for the participants and on the sequence of events. The casket is placed in front of the group, with the closest relatives nearest to it, and those of less connection with the deceased further back. In the church the clergyman is in the most prominent position at the altar or in the pulpit; the pall bearers and any other dignitaries of the occasion are also near the front. When the service is over the same relative status of positions is maintained in the procession to the cemetery. Events in the ritual take place in automatic sequence rather than by verbal direction of a leader. At services in mortuary homes the sequence is less fixed and the undertaker, who assumes very little prominence at a church, directs affairs more actively in his own premises.

At the wake much verbal interaction takes place. At the service practically none occurs; the audience is silent except as it may take part in responses led by the clergyman. In fact the clergyman initiates all action, except that directed by the funeral director. Activity on the part of the auditors is of an unexpressed emotional or intellectual kind.

When a eulogy is given, the keenest attention of the members of the audience is devoted to identification of each with the dead person. After the funeral, they tell of listening for items in the narration of the life or in the characterization of the eulogy with which they were familiar, or events or loyalties which they shared with the deceased. The desire to listen to a eulogy rather than to an analysis and critical evaluation of the life that is ended, comes in part from this identification, and the consequent egoistic satisfaction in praise and commendation that directly or remotely reflects on them.

However, a much stronger emotion creates or strengthens the wish to hear well of the dead. It is the wish to be well spoken of at one's own funeral. Under the weight of the apprehension, whether clearly or vaguely realized as such, the individual gains some assurance through hearing words of approbation. In this connection one emotional experience at the funeral service needs to be mentioned here. This experience is the concern that is usually aroused over the mystery of life and death and the often painful reappraisal of the ideals held by the individual and the degree to which they are implemented in the routine of daily affairs. Clergymen occasionally find persons ready to affiliate or renew affiliation with the church when death has occurred in the family.

Due to the depth of feeling aroused by death in the minds of some of those in attendance, and due also to the grief of the close friends and relatives, there is always the possibility of an outburst of emotional expression, especially in the case of a few minority groups. The clergy, for the most part, take precautions to prevent the occurrence; some meet with the members of the family before the ceremony to fortify them against the emotional ordeal. Tensions of other kinds are experienced during the ceremony by some of the members of the congregation; sympathy with the bereaved, remembrance of similar losses in the past, fear or expectation of an emotional outburst, or, among those present who are not adherents of the faith expressed in the ritual, an uneasiness at participation in it.

In a gathering of any considerable size, there are also persons who are emotionally affected very little. Many persons who are deeply affected are fatigued by the contemplation of death. To meet these tensions and this fatigue clergymen reduce the service to thirty minutes or less in length. Clergymen called to officiate at a service in a funeral home may speak voluntarily or by request for only ten minutes.

One other almost universal characteristic of funerals is the lavish display of expenditures noticeable in the costly casket. This is particularly striking at the obsequies held for the dead of low or middle income families. At services held in the chapels of undertaking establishments, the impression of conspicuous display is augmented by the mass of costly floral pieces. A real or imagined need may be served by the seemingly extravagant exhibit. Nevertheless the uninitiated observer cannot but be struck by the contrast of the social and spiritual emotions aroused by the death and emotions characterized by the superficial desire to live up to the Joneses.

A lasting impression of differences between funeral services is left by the contrasting atmosphere in which they may be held. In the home of the deceased a tone of familiarity with him and his "folks" prevails. Sympathy for the family is felt more intensely than in either of the other two settings, and simplicity of casket and procedure seems eminently appropriate. The participant's mind is apt to dwell on the family life of the deceased, its beginning and its now partial dissolution, as well as on the generation immediately preceding and the one following his. At the church the symbols of faith make their imprint, and solemnity as well as architectural grandeur seem fitting. Here not only the deceased and his family, but the gathering itself becomes merely a part of the expression of ultimate human longings. The mind of the participant in this context dwells less on the period of a lifetime and more on vast stretches of time and on the meaning of eternity. In a sense the funeral parlor is more informal than either the home or church. It symbolizes death to the participant more than they, and in greater measure holds the attention to this one unusual happening. It magnifies the present anguish and guilt and glosses over the permanence of affection and sorrow, and the continuing processes of daily living. It emphasizes, not so much the span of life nor the long stretch of time, but the short period of the funeral activities.

FINALITY OF THE COMMITTAL SERVICE

Committing the remains to earth is a continuation of the funeral service. It is dramatic beyond any incident in the funeral period except the moment of death itself. It is packed with acts and symbols of finality, and if ritual could blot out any lingering fantasy that the dead one might be seen or heard again, the committal would do so.

Fewer persons attend the committal service, partly because to do so is time consuming. This is particularly true in urban centers where the cemetery lies at a considerable distance from residential areas. In addition, many acquaintances entertain the opinion that the final act affects specifically only the closest relations and friends. On occasion, when the clergyman has been brought in to officiate at the service of a stranger, or when the journey to the grave is long, the committal service is said incongruously in the funeral parlor before the procession starts. Thereafter few but the immediate family accompany the casket. If the deceased has been prominent, or a member of a cohesive group, larger numbers of persons make the trip. It is still quite a common thing for the surviving members of the family to take pride in the number of cars in the procession.

During the last and climactic episode of the funeral series the casket is the center of attention. Lines of status are drawn as at the preceding service. The hearse leads the procession, followed by the immediate family, other relatives, near friends and others in order. The clergyman and pall bearers ride in cars near the head of the cortege. At the end of the journey the clergyman and the immediate relatives stand closest to the grave. The undertaker becomes much more prominent in the direction of the proceedings as he and his assistant instruct the pall bearers in placing the casket on the tapes and later lowering it into the grave.

The rite is brief; the trend is to make it less harrowing for those who have lived with the one who now is dead. But feelings run deep and strong and are more likely to burst out here than at any other time. Often the clergyman bolsters the closest relatives before the committal begins. As the casket is lowered and the symbolic flowers or handful of earth is thrown on the casket and particularly when the phrase "dust to dust" is heard, the tension is almost unbearable for any one who has known the deceased at all well, but especially for the family. At this moment, in certain cultural groups, a widow may attempt to throw herself on the casket and plead to go with her husband. The observer may recognize it as a role she is expected to play, and may be prepared to discount the sincerity of the act. Witnessing the enactment of just such a scene, however, leads to the firm conviction that under the cruel circumstances, the role the widow plays must be easy to assume with a maximum of tense emotion and a minimum of pretense.

The committal service might be characterized as a rite to confirm to the participants the end of their relationship to the dead, and as such it is an essential part of the celebration of death in certain religious groups. For some persons, however, it is a harrowing anticlimax to the calm sublimity of the funeral service.

THE RETURN HOME

From the moment of death, and in case of critical illness preceding it for a period before death, through the afternoons and evenings of the wake, through the tense emotional experience of the funeral service and the tragic moments of the committal service, the family has spent its physical and mental strength. The stimulus of responsibility in prominent roles has enabled the members to hold out to the end. When the cultural requirements have been met and the spotlight removed, the return to the home may signalize a letdown into more heartrending sorrow than any happening up to that time. The old relationships have been disrupted, and the new not yet entered upon. It is then that some of the neighbors or the relatives not included in the immediate family often try to make the homecoming seem less lonesome and desolate. They prepare food, either in the home of the family or in their own homes, and bring it in for the tired and hungry group. Such assistance has become a custom that is to be found in many parts of the country.

Usually few persons are present, unless many relatives have come from outside the city to remain for a gathering of the extended family. Action originates with the neighbors, relatives and close friends; and ordinarily, as in any housekeeping matter, the women take over the planning and serving of food. There is little or no formality, and a warm, intimate feeling pervades the group.

The impulse of the close associates to lessen the work and brighten the spirit of the return home does not arise solely from a rational consideration of the need of the family. It springs from a desire of practically every one who has known the family in a friendly fashion. From the hour when death is expected or has come many offer help, and many more would do so if they could think of some service that is needed.

It would appear first that some glimmering of the pressure of formal requirements of the funeral on the family is felt. Second, the sympathy that is felt finds verbal expression difficult for many persons and inadequate for many more. Occasionally the observer detects something of the feeling of guilt that the chief mourners experience also gripping in smaller measure the less intimate friends and neighbors. The wish "to do something" is its manifestation.

JEAN MASAMBA and
RICHARD A. KALISH

Death and Bereavement:
The Role of the Black Church*

In the following selection, Masamba and Kalish explore the beliefs and social practices surrounding death in the Black community. Using various types of evidence—personal interview, observation, review of the literature, and analysis of spirituals—the authors recount the components of a Black funeral they regard as typical. They argue that many of the components which are frequently criticized do, in fact, effectively assist the bereaved.

As the study of death and bereavement has become a matter of increasing academic and clinical concern, it is appropriate that some attention should be given to values, beliefs, expectations, individual behavior, and social practices regarding death in the Black communities. In the past few years, Kalish and Reynolds have reported on a three-year study of four groups (Black, Mexican-American, Japanese-American, Anglo) in the greater Los Angeles area and an earlier study by Pandey compared the death anxieties of Black and non-Black college students.[1-4] Other recent studies have explored the role of Black morticians[5] and death in Black writings,[6] and an analysis of death in Black Africa has been completed.[7] These have obviously just scratched the surface of this important topic.

In this paper, I[8] will explore the religious and psychosocial dynamics of bereavement in the Black experience and the implication of these phenomena for mental health. As a Black African clergyman and pastoral psychologist who has lived for several years in the United States, I can offer a combination of "the view from within" and "the view from without." The present paper discusses the patterns of

Source: Reprinted from *Omega*, 1976, Vol. 7 (No. 1), Baywood Publishing Co., Farmingdale, N.Y.
*Author's Note: This project was funded by grants from NIMH and NICHD.

religious, psychological, and social factors that influence behavior of the bereaved, with particular attention to the ways in which the church and church members cope with the dissolving powers of death.

SOURCES OF INFORMATION

Sources of information for the present paper include:
1. *A literature review.*
2. *Personal experiences.* During my relatively brief stay in the United States, I have had fairly extensive experience with the dying and the bereaved in Black churches, where my involvement has been both that of parishioner and pastor. The junior author has drawn primarily on informal discussions, his academic background, and a research study he conducted several years ago.
3. *Direction of a ten-week seminar on death and bereavement for church deacons.*
4. *Interviews.* Ministers from selected congregations were interviewed on death and bereavement, and their views were compared. Key people in the churches, such as deacons and active members of the congregations, were also interviewed. Some interviews were also conducted with funeral directors.
5. *Field trips and participant observation.* I accompanied Black pastors on visits to hospitalized and bereaved parishioners, paying particular attention to relationships between the pastor and those he visited. I also attended a number of funerals where these same pastors officiated, observing the nature of eulogies, arrangement of the services, and social interactions. In addition, I participated in worship services and attended faith-healing sessions.

DEATH IN BLACK SPIRITUALS

The attitudes and expectations held by Black Americans concerning death have been extensively described in their spirituals and the blues. Through their songs, the Blacks have been able to ritualize and describe the emotional and religious contents of their relationships with life and death. Some of the major themes include:
1. death as a symbol for liberation,
2. death as an integral part of life,
3. death as the basis for fear,
4. death as cessation of this life, not extinction of all life, and
5. social extinction as the meaning of death without proper ceremonies or survivors.

Death Used as an Underground Symbol for Liberation Here and Now

Spirituals, according to Jackson, ". . . should be considered as a covert form of desire for freedom, with death simultaneously representing actual death and freedom—with the obvious realization that the only freedom most of the slaves would find was to occur with death'' (p. 205).[6] The will to be free and to survive is expressed in death-rebirth metaphors. The Black who cries,

> Oh Freedom, Oh Freedom, Oh Freedom over me
> Before I'd be a slave
> I'd be buried in my grave
> And go home to my Lord
> And be free.

is engaged in a battle of freedom and integrity that must be conducted until death. Death and the hereafter are only symbolic representations of the freedom and liberation in the here and now. The fear of death is therefore minimized as death becomes the symbol of courage, hope and liberation.

> Through all the sorrow of the Sorrow Songs there breathes a hope—a faith in the ultimate justice of things. The minor cadences of despair change often to triumph and calm confidence. Sometimes it is faith in life, sometimes faith in death, sometimes assurance of boundless justice in some fair world beyond . . . (p. 498).[9]

Death is therefore a positive symbol for freedom in the midst of social injustice and exploitation. This understanding of the meaning of death had influence on Black leaders in the 1950s and 1960s. King and Malcolm X were willing to die for their beliefs, if death is the price to be paid for freedom. Meredith believes that Black leaders contemplated death as one means of guaranteeing the legacy of their work.

> To understand the tenor of the '50s and '60s you have to understand the great importance of death. Death and the threat of death shadowed the life of every leader . . . It was a reality. In a sense, it was even a tactic, even a goal.
> Martin Luther King and Malcolm X, for example, wanted to die; for each of these men, their violent death was the only sure way to preserve their legacy (p. 157).[10]

In general, the Black's contact with the dead has been immediate, inescapable and dramatic. Struggle, violence, and aggression have been the black American experience from the time of slavery to the present life in the ghetto, where sudden death is a reality. Violent death, sudden death, becomes a symbol of the ultimate justice to come. Death becomes an indication of things that are worse than death and against which the Black American needs to fight.[11] Thus, in the Black experience, death is most often a symbol of release from slavery without meaning release from life.[9] It sometimes was a welcome release from the burdens of this world, a means to be received in the kingdom of God.[12]

Death Recognized as an Integral Part of Man's Life

Being influenced by his African heritage, the Black American has a tendency to see death and life not as enemies but as partners.[7] Death is therefore personified.

Because the reality of death was a part of their everyday experience, Blacks spoke of it in personal terms.

> Oh Deat' he is a little man,
> And he goes from do' to do',
> He kill some souls and he wounded some,
> And he lef' some souls to pray.
>
> Death he ain't nothin' but a robber, don't you see?
> Death come to my house; he didn't stay long,
> I looked in de bed, an' my mother (father, sister, brother) was gone,
> Death, he ain' nothin' but a robber, don't you see?

James Cone explains the historical basis that has given rise to this attitude of viewing death as part of life's experience:

> . . . black people were well acquainted with death, for they lived under its threat every moment. The slave owners, in particular, and white people in general were vivid reminders that life could not be taken for granted. It had to be defended all the time by all possible means. To stay alive in dignity was the essential task of the black slave community (p. 75).[12]

Death as the Basis for Fear

The impact of the community life of the slave era protected individual Blacks from mental exhaustion in response to violent death. Today, it seems that the presence of violent death in the Black ghetto induces fear as may be observed in the following history.

Mrs. A. is a young, married Black woman, mother of five children and an active member of her Baptist church; relationships with her own parents and with her sisters and one brother were apparently good. She expressed her feelings that she did not fear death itself, but was afraid of dying and of pain. "Being unaware of when death is going to get me bothers me, like being on an airplane and finding that in five minutes I'm going to die." She finds it threatening to contemplate dying without being prepared for it; in a similar vein, she finds lack of control over when and how she will die very threatening.

Mrs. A. says that natural death is acceptable to her and the pain associated with natural death is not especially disturbing. By natural death, she means dying in old age—at least 60—of causes that occur neither suddenly nor unexpectedly. She knows that drugs can calm pain. The experience of a friend of hers, an old lady who has been holding on to life during four years of suffering from terminal cancer, has helped Mrs. A. conquer her own fear of pain connected with natural illness and, thus, natural death. The anxiety Mrs. A. expresses over death that does not arise from natural causes may have its origins in the deaths of Blacks in the Vietnam War, and from the deaths of Black leaders such as Martin Luther King and Malcolm X:

There is nothing for which I can sacrifice my own life, except saving the lives of my children. Whenever danger threatens my children, such as fire, police brutality, I'll run to save them even if it means losing my own life. This is where the unnatural death loses its sting. I am always afraid of unnatural death: violence, killings reported on radio . . . those police . . . they can kill even the innocent, I don't like to see the police wandering around because I don't know what they want. They can always kill you by mistake and no one will plead your case. I never dare a policeman to touch me . . . .

The fear of death has also been influenced by her relationships with her husband and children:

I cannot think of my husband dying. I will not look at him. When he is gone, I am gone too, I have no one else. I can stroke my child, though. I am stronger than the child. I don't like to talk about these things. I feel good that I can express these feelings. But I am always afraid that death might come in a very violent manner.

Not every Black thinks and talks freely about his own death. One interviewee expresses the need for dealing with his inner feelings:

I'm sentimental about death. I don't like to talk about it for several reasons. Mother died a couple of years ago. I don't know much about death, the life after death. Life is threatening when you think of physical pain about dying. You don't know what life over there looks like. People talk much about religion: don't drink, don't wear short dresses, don't sit with the ungodly people. All that scares me. I like Malcolm X because he talks about this earth as our heaven, instead of always talking about life over there. Religion is too legalistic and hell scares me.

Another person, forty-eight years old, explains his feelings of not wanting to deal with death in terms of his economic situation:

I take medicine every three hours. That keeps me going. I have a nice doctor, a Jew. He treats me often free. He does it because I'm a minority individual like he is. It is not easy to be poor and suffer, you know. I take it easy. The doctor does not tell me what I have, but I think I have cancer. Every time I go to the bathroom, white stuff come out. Probably my kidneys are very badly infected. I should go for another check-up. I drink a lot in order to forget it. I'm happy when I'm talking to people like you. But when I go to sleep, I start thinking about it. Nobody likes to die, you know. We want to live a little longer. I have obligations toward my family members and I like them. But it is not easy to be poor and sick. And the thought of dying bothers me because I don't know I'll have enough money to take care of all the expenses that go along with funerals and so on. That causes a lot of my anxiety. And when I am depressed because of the thought of dying without proper material preparation, I feel small and I dream about my own death and I become afraid.

Death Recognized as Cessation of This Life and Not as Extinction of Life

Death gives way to another quality of life with the Lord. The African concept of death as an extension of life was Christianized by Black Americans:

When I'm gone
When I'm gone . . .
Mother, don't you weep . . .
For I'm going to Heav'n above,
Going to meet the God I love,
O Mother, don't you weep when I am gone.

Death is therefore only a bridge between the hopeless and the hopeful life. As this is the case, one must die in dignity so that death is an unbroken bridge. Even today, death is referred to as "passing." The minister usually teaches that "we live unto the Lord and die unto the Lord. We weep because we care, not because we despair." That is why slaves wanted to die like Jesus[12]. To die in dignity is to experience the victory over injustice. This is why in the South the traditional procession to the cemetery was accompanied by songs of sorrow by the band, the procession back to the city was accompanied with songs of joy and victory. A sense of joy and purpose in living is experienced even after experiencing the death of a loved one. The following prayer, usually printed in the bulletin, is recommended for reading:

PRAYER

O GOD! Great and Omnipotent Judge of the living and the dead! Before whom we are all to appear after this short life to render an account of our works. Let our hearts, we pray Thee, be deeply moved at this sight of death, and while we consign the body of the deceased to the earth, let us be mindful of our own frailty and mortality, that walking always in Thy Fear and in the ways of Thy Commandments we may, after departure from this world, experience a merciful judgement and rejoice in Everlasting Happiness, through Christ, our Lord.
—Amen.

Social Extinction Feared

Social death has been described as the loss of social relationships, an event that often anticipates clinical death for those who are dying, taking place as friends, family members, co-workers, and others withdraw from social interactions[13]. Here we would like to postulate a parallel concept, that of social extinction, to be applied in situations where the individual ceases to have any earthly ties after his clinical death. When one dies and leaves no relatives behind, when he is without proper ceremonies, when he is no longer remembered, we can state that he suffers social extinction. Eventually, this will occur to everyone, although some may live in memories, record books, archives, and historical treatises longer than others.

Essentially, social extinction means that earthly immortality has ceased, according to the definition of the individual concerned. For a person to feel that social extinction will follow immediately upon his clinical death can be depressing. Death-related ceremonies and rituals can mitigate against this extinction. For devout Christians, the Resurrection probably provides a concrete basis for avoiding social extinction. It not only means that death does not extinguish self-aware existence, but that the death of the body itself is not a permanent phenomenon. The extent to which acceptance of such beliefs compensates for anxiety concerning social extinction, however, is not at all understood.

Burial insurance and the tradition of burial societies reflected not only the social, political, and economic experiences of the Black family, but also the religious meaning of the indivisibility of life and death, that is, the interpenetration of relationships between the living and the dead, when one dies and is buried with dignity. The religious attitude inherited from Africa was Christianized to fit the realities of Black American experience. To die without proper ceremonies, without the dignity of personhood, without the entourage of other human beings threatens a forgotten afterlife and the possibility of a distant relationship with God.

The world views, the theology of suffering and salvation have created institutional practices that have shaped Black perceptions in regard to death, dying, burial, bereavement, and have played a significant role in facilitating the spirit of Black nationalism.

PATTERNS OF SUPPORT DURING THE CRISIS OF BEREAVEMENT

Each person has his own mechanisms for coping with the process of bereavement. But it is also true that each culture has its own particular mechanisms that affect the emotional responses of the bereaving individual. If death is a biological reality, it seems that the anxiety connected with the personal event of death or the passing of a relative is a cultural phenomenon. This has some bearing on the stages through which the bereaved person passes. Black funeral practices, together with wake and other social services, provide a network of psychological mechanisms that facilitate grief work.

Psychological Dynamics of Black Funerals

The loss of a loved one through death gives rise to a variety of personal, social, and emotional needs, depending on the individual and on his social community or culture. For many, the church offers rituals and ceremonies that provide the bereaved the opportunity to fulfill many of their needs. Although Black Baptist churches are hardly unique in this matter, I will discuss what I have observed in that context.

There is little doubt that funeral services provide social support for bereaved persons in the Black community as in most others. I spoke with over two hundred members of Black Baptist churches concerning this and other matters, and I made a point of tabulating the responses. Although over three-fifths of those who had suffered a loss told me their family and friends gave support and sympathy, about four-fifths received support from their minister and members of their church. The religious funeral ritual is organized not primarily around the deceased person, but around the living. Even though flowers are brought, a eulogy is always part of the service, and an expensive casket is usually provided for the deceased, the survivors are at the center of the funeral service. A funeral rite is social par excellence. "Its ostensible object is the dead person, but it benefits not the dead, but the living" (p. 64).[14]

The wake services that precede or follow the funeral also offer a social support for the bereaved. The presence of many friends at the funeral and/or at the wake helps compensate for the sense of isolation caused by the death of a loved one. The social processes around the bereaved that often began in the hospital or nursing home continue at church, at the interment, and at home. At these places children as well as adults show their concern not only for the afterlife of the deceased, but for the psychological and material comfort of the survivors.

Many Black church members belong to societies within the church they attend. In the two Black churches I observed, these societies frequently organized a church banquet following the interment for the purpose of providing the survivors with emotional and social support. Although other church members may participate in preparing the dinner, the particular group or groups to which the dead person had belonged is responsible for leadership in planning and organizing. Sometimes funds are collected to meet some of the expenses of the funeral services. One pastor talked of the possibility of working out a program in the church community that would provide a substitute parent (or parents) for the surviving small children, and encourage new relationships for the bereaved adults.

The sense of an extended family becomes strong at the time of bereavement. In the family structure where people are not even related by blood, a feeling of being close to the bereaved transcends social services and obligations that one has to provide to the bereaved. In some of the funeral services that were under the directorship of Black morticians, I observed that a female chauffeur was provided whenever a woman lost her husband. This female chauffeur, dressed in black, remained with the widow during the service. She escorted her outside, brought her to the limousine, chauffeured her to the cemetery, and sat down with her at the interment service. This woman usually checked on the widow a few times during the week following the funeral service.

Although, according to one study,[2] Black Americans are less likely than Mexican or Japanese Americans to desire a mortician of their own race (39 percent did want a Black mortician, while 54 percent stated they were indifferent), given the actual situation—rather than a survey questionnaire—many Blacks undoubtedly feel that the Black funeral director is more sensitive to their needs and more trustworthy in his business dealings with the Black community. For example, at one of the wake services, people were quiet and subdued during the thirty minutes a White minister officiated, but they relaxed and resumed their normal talking, joking, and singing after he left.

Funeral Services as Channels for Emotional Catharsis

A major component of funeral services in Black churches is the opportunity for emotional catharsis. As one parishioner commented, "In times of anguish, the church has been a psychiatrist's couch. I can release my anxiety, anger, frustration, not only in the worship services where I am accepted even when I pass out, clapping my hands and shouting, but also in business meetings." One characteristic often attributed to Blacks is the capacity to express inner feelings of joy or sadness, anger or sympathy, without much inhibition. The blues, spirituals, trance experiences in church services, are expressions of such emotional expression.

Some of the factors that facilitate emotional discharge during funerals are the songs, the nature of the eulogy, and the visual confrontation with the body.

Songs—Songs perform two kinds of functions for the survivors. First, the words of many songs seem particularly appropriate after a death has occurred, either because they recall the lost relationship or because they speak of the happiness and contentment of the dead. Secondly, for those Blacks who have shared church experiences with the dead person, the songs may bring back memories of being together in church singing the same songs.

Eulogy—The sermon is a memorial to the deceased, given in remembrance of him and supported with material from the Old and New Testaments. As might be anticipated, pastors tended to talk more about those persons whom they knew best. On some occasions, certain mourners gave brief testimonies, talking about the life and aspirations and deeds of the dead person. One pastor remarked that Black preachers make every deceased person into a saint, focusing solely on his positive attributes and exaggerating even these into a paean of glory. This tendency prevents the Black Baptist church from developing a theology of intercession that would permit pleading with God to intervene on behalf of the deceased. The lack of intercessory theology causes some bereaved persons, especially those who had knowledge of the moral and social inadequacies of the dead person, to wonder whether the service would be sufficient to provide entrance into eternal rest. One example of this was especially graphic. A middle-aged Black woman broke into violent crying when viewing her brother's body following the funeral. She later revealed to me her anxiety about his salvation because the minister did not plead on his behalf, and she was well aware that her brother's life was far from exemplary. This uncertainty created feelings of anger toward the minister and personal guilt for not having helped her brother to have lived a "Christian" existence.

The eulogy for another funeral, while hardly typical, is also worthy of note. The dead person was a twenty-year-old state university student who had been killed by a policeman on the campus. Objectively speaking, there was little or no basis for the shot having been fired, and the dead student had been student body president. The funeral was held late in the morning with three hundred and fifty to four hundred persons in attendance. The pastor's eulogy was particularly relevant:

> Jesus was a young man. He was a compassionate person. He tried not to do any harm to anyone. He loved children, "Let the children come to me." He loved his people. He talked about mercy, justice and truth. He had power to use violence, to use the power of heaven. But his power is seen in His voice of peace, "Blessed are the peacemakers for they shall see God." This boy was a leader—he was the president of a student body of twenty

thousand persons. He suffered as an innocent one and was crushed. We have not gotten beyond the primitive drives of crucifying people. Anybody's son here can be next. Many young men who are being killed not only in Vietnam but also here, are Blacks. Why? How long, Lord, will it be until justice comes? How long will it be that we will react by saying, Father, forgive them for they know not what they do? Creative energies have to be used so that we can live in a better world. Are we going to be spectators and say that problems don't exist in our societies? Are we going to rise up and recognize that California is a new South? God knows how you feel because he lost his only son on Good Friday. The spiritual and the body cannot be separated. (If God is interested in man's spiritual freedom, the body must also be free.)

At this funeral service emotion was easy to express. The emotional expression was accepted by the pastor and the rest of the congregation. It seems that violent death creates more overt emotional outburst and feelings of anger and rage than natural, suicidal, or accidental death. Two ladies fainted while viewing the remains. The pastor, parents, and many other people in the congregation cried.

Visual confrontation—Black funerals generally call for visual confrontation of the dead body. On the bulletin of the order of service, the picture of the deceased person always appears. Of all the services attended, there were only two that did not have a picture printed on the order of service and these were under the care of a White funeral home. One member of a deceased person's family said that the printing of the picture on the order of service helped him accept the reality of loss as well as creating in him the feeling of "spiritual" presence of the deceased among the living.

The visual confrontation of the dead body is vivid when the remains are viewed by the living. In almost all the funerals I attended, caskets were closed from the beginning of the service to the end of the sermon when they were opened. Those present were asked by the representatives of the funeral home to view the body. (The body was cosmetized, dressed in regular clothes, using the best clothes the deceased person possessed while living.) It was observed that people had varieties of responses to the body. Some people stopped and looked at the body, touched it, talked to the deceased. Some people were unable to look at the body. Members of the family were always seated on the left side of the church and in the front row. They were the last to view the body. The body is brought closer to where they are seated so that they can see it without standing up.

The viewing of the body is the climax of the service, calling for overt expression of strong feelings. Sometimes the behavior exhibited is sufficiently vehement or involves so much physical movement that the pastor appears upset. When emotion is not expressed, it appears that one or more of the following may be the cause:

1. the feeling that emotional expression is an indication of personal or, more frequently, masculine inadequacy,
2. the belief that such emotions should not be expressed in front of people who are not family members or very close friends, and
3. the minister's beliefs that it implies a lack of acceptance of resurrection and hope in Christ.

CONCLUDING STATEMENT

In general, the Black church's handling of funeral services facilitates grief work as individuals are allowed to express their feelings. It is my personal hope that some of the practices, such as wake services, viewing the body, organizing banquets, will not be removed from people's experience as they tend to play a great role in the ways bereaved persons express their feelings and resolve guilt, frustration, isolation, and help the bereaved individual to experience a sense of community.

NOTES

1. R.A. Kalish and D.K. Reynolds, 1973. Phenomenological reality and post-death contact. *Journal for the Scientific Study of Religion* 12: 209-221.
2. R.A. Kalish and D.K. Reynolds, 1976. *Death and ethnicity: A study of attitudes.* Los Angeles: Andrus Gerontology Center Press.
3. D.K. Reynolds and R.A. Kalish, 1974. Anticipation of futurity as a function of ethnicity and age, *Journal of Gerontology* 29: 224-231.
4. R.E. Pandey and D.I. Templer. Use of the death anxiety scale in an inter-racial setting. *Omega* 3: 127-130.
5. M.J. McDonald. The management of grief: A study of black funeral practices. *Omega* 4: 139-148.
6. M. Jackson, 1972. The black experience with death. *Omega* 3: 203-210.
7. J. Masamba. The African concept of death. *Omega.* To be published.
8. The use of first person in this paper refers to the senior author, Jean Masamba.
9. J. Lovell. *Black song: The forge and flame.* New York: Macmillan, 1972.
10. J. Meredith. Black leaders and the wish to die. May 1973. *Ebony:* pp. 154-159.
11. H. Thurman, 1947. *The Negro spiritual speaks of life and death.* New York: Harper & Row.
12. J.R. Cone, 1972. *The spirituals and the blues: An interpretation.* New York: Seabury Press.
13. R.A. Kalish, 1965. Life and death: Dividing the indivisible. *Social Science and Medicine* 2: 249-259.
14. R. Firth, 1964. *Elements of social organization.* Boston: Beacon Press.

ROBERT J. LIFTON

The Struggle for Cultural Rebirth

The impetus to study death alternately throws one back to a reexamination of life and hurtles one forward to an exploration of the nature of immortality. Funerals reaffirm the shared sense of continuity, the concept of immortality established by particular belief systems. Throughout cultural history, myths have promoted belief in the solidarity of life and insulated man from an overwhelming fear of death. In the following article, Lifton explores the reconstruction of modes of symbolic immortality during a time of historical dislocation such as the present. Lifton conducts his exploration of immortality on a number of levels simultaneously. He ends by reaffirming the age-old pattern of death and rebirth with the statement that "Every significant step in human existence involves some inner sense of death."

In times of relative equilibrium, the symbols and institutions of a society provide comforting guidelines, a prescribed life cycle, for our internal experience as well as our external behavior. But in times of severe historical dislocation, these institutions and symbols—whether having to do with worship, work, learning, punishment, or pleasure—lose their power and psychological legitimacy. We still live in them, but they no longer live in us. Or rather we live a half-life with one another.

The quest for images and symbols in new combination, for what might be called communal resymbolization, is precarious and threatening—so much so that it can itself be viewed as the cause for the cultural breakdown everyone senses.

Whether we acknowledge it or not, feelings of disintegration and loss permeate contemporary life. Consider, for instance, the widespread inclination to name and interpret man in our present situation not in terms of what he might actually be but rather in terms of what he has been, that is, what he has survived. We speak of man as post-modern, post-industrial, post-historic, post-identity, post-materialist, post-technocratic, and so forth. There are pitfalls in this way of naming the present (or the future) after what no longer is (or will be), but the terms have an authentic source in the sense of survivorship, present or anticipated, that so pervades our deepest image of ourselves.

In other writings I have emphasized the importance of holocaust in our symbolic vocabulary—of the recent past (Nazi death camps, Hiroshima and Nagasaki), the present (Vietnam), and the future (imagery of ultimate destruction by nuclear weapons, environmental pollution, or other means). Now we see the imagery of holocaust coming together with the experience of post-modern cultural breakdown: our loss of faith not so much in this symbol or that but in the entire intricate web of images, rituals, institutions, and material objects that make up any culture. The urgency of contemporary innovation stems from this sense of survival and loss at the most profound experiential level. I keep thinking of a (more or less) rhetorical question put to me recently by a thoughtful student: "Are four thousand years of human experience merely adding up to the capacity to repair a deficiency in a space ship several million light-years from home?"

In recent years we have witnessed the emergence of a "Protean" psychological style of flux and flow of the self, or self-process—of what the young call "goin' through the changes" in an interminable series of experiments and explorations of varying depth, each of which may be readily abandoned in favor of still another psychological quest. The Protean style is that of a survivor of the kinds of technological and cultural holocausts, real and anticipated, that swirl around us.

The Protean process is a product of a convergence of history and evolution. The two have always intertwined: Darwin's message was that man emerged from other species in a historical process; and there has been no lack of evolutionary interpretations of history. But we tend to view evolution as prehistorical, and history as post-evolutionary. The separation has been based upon our assumption of radically differing time scales in their impact upon man: during a historical unit of a decade or century, man was rarely changed in a fundamental way—an evolutionary unit of a millennium or more was required for that to be accomplished. But our present revolutionary technology and unprecedented historical velocity cast doubt upon that distinction. We sense, uneasily, our capacity to eliminate man in evolution no less than in history, and short of that to alter man—whether genetically or through organ exchange or mind influence—as never before.

Like so many of our boundaries, that between history and evolution is obscured rather than eradicated. As history and evolution converge, innovators embrace our new access (made possible by technology) to all forms ever known to human culture. Poised at a confusing and liberating psychic brink, ready to plunge wildly ahead in an unknowable process devoid of clear destination, man suddenly finds, swirling about him, the total array of images created over the full course of his historical and evolutionary past. These images become an elusive form of psychic nutriment, to be ingested, metabolized, excreted, and, above all, built upon and recombined in a process of organic growth.

Richard Sennett has observed that when a machine's parts wear down, the machine cannot operate. "But," Sennett continues, "the essence of human development is that growth occurs when old routines break down, when old parts are no longer enough for the needs of the new organism. This same kind of change, in a larger sphere, creates the phenomenon of history in a culture." Death and loss can occasion profound research, recreation, and renewal. But for such transformation to occur, the relationship of man to machine and of man to work must be altered in the direction of organic growth.

This is Lewis Mumford's principle of transition from mechanism to organism. But something more is involved as well: social arrangements that permit and encourage technology to become part of a larger principle of imaginative transcendence.

MODES OF SYMBOLIC IMMORTALITY

Everywhere, men and women band together to confront the pervasive sense of "living deadness" emanating from holocaust, undigested change, large techno-bureaucracy, and above all the image of the machine. They seek new forms of connection, movement, and integrity around which to build new communities for living and working. One way to probe some of the fundamental dimensions of this process of communal resymbolization is to view it within a framework of shifting modes of symbolic immortality.

Symbolic immortality is an expression of man's need for an inner sense of continuity with what has gone on before and what will go on after his own limited biological existence. The *sense* of immortality is thus more than mere denial of death, and grows out of compelling, life-enhancing imagery of one's involvement in the historical process. This sense of immortality may be expressed *biologically*, by living on through one's sons and daughters and their sons and daughters, extending out into social dimensions (of tribe, organization, people, nation, or even species); *theologically*, in the idea of a life after death or of other forms of spiritual conquest of death; *creatively*, through "works" and influences persisting beyond biological death; *naturally*, through identification with nature, with its finite extension into time and space; or *transcendentally*, through a feeling-state so intense that time and death disappear.

Historical change itself can be understood in terms of shifts in these modes, or in combinations of these modes. Darwinism, for instance, became the center of a shift (always gradual and partial) from the theological to the biological and natural modes. Or the Chinese Revolution of the twentieth century can be understood as a shift from the biological mode (the socio-religious principles of family continuity and filial piety) to a form of "revolutionary immortality" that embodies aspects of all the modes. I believe that the significance of contemporary social experiments can best be grasped within this larger quest not just for change but for a change in enduring connectedness and commitment, in relationship to contemporary paths to immortality.

The biological-biosocial mode is at issue in the new kinds of families and family-like structures now taking shape. A wide variety of experimental communal arrangements press toward new forms of biosocial continuity—toward new "tribes," a new "people," or at least new forms of community. These groups (sometimes but not always called communes) concern themselves with root psychobiological matters—organic food, greater sexual freedom, collective child-rearing, and spontaneity of mental and physical expression.

Observe the altered definitions of manhood and womanhood taking shape not only in such experimental enclaves but throughout much of society. Within a single generation we have seen the virtually exclusive American male ideal of the tough (even brutal), tight-lipped, fist-ready, physically powerful, hard, anti-artistic, no-nonsense, highly competitive sexual conqueror give way to the gentle, open, noncombative, physically unimpressive, soft, aesthetic-minded, indirect and associative, noncompetitive, sexually casual self-explorer—with a variety of types in between. Similarly, the feminine ideal of the soft, compliant, self-sacrificing, family-oriented helpmate has given way to that of the aggressive, physically and psychically strong, self-expanding, liberation-oriented feminist. Much of the original hippie and Women's Liberation movements can be understood as explorations in broadened definitions of sex roles, so that one can be soft and tentative while still manly, hard and assertive while still womanly. This kind of experiment on the part of any of these groups must inevitably include excesses and absurdities. But in reaching for both the center and periphery of maleness and femaleness there is a groping toward fundamental alteration of the bio-social mode of immortality.

There is, in other words, a biological base to Protean experimentation. And the theme of community—of quest for bio-social continuity—becomes fundamental to all contemporary transformation. The struggle for "community control" is often a struggle for community formation. It is an effort to reassert authority over the most fundamental aspects of life, to combine autonomy with lasting human connection.

Protean efforts at transformation are very active in the theological—or, more accurately, religious or spiritual—mode, as is evident in experiments with both social-activist and experiential-meditative forms of Christianity and Judaism, as well as with Buddhist, Hindu, and other Eastern religions. One can also point to revived interest in various premodern religious-like rituals and superstitions—Eastern and Western astrological charts, the Chinese Book of Changes (*I Ching*), and tarot cards and other forms of fortune-telling.

Most commentary emphasizes the antirational nature of this embrace of seemingly primitive spirituality, which can indeed be present, especially for those who develop a preoccupation with charts and cards or feelings and vibes that excludes ideas, growth, and change. More characteristic, I believe, are the people who make forays in and out of these varied spiritual alternatives, as experiments in both knowing and feeling, in which one absorbs a fragment here, an image there, and maintains a sense of flow that is more consistent (more "stable") than the involvement with any one of them.

John S. Dunne, the distinguished Catholic theologian, posits as the new religion of our time "a phenomenon we might call 'passing over' . . . a going over to the standpoint of another culture, another way of life, another religion . . . followed by an equal and opposite process we might call 'coming back,' coming back with new insight to one's own culture, one's own way of life, one's own religion." The process, and the new religion itself, are epitomized not by Jesus or any other founder of a world religion but by Gandhi, who followed such a trajectory from Hinduism to Christianity (and even to some extent to Islam) and then back to Hinduism. But even Gandhi, in the very focus of his faith, has a certain nostalgic ring for us. Could it be that the holy man of our time has only just begun to invent himself, that he will not merely "pass over" and "come back" in that relatively orderly sequence but will do so in a sustained, repeated, perhaps even endless process, in which spiritual depth no longer depends upon exclusive doctrine of any kind and realization combines "the principle of permanence" with that of continuing open search?

Whatever form our next prophet may take, we can be certain that we will be witnessing great waves of religious feeling. For what we call religion directs itself, at least at its best, to precisely the kinds of altered relationships to death and the continuity of life that occur during any historical turning point. But lest contemporary priests misunderstand the stirrings within their churches and temples (and the much stronger religious expressions outside of them), this kind of renewed religious feeling presses not toward the stability of denominations and orders but toward their overthrow, not towards orderly worship within existing social arrangement but towards forms of worship—of celebration and immortalization—that subvert the numbing pseudoritual of "normal religion" in favor of newly immortalizing visions.

The third mode of symbolic immortality, that of immortality via man's works, has been a crucial area of social preoccupation. Involved here is the disorganized but powerful critique now under way of all major social institutions: those within which one learns, is governed, judged, or punished, and, above all, finds significance. In the fundamental questions now being raised about universities and schools, political and judicial arrangements, intellectual disciplines and professional practices, there is a common overriding theme: the quest for significant work experience, both in immediate involvement and in a sense of the work's contribution to the continuing human enterprise. For what we call work is a uniquely important boundary between self-process and social vision. Perhaps for the first time in history very large numbers of men and women are beginning to demand harmony and meaning at that boundary; to demand a reasonable equation between work and "works."

This fundamental relationship between work and symbolic immortality is typified in the passions of the "work commune" movement—the creation of small communities that permit poolings of professional, political, and psychobiological experiments. In these and such related groups as radical institutes and radical caucuses in all the professional disciplines, there is not only a powerful transformative element but a conservative one as well: a determination to confront and thereby preserve a particular social or intellectual tradition—rather than dismiss or ignore it—in a spirit critical both of the tradition itself and of its conventional applications.

This task of resymbolization, traditionally the mission of great innovators, has now become something close to a mass experience. Large numbers of people, in one way or another, move (in Daniel Berrigan's phrase), "toward the edge" of their profession or craft, not necessarily because they originally plan to but because their situation evokes altered relationships and judgements—involving the lost ethical and hypertrophied technical components of work and profession, the separation of work and life, and the nature of the society and culture in and for which one works. All this is part of a largely inchoate yet profound quest for newly immortalizing combinations of human influence. We may suspect that the structures and institutions that emerge will have to build into their own evolving tradition the expectation of the unexpected, the capacity to engender a stability in equilibrium with periodic transformation—which may, indeed, be the only form of true stability possible.

The natural mode of immortality has obvious relationship to ecological passions and to general fears about destruction of the environment, fears all too appropriate. But there is also a more positive impulse toward nature among many innovators as exemplified by the rural commune movement. Many have ridiculed this movement and have looked upon it as nothing more than a pathetic form of pastoral romanticism, a regression to a discredited myth that is particularly misdirected in our present urban-technological society. There is no doubt that many of these communal efforts *have* been romantically envisioned and poorly planned. Moreover there is pathos and error in the claim, occasionally made, that they are *the* answer to our urban-technological dilemmas. But what is often missed in these exchanges is the psychological significance of reclaiming a relationship to nature as part of a more general psychic renewal. When young Americans create a rural commune in New Mexico or New Hampshire, they approach nature with contemporary sensibilities. They seek to bring nature back into the human imagination. They embrace nature in an experiment with the self. The ramifications of that experiment may yet make their way into the most urban minds.

The final mode, that of experiential transcendence, differs from the others in being a psychic state per se. It includes various forms of ecstasy and rapture associated with the Dionysian principle of excess, and with the mystical sense of oneness with the universe Freud referred to as the "oceanic feeling." Mystics speak of a state of awareness where, totally unencumbered by any particular idea or image, one is able to perceive the entirety of the larger universe and of one's own being within it.

This is the "high" one can get from drugs or from various forms of intense encounter; the "trip"; the state of being "stoned." The terms are interesting. "High" implies elevation of psychic state in the direction of transcendence. "Trip" implies being in motion but something briefer and more temporary than, say, a "journey," and having the implicit suggestion of return. "Stoned" implies an absolute intensity (the smoothness, hardness, solidity, and finality of stone), in this case intensity of feeling, ecstasy—but also the numbness, insensitivity, or deadness of a stone (stone blind, stone deaf, stone dumb, stone cold, stone dead). The duality may be appropriate; one undergoes a "small death" (of more or less ordinary feeling) in order to open oneself up to a "new life" (to feeling on a different plane of intensity), to a sense of transcendence. One becomes impervious to the prosaic idea of mortality and feels oneself so exquisitely attuned to—indeed merged with—the universe as a whole that the issue of life versus death is no longer of consequence. Should the process fail, whether because of depending too much upon the technology of becoming "stoned" (the drugs themselves) or for other reasons, one is left in a state of perpetual numbing (stone dumb, stone cold, etc.).

In a wide variety of experiments—sexual, political, aesthetic—there is a powerful insistence upon making the quality of "awareness" or transcendence basic to the act. Indeed, there is a very real sense in which experiential transcendence is the key, the baseline, for the other four modes. That is, one requires some form of ecstasy and oneness—whether all-consuming or of a more gentle variety—in order to experience oneself as living on in one's children, works, spirituality, or relationship to nature. And that level of experience is also required for the inner psychological reordering necessary to individual transformation.

TRANSFORMATION AS RECREATION

Transformation is achieved only by touching a mythic or formative zone, very close to that Mircea Eliade speaks of as "the zone of the sacred, the zone of absolute reality." For the seeker, it is "the road to the self, the road to the 'center' of his being." The principle is one of *psychic action,* by which I mean the genuine inner contact leading to confrontation, reordering, and renewal. As Eliade expressed in reference to ancient rituals surrounding the new year, one experiences "the presence of the dead," the ceremonial depiction of "a 'death' and a 'resurrection,' a 'new birth,' a 'new man,' " and the overall principle that "life cannot be restored but only recreated." This, too, is the principle of genuine Protean transformation.

Consider just a few of the psychological difficulties of individual and social transformation. For those moving into adulthood, the newness and instability of the contemporary situations is such that there can be few "formative fathers" available for them to emulate. Those who do exist are likely to be approached with a tenuous ambivalence or equally tenuous romanticism.

Apart from models or leaders, there are very few existing social institutions within which fundamental transformations can be explored or developed. The result is a form of floating confusion that is in turn related to profound difficulties in connecting innovation with a sense of actuality. The innovator is thus likely to fluctuate between extreme self-doubt and a seemingly opposite but psychologically related self-righteous moralism that claims dominion over truth. Issues of betrayal and self-betrayal confront him at every point: his effort to innovate "betrays" his family and his past; his failure to take a particular leap or his tendency to remain associated with existing society "betrays" his new associates in innovation. More generally, he experiences what I have called the guilt of social breakdown, the self-condemnation of the man without anything to be loyal to.

Most of all the Protean experimenter must call forth dark areas of the psyche, demonic imagery of destruction and suffering as threatening to himself as to society. These "death sources" both reflect his dislocation and energize his renewal. While the ordinary person erects protective devices to avoid confronting them, the innovator moves toward them, sensing that his innovation depends upon them. And today that confrontation must take place within the precarious diversity of the Protean pattern. No wonder young innovators ask the question, as one did of me: "In order to make revolution do you have to destroy yourself?"

To grasp some of the complex relationship betweeen would-be innovators and their society, one must consider the theme of the "underground." One thinks of underground movements, especially in the political realm, as those relegated to a secret, invisible place by their very illegitimacy—by their unacceptability to those in control of society. For some groups such a definition undoubtedly still holds. But in broader present usage the theme of the underground may have greater importance as a psychic and social realm sought out by innovators in order to experiment with the work of transformation. Hence the word becomes almost interchangeable with "free" or "alternative"—and we have the underground church, the underground press, underground films, free or alternative schools, the free university, etc.

One should not be misled by the short life of most underground institutions or their confused and precarious relationship to, and frequent absorption by, the "overground" of proper society. We will continue to need underground themes in our society—imagery of a subterranean realm of both exquisite mysteries and terrible demons—a realm signifying the unconscious mind in Freud's sense and a land of death and continuous life in the paradigm I am suggesting. However often our social critics announce the death of the avant-garde, the counterculture, or the underground, we can expect continuous psychic experimentation in that realm, with individuals and groups periodically emerging from it renewed by insight and vision with which to confront the formative zone of the larger society.

The ultimate task of transformation is the recreation of the adult self. In significant degree, an adult is one who has ceased to play and begun to work. Of course adults play too, but their play tends to be in the service of maintaining the social order, as opposed to the spontaneous subversiveness of the play of children. Adult work is the work of culture: everyday tasks are conducted under the guiding principles of the culture's assumptions about transcendence and are subservient to the prevailing modes of immortality. Each steel girder installed, each mile driven in a taxi, each product order typed and approved contributes to a culture's collective effort to cope with individual mortality through lasting enterprises, structures, and sequences. Adult work is always tied in with a larger spiritual principle—whether that principle is the Protestant ethic, the deification of capital, or the revolutionary vision. Indeed, one way of defining adulthood is as a state of maximum absorption in everyday tasks subsumed to transcendent cultural principles, permitting minimal awareness of the threat of individual death. This is in contrast to both old age and youth: in old age one is impinged upon by the imminence of death and becomes preoccupied with immediate evidence of continuity and integrity, while in youth one requires more intense and direct modes of transcendence rather than the more indirect workaday kind.

Therefore when many of the young are accused of refusing to grow up and become adults, there is a sense in which the accusation is true—and, indeed, must be true for innovators during any period of radical dislocation and change. What they reject is the existing version of adult existence—their sense of adulthood as a locked-in, desensitized state; one of unquestioned assumptions about work and productivity, family and other human relationships; and of fuzzy, nonviable, half-religious images about death, life, and "ultimate meaning."

Contemporary innovators are clear about their quest for a form of adulthood with more play in it. Play and playfulness are central—for the kind of adulthood sought, and for the process of change itself on the way to that state. Great innovators have always been able to play and, in many cases, have come to their innovations via elaborate and disciplined forms of play. While this play is in some ways more characteristic of the child than of the average adult, it is nonetheless the play of adults, playfulness seasoned by form and accessible to insight. The innovator has always lived in exquisite equilibrium between his refusal to be an adult as ordinarily defined and his burdensome assumption of responsibility for a large segment of adult action and imagination. We sense now a demand that all, whatever their innovative talents, share in this playfulness and Proteanism until "adulthood" either disappears entirely or is renewed and transformed.

Ultimately, genuine transformation requires that we "experience" our annihilation in order to prevent it, that we confront and conceptualize both our immediate crises and our long-range possibilities for renewal. Joseph Campbell reminds us: ". . . the idea of death and rebirth . . . is an extremely ancient one in the history of culture," frequently in the form of a "shock treatment for no longer wanted personality structure." In our present Protean environment the principle still holds: *every significant step in human existence involves some inner sense of death.* As Francis Huxley puts the matter, "Where there is anxiety—as there is in every human culture—the imagination is called upon to destroy it by an act of reconstruction." Destruction and reconstruction—death and rebirth in the quest for immortalizing connectedness—is at the center of man's creation of culture. From this process alone can the urgently needed transformation of our own culture ensue. Heinrich Boll tells us that "an artist always carries death within him like a good priest his breviary." The priest, the artist, the human being within us require that we do no less.

Questions

1. Define each of the following terms used in this chapter. Terms marked with an asterisk are concepts the authors expect the reader to know already. If you are not familiar with them, consult a dictionary.

    *traumatic experience
    *syndrome
     normal grief reaction
        (grief syndrome)
    *psychoneurotic
     grief work
    *identification
    *conversion symptom
     anticipatory grief
    *culture
    *norm
    *value
    *status position
    *social role
    *socialization
     constitutive symbolism

    *ambivalence
    *family of orientation, of
        procreation
    *taboo
     role requirement
     wake
     committal service
     eulogy
     embalming
     psychoanalytic school
    *the unconscious
    *object-relations
    *incomplete mourning
    *kinship system
     Protean man
     symbolic immortality

2. a. When Lynn Caine found herself a new widow, she quickly became aware of a new role expectation. She was determined to be the "ideal American widow," full of courage and restraint. Outline the characteristics of the admired American widow. How does the role expectation differ for a widower?

    b. Volkhart and Michael describe how the cultural role expectation can be at odds with the experience of the mourner and result in pathology. In what ways does the American stereotype provide support for the widow? In what ways does it block expression of her needs?

3. Lindemann lists identification as a part of normal grief that in its extreme forms may indicate pathology. Compile a list of different kinds of behavior that might be considered identification, beginning with the examples given by Lindemann and Albert Cain.

4. Lindemann and Cain describe in detail how the mourning process can fail to resolve loss. What different forms can "pathological grief" take? What kinds of behavior might indicate to you that a bereaved person was reacting in a psychologically unhealthy manner? What factors would you need to take into account in making your determination?

5. a. As expected death after a long illness becomes more frequent in our country, family and friends are more likely to begin an antici-patory grief reaction before death occurs. Recalling the discus-sions of Kübler-Ross and Lindemann, outline the benefits and the dangers involved in beginning to mourn while the terminally ill patient is still alive.

   b. Under these circumstances, the needs of the mourner would no longer be met by the social role demands of the bereaved as we know them. Contrast the kinds of role behavior that would be appropriate following sudden unexpected death with those follow-ing a long terminal illness. How might the funeral rites be changed to reflect these differences in needs?

6. In discussing funeral practices, Bowman and Masamba and Kalish make several generalizations. Examine their articles closely to identify some of those generalizations and suggest in each case a procedure by which you could test the validity of their generalizations.

7. It has become a cliché to criticize American funeral practices for deny-ing death. More importantly, they have been criticized for depriving the mourner of his grief. Consider the variety of responses described by Bowman. In what ways do they represent denial of grief? Does the funeral, as you know it, promote healthy grieving? Suggest three specific changes that could be made in the funeral so that it would meet the psychological needs of mourners more effectively.

8. a. Sigmund Freud argues that it is impossible to imagine one's own death. How does he reach this conclusion? Do you agree? What evidence would you offer for your view?

   b. Freud discusses the role of drama and literature in man's attempt to reconcile himself with death. What is this role? Do you agree with Freud's interpretation? Why or why not?

9. Consider the war novel as a literary subgenre. Using war novels you

know, identify attitudes toward death that are expressed directly or indirectly. What examples of guilt do you find when characters confront the death of another?

10. Bereavement after suicide is considered an especially high-risk grief period. What special supports do the survivors of suicide need? How could you provide for their particular reactions?

11. a. "Daddy" is a mourning poem; cite lines in the poem that exemplify anger and guilt.

    b. *Holocaust* is a term now used to refer to the persecution of Jews in the concentration camps of Germany during World War II. Consider the use of holocaust imagery in "Daddy." What is its effect in setting the tone of the poem? What analogy is suggested between the holocaust and bereavement in general?

12. Lifton explains that every step in life involves an inner sense of death. Many rituals celebrate the beginning of a new life and the "death" of a former existence. How is the death–life progression evident in the following: baptism, bar mitzvah, graduation, marriage, divorce, the birth of a child, a job promotion?

Projects for Further Study

1. Lynn Caine poignantly portrays the feelings of helplessness of the widowed, whose needs are too often overlooked. Investigate the "Widow to Widow" program described by Phyllis Silverman in *Helping Each Other in Widowhood.* Information on a similar program, "Journey's End," is available from the Ethel Percey Andrus Gerontology Center, University of Southern California. What supports are offered in your community? What specific services would be helpful to the widowed? Try to interview three widows (perhaps through a church group) on their experience of bereavement in order to generate a specific list of problems and needs.

2. a. Although the funeral is one of our most conservative rituals, it is subject to change, as is any social institution. Interview some older relatives on funeral customs they recall from their youth. How have funeral customs changed over the last fifty years? Have attitudes towards funeral customs also changed? Why?

   b. Not only the social customs but the ritual itself also changes. Study the new funeral liturgies both in the church and in the secular funeral. For example, the funeral industry is developing the "Life Centered" funeral; ideas for personalized services are suggested in Ernest Morgan's *A Manual of Death Education and Simple Burial.* Compare and contrast the orientation, the symbols, and the styles of the newer liturgies with the more traditional.

3. Writers such as Jessica Mitford, in *The American Way of Death,* and Ruth Mulvey Harmer, in *The High Cost of Dying,* cite examples of financial abuses in the funeral industry. To protect the "consumer" from unnecessary expenses, they advocate the development of nonprofit memorial societies. Visit a funeral home to investigate the typical

217

funeral costs in your area. If there is also a memorial society in the area, compare the services offered by each and their costs. The following resources may be useful in gathering information.

"The Price of Death: A Survey Method and Consumer Guide for Funerals, Cemeteries and Grave Markers" contains a suggested procedure for conducting a survey of prices and services, including questionnaire forms with instructions for their use. This consumer handbook is available from the U.S. Government Consumer Information Center, Pueblo, Colorado, 81009.

Information in various forms about traditional funerals is available from the National Funeral Director's Association, 135 W. Wells Street, N.W., Washington, D.C., 20036.

Information about memorial societies is available from the Continental Association of Funeral and Memorial Societies, Inc., 1828 L Street, N.W., Washington, D.C., 20036.

4. a. Social immortality is one of the most common forms of symbolic immortality. Identify as many examples as you can during a one-week period. (Consider physical memorials, dedications, memorial events, donations, endowed programs, etc.) Discuss the degree to which social immortality is valued in our society.

   b. In the nineteenth century the word *cemetery* began to replace the traditional generic terms, *graveyard* or *burial ground;* a shift which reflected the fact that the cemetery had become a cultural institution. Visit a local cemetery to see how death is presented: identify as many different representations of death as you can, both individual symbols (e.g., ornaments and headstones) and the symbolism of the place itself (e.g., the setting and the architectural styles). Where you find inscriptions on the headstones, collect representative examples of different styles of epitaphs. What different themes do you find? What information is typically given about the deceased? Besides serving as a disposition site for bodies, what other social, religious, or personal functions does a cemetery serve?

Structured Exercises

Before beginning these exercises, please read "Note to the Instructor" on page xiii.

1. This exercise is designed to synthesize the information about funeral customs provided by the readings in Chapter Three. The exercise can be modified either to allow further investigation of the function of funerals or to put the student in a position to experience his own feelings about funerals.

   a. Imagine that you have died with everything in your life as it is right now. Design a personalized funeral or memorial service for yourself. Describe in detail the arrangements you would like: the time the service would be held; the kind of gathering it would be; the setting where it would be held; who would be there; what would occur during different parts of the gathering; whether there would be music and flowers, and if so, what kind; and so on. Even if you want a traditional religious funeral, describe the details; there are still many options such as choice of hymns or prayers which personalize such a service.

      This exercise could be written up before class discussion, or it could be done in class as a visualization exercise once the class is familiar with what goes on at a funeral. In class discussion, try to compare and contrast the themes that emerge from the different descriptions as well as focusing on the personal feelings of loss.

   b. The eulogy is the traditional funeral oration which reviews the life of the deceased and represents a formal farewell from the community. Assume that everything in your life is as it is right now and write your own eulogy. How would you sum up your life at this point?

      In order to share the experience with the class, you could form small groups to read the completed euologies, either by passing them around to be read silently, or by reading them aloud to the group. A second alternative for sharing the eulogies would be to have each person take turns at lying on a table, eyes closed, imagining a funeral setting in as much detail he wishes appropriate, while his eulogy is read aloud. After all the eulogies have been read, discuss your reactions both to composing the eulogy and then to hearing it read. What has the process told you about yourself and your goals?

c. The epitaph is the brief statement placed on a memorial marker. What would yours be? Explain your choice to the class. Do they agree with its appropriateness for you?

2. To enable the student to explore his or her personal reactions to loss have each student respond to the following exercises. Picture the most important person in your life. Suppose he or she were to die tomorrow. Take ten minutes to decide on responses to the following questions. Use a worksheet to make notes if you wish.

a. What would you miss most about that person?

b. What one thing do you wish you had had a chance to tell that person?

c. What one thing do you wish you could have heard from that person?

d. What one thing would you have wanted to change in the relationship?

e. What was the happiest moment you recall sharing with that person?

f. What was the most painful moment, before now, the two of you shared?

g. What circumstances (time, place, event) do you expect to bring the most painful memories?

When everyone has completed the questions, you may share the responses either as a class or in smaller groups. During this part of the exercise, you may discuss your reactions to actually doing the exercise, how you selected the person you chose, and what you learned from the experience.

For Further Reading

The following books and paper provide in-depth coverage of the topics introduced in this chapter.

Bowlby, J. *Loss: Sadness and Depression.* New York: Basic Books, 1980.

Freud, S. Mourning and Melancholia. In *The Complete Psychological Works,* ed. J. Stachey, Vol. 14. London: Hogarth, 1966.

Goody, J. *Death, Property and the Ancestors.* Palo Alto, Ca.: Stanford University Press, 1962.

Gorer, G. *Death, Grief, and Mourning.* Garden City, N.Y.: Doubleday, 1965.

Grollman, E.A., ed. *Concerning Death: A Practical Guide for the Living.* Boston: Beacon Press, 1974.

Habenstein, R.W. and Lamers, W.M. *Funeral Customs the World Over.* Milwaukee: National Funeral Directors Association, 1960.

Krystal, H., ed. *Massive Psychic Trauma.* New York: International Universities Press, 1969.

Lamm, M. *The Jewish Way of Death and Mourning.* New York: Jonathan-David, 1972.

Lifton, R.J. *History and Human Survival.* New York: Random House, 1970.

Lopata, H.Z. *Women as Widows: Support Systems.* New York: Elsevier North-Holland, 1979.

Lynch, J.L. *The Broken Heart: The Medical Consequences of Loneliness.* New York: Basic Books, 1977.

Morgan, E. *A Manual of Death Education and Simple Burial,* rev. 9th edition. Burnsville, N.C.: The Celo Press, 1980.

Parkes, C.M. *Bereavement: Studies of Grief in Adult Life.* New York: International Universities Press, 1972.

Pincus, L. *Death and the Family.* New York: Pantheon, 1975.

Schoenberg, B., Carr, A., Peretz, D., and Kutscher, A., eds. *Loss and Grief: Psychological Management in Medical Practice.* New York: Columbia University Press, 1970.

Silverman, P., Mackenzie, D., Pettipas, M., and Wilson, E. *Helping Each Other in Widowhood.* New York: Health Sciences Publishing, 1975.

Stannard, D.E., ed. *Death in America.* Philadelphia: University of Pennsylvania Press, 1975.

Chapter Four

Death and the Child

As recently as the sixteenth century, Montaigne could write to a friend in terms that surprise the modern reader: "I have lost two or three children in infancy," he explained, "not without regret, but without great sorrow." With the probability that several children born to any one family would die before reaching the age of majority, it was argued, families could not allow themselves to become too attached to children whose hold on life was still fragile.

In twentieth-century America, decreased infant mortality, control of childhood diseases, and vastly improved health conditions have rendered the death of a child a rare tragedy: at once a senseless waste, an affront to pride in medical progress, and a haunting intimation of mortality. The child is not only regarded as a person from the moment of birth (or conception as is often evidenced in arguments against abortion), he is often seen as the center of the family unit, the natural recipient of extensive care, and the tangible representation of the hopes of those around him. There is considerable variety in contemporary styles of child rearing, but, common to most, is the dedication of adults to protect their children from all that is harmful. And, as one might have predicted from studies of adult attitudes, the discussion of death has most often been considered as something harmful, something to protect children from. Indeed the taboo against the discussion of death with children has been so effective that Simon Yudkin, a physician, has observed that children today know more about their origin than their end.

225

More than parental tenderness, however, restrains the discussion of death with children and makes even less likely the discussion of the child's own death. Such a discussion poses a threat to one's own hold on life. Faced with the death of a parent or a friend, a person recognizes the possibility of his own death, but when confronted with the death of a child (someone who has shared fewer years), the arbitrary power of death becomes unavoidable. The person is forced to concede not only that he *will die at some time,* but that *he might die at any time.*

CURRENT RESEARCH

Thus, it comes as no surprise that widespread study of children and death followed well after studies of the dying adult were conducted. Recent work on the subject of children and death has taken three forms: research in the social sciences directed to an understanding of children's conceptions of death and their mourning reactions, medical studies oriented to advancements in treatment for terminally ill children, and popular children's literature and films which have been designed to bring their presentations of death to children into line with the best available research.

RESEARCH IN THE SOCIAL SCIENCES

As developmental psychology has moved from a normative to a structural approach, beginning with renewed interest in the work of Jean Piaget, considerable research into the child's formation of the concepts of *life* and *death* has followed. Sylvia Anthony, observing school-age children's play and fantasy, found death a common theme and the child's discovery of death to be simply an incident in the normal day-to-day process by which a child explores his environment. Maria Nagy, working in Hungary, traced a developmental sequence in children's theories concerning the nature of death. Nagy found that the child who at the age of four might pour water on a dead animal to "make it alive," grows into the six-year-old, telling tales of the boogeyman, and then becomes the nine-year-old, at once forced to accept the inevitability of death and ready to mock it with jokes and gestures.

But to say that the child's discovery of death in the abstract is more exploratory than emotional is not to suggest that children feel little emotional response to particular deaths. On the contrary, when a child loses a significant person in his life, warns child psychiatrist Benjamin Shambaugh, "every defense will be mobilized to ward off the impact and . . . every new object relationship as it develops will be influenced by the fact that an earlier one was lost." Agreement on the child's capacity to mourn, however, is not unanimous. According to Martha Wolfenstein, the young child, though he may be aware of death, is not developmentally ready to begin the work of mourning. She suggests that adolescence, a period when the individual comes to see time as irreversible and when he gives up a major love object, his parents, is a trial mourning period and a necessary precondition to actual mourning. John Bowlby, however, suggests that mourning can be divided into three phases—protest, despair, and detachment—and that it may occur, at least in its first phase, as early as six months of age. The research into the child's understanding of death and capacity to mourn has been joined recently by a growing number of observations of the dying child and his family in the hospital environment.

THE DYING CHILD

The care of the dying child, or adolescent, presents a doctor with one of his most difficult tasks. Yet, as recently as 1968, William Easson, a child psychologist, noted that in most cases "the physician or physician-to-be was given little understanding of the management of the dying child." Though new research on the dying child is still scant, beginning in 1960, a small number of psychiatrists and pediatricians began documenting the dying child's awareness of impending death. In addition, they recognized that the child's awareness of his death was often accompanied by withdrawal and denial of the diagnosis on the part of both parents and hospital staff. Currently, research into the support systems needed by the dying child and his family has burgeoned, resulting in a text on the subject and a hefty, internationally edited volume in child psychiatry.

LITERATURE AND FILM

The past quarter century, which has been so productive in studies of child development, has been equally abundant in children's literature. At one time the subject of death was presented primarily to motivate children through fear to good behavior. Later it was avoided altogether.

> A little child
> That lightly draws its breath
> And feels its life in every limb
> What should it know of death?
>
> *Wordsworth*

It has more recently been presented in a realistic manner which acknowledges the child's understanding of death and often reflects the complexities of his reactions toward it.

Some works such as *Charlotte's Web* portray death as a necessary part of the cycle of nature; others like *Annie and the Old One and My Grandpa Died Today* present death within the family unit. A smaller number present the death of a child, for example, *A Taste of Blackberries, The Brothers Lionheart* and *Sadako and the Thousand Paper Cranes.* Interest in the presentation of death to children has not been confined to books, for both film and television portrayals have appeared in the past few years. So great has been the activity in this field, in fact, that the danger of exploitation of emotion, always present in marketing for children and equally likely in presentations of death for any audience, lurks dangerously close. To identify those works that will be most conducive to understanding, we must seek enduring simplicity, those books which Paul Hazards notes will "distill from all kinds of knowledge, the most difficult and the most necessary—that of the human heart."

OVERVIEW OF THE CHAPTER

The readings in Chapter Four examine the child's growing understanding of death as a concept and as a personal reality, adult reaction to the death of a child, and, finally, the dying child's reaction to his own situation.

To ground the discussion, Maria Nagy, in "The Child's Theories Concerning Death," reports on her early study which identified sequential stages in the development of the child's understanding of death. The brief selection which follows, from James Agee's Pulitzer Prize-winning novel, *A Death in the Family,* presents an interesting counterpoint to Nagy's theoretical study. In Agee's novel, two children of different ages reveal their own assumptions about death as they try to make sense of the explanations they have been given about their father's death.

A somewhat different explanation of death is found in the selection from Joan Fassler's *My Grandpa Died Today,* which provides an example of a growing emphasis within children's literature on themes of aging, separation, and death. These themes are handled by Fassler with honesty and simplicity.

The growing interest in death education for children is discussed by Irving and Blu Greenberg, the former a rabbi and professor, the latter a lecturer and writer. In "Telling Your Children about the Holocaust," they outline the program they followed to make their own children knowledgeable and continually conscious of the fact of the Holocaust. In a very specific sense, the article raises the more general value-laden question of the amount and timing of the transmission of death-related knowledge to children.

The two final readings in the chapter approach that most threatening topic, the death of a child: the first, "Childhood Leukemia: Emotional Impact on Patient and Family," assesses the impact of a child's death on others; the second, "Children's Awareness of Fatal Illness," analyzes the extent to which a dying child is likely to realize his condition. The former paper is a collaborative effort by a research team composed of four pediatric hematologists, a child psychiatrist, and a social worker; the latter paper is the work of Eugenia Waechter, a professor of nursing.

In sum, the readings present a variety of relationships between children and death; to begin, however, the reader is offered five reactions of children to their first encounter with death.

Encounter

THE FIRST TIME SOMEBODY
YOU KNEW DIED

The statements below are the recollections (reproduced as written) of elementary school children asked to write about the first time somebody they knew died.

"I remember when I was five years old my uncle died. Then a lot of people came to the funeral and there was many flowers inside the box and outside too. I got to tuch him and he was very cold then my mother told me why he was that cold. He was cold because some people take out al there things from inside. I went to tell someone els and he told me the same thing. And know I had believed her. Everybody was cring that my tears came out. Sins that time I did not want to go to a funeral ever again."

"When my granmather died I died too."

"My father went to Vietnam and he was Berly to go in the jungle and he step om pungy stikes and I was very sad sow they gave me all of his guns begde boots and his very owm money everybody loved him in the force so my mother crying and she told me that I was the man for the house."

"My Great grand father died when he was having a heart attack. My Great Grand mother was very sad and had to marry again."

230

Source: Contributed by children at St. Toribius, Annunciation, St. Emydius Schools in Los Angeles, California.

"After a person is buride He will always be with you. And if you will not belief me ask your parents."

Thinking back on your own childhood, when was the first time you encountered the death of somebody close to you? Picture the time, recalling who died. Was it a person or a pet? How old were you at the time? What did you think was the cause of death? Did that death make you worry about your own health or safety?

MARIA NAGY

The Child's Theories
Concerning Death

The selections on the preceding page were written by children between the ages of nine and twelve, the time when children begin to understand death as an irreversible and inevitable occurrence. The children's responses are typical in their simple realism, their puzzled efforts to understand what death means, and their ultimate reliance on parental authority.

Maria Nagy conducted a field study of 378 children in Budapest to investigate the theories of death that children construct. Nagy, a structuralist in the tradition of Piaget, hypothesized that children's theories about the nature of death would reflect changing states of development as the children matured. In her study, she found that very young children do understand it to mean something very different from the concepts of the older child or adult. The ages Nagy assigns should not be taken as norms; rate of development depends, in part, on the experience provided by the environment.

INTRODUCTION

The Problem and Its History

Death is immemorial man's eternal problem. Life, the other great problem, gains its significance and its value only through death. Life and death are not two extremes, irreconcilable opposites which the human mind joins artificially into one formula. The relation between life and death is organic, for man as individual behaves in a quite identical way, that is, according to his nature, toward these two apparently contradictory facts. He who does not know how to live is also not capable of dying. And he who fears death is really terrified of life.

Source: Maria Nagy, "The Child's Theories Concerning Death," *Journal of Genetic Psychology,* LXXIII (1948), 3-27 (Vol. 73).

Every work on folk psychology which aims at being complete deals with not only the people's attitude toward life, but also its conception of death, as one is not to be understood without the other. Psychopathology is therefore concerned with the abnormal preoccupations with death, for only by abolishing these can a healthy behavior in life be attained. Psychologists, working with the age of adolescence, fundamentally examine everything which turns the adolescent attention toward death, for just those apparently inhibiting factors indicate the resolution of new life vigors.

Child psychology in the last half century has carried out research in every phase of the child's life, but cognizance of the child's conception of death is still isolated. Yet it is quite certain that the child connects life and death, indeed it is just in childhood that the individual develops his behavior in respect to death.

If we wish to investigate experimentally the child's attitude toward death, the theme must necessarily be divided into detailed questions. Among the questions connected with death, in the present study I wish to deal with only one. *What does the child think death to be, what theory does he construct of the nature of death?*

According to Reik's observations, the child thinks of death as temporary and gradual. Chadwick analyzes more the child's feelings in relation to death, not the understanding rendered by a definition of death. Graber found that to the child death and sleep were the same, so death is not known for what it is. Gerard carried out observations on three children. He also stated that death's finality was unknown to them. According to Stern, at the age of 10 death is not understood realistically; either they believe in physical survival, or in the Great Reaper. Wechsler and Schilder's experiments show that death is considered as a violent phenomenon. Cousinet investigates the idea of death genetically and distinguishes three stages. In the first stage the child denies death; in the second the truth is taken into account, he considers the process as similar to illness. Finally, in the third stage, it becomes quite concrete, the child considers it a peculiar process taking place in the living. It is unfortunate that these three stages were not indicated according to age and that he does not show their frequency. Finally, Weber deals with the recognition of the signs of death and finds that the child considers death a destroying-force which cuts him off from life and his family. In the literature of psychoanalysis there are many references to the child's attitude toward death, as it seeks the origin of all forms of behavior in childhood, hence the attitude toward death also. According to one of Freud's instinct-groupings which distinguishes the instinct of life and that of death, they are disposed to explain every manifestation of a person's life through its fundamental relationship to life and death. But his hypotheses tend rather toward the instinctive factors, they do not investigate the theories concerning the nature of death.

From the above it appears that further examination of the child's attitude toward death is necessary, as previous authors, with the exception of Cousinet, do not give the course of development and deal principally with feelings in connection with death. I, however, *wish to investigate, from the genetic standpoint, the theories concerning the nature of death of children from three to ten years of age.*

METHOD AND MATERIAL

The material was assembled in three ways: (1) written compositions, (2) drawings, (3) discussions.

①. *Compositions* were written by children from seven to ten. I go into the class with the teacher. "Do you know why I have come, children? I know that you can write very nice compositions. I am curious about them. It will be a little strange, but certainly you will do it very cleverly. *Write down everything that comes into your minds about death.*" (I repeat slowly, twice.) It is not allowed to ask questions. Work time, one hour. The eventual questions and general attitudes are noted.

2. In one of the schools, after the compositions were finished, the children began of their own accord to make drawings about death. This gave the idea of having separate drawings. The six to ten year olds did this in the same school. I announce that there will be secret drawing. "Who can cleverly separate himself from the others, so that no one can see what he is doing?" In an instant they surround themselves with their satchels, with their blocks. It is not necessary to give special instructions, they themselves discover how to sketch death. The bigger ones wrote an explanation of the text (see drawing that follows).

THE FIRST DEATH

1. *The death-man.* "Smokes a pipe in his joy. He is happy if he has work, work received from the good God."

2. *The sun.* It is so black because "the sun is also in great mourning. In nice weather it looks on the world and sees what happens. In bad weather the good God tells him." The child also personifies the sun. The world is for people. The duty of the sun is to follow people with its attention. Cosmic factors also take part in human suffering.

3. *Weeping willow.* "It is sad because it is beside a grave, that is why it keeps its branches lowered. Since the first man died it has always been sad." The ideas are explained by the same factor as in the case of the sun.

4. *Eva.* Weeps for the dead. In her handkerchief is the little girl's monogram.

5. *Guardian-angel.*

6. *Mourning angel.* Not only man and nature but also supernatural beings take part in the mourning.

3. The discussions were made with two somewhat varying methods with three to six and seven to ten year olds. I began with the ten year olds and descended gradually, in order to accustom myself to their way of speaking, among the smaller ones. With the seven to ten year olds I talked separately, one by one, in a quiet place. I hide my writing behind some object so that they do not see that I take notes of what they say. As introduction I merely say, "You wrote a very clever composition, that is why I called you here. It will be easier now than last time, because you needn't write, only talk. *Tell me all you can think of about death.*" If they were perplexed I encouraged them: "Just think, surely lots of interesting things will come to mind." I let them speak freely. If they said anything I had them explain it. With that I always take care that my questions are indefinite, that is to say, suggest nothing. I emphasize, it was not an interrogation, but the child's spontaneous expression artificially brought out. The aim of the questions posed was just, in fact, that I should know the exact meaning of the child's expressions and not give them an arbitrary interpretation.

When the child runs out of something to say I ask questions. The questions were assembled and composed on the basis of the compositions. The range of questions was as follows: (a) What is death? (b) Why do people die? (c) How can one recognize death? (d) Do you usually dream? Tell me about a dream about death! Naturally only those of the questions were put concerning which free discussion had not dealt.

Then I discuss with them the doubtful points in the composition and drawings if I have so far not got an answer about them. Finally I ask them, if any thing more has come to mind, to tell it.

With the three to six year olds the situation was more difficult as I had no composition on which to base the discussion. As at that age there is still no concentrated thinking, instead of direct announcement of the object I was obliged to choose an indirect route. And first of all I try to create some contact with the child. I ask him to tell me something, and perhaps I will tell him a story.

Then when I see the moment has arrived, I ask him to tell me about the *table*. If he understood the instructions he must then tell about the following words: *death, life, birth, brother.* Naturally I linger longest on the word death and try to get it discussed the most. When necessary I ask questions. My questions are the same as for the bigger children, only differently drawn up.[1]

The distribution of the experimental material is shown in Table 1.

Table 1

Age	3	4	5	6	7	8	9	10	Total
	Distribution of material according to age								
Composition	—	—	—	—	63	81	93	57	294
Drawing	—	—	—	8	9	9	12	2	40
Discussion	7	13	16	26	32	23	29	5	151
Total	7	13	16	34	104	113	134	64	484

Table 2 (*N* gives the frequency in absolute values)

Age										
	What is death? (Composition)									
	7		8		9		10		Total	
	N	%	N	%	N	%	N	%	N	%
2nd stage	12	92.3	21	91.3	27	71.0	4	16.7	65	65.3
3rd stage	1	7.7	2	8.7	11	29.0	20	83.3	34	34.7
Total	13	100.0	23	100.0	38	100.0	24	100.0	98	100.0

Thus we have a total of 484 protocols from 378 children, 51 percent of the children were boys, 49 percent girls. They are selected from different religions, different schools and social levels. The material was collected in Budapest and its environs.

RESULTS[2]

What is death? Among the children from three to ten the replies given to this question can be ranged in three groups. As the different sorts of answers can be found only at certain ages, one can speak of stages of development. The child of less than five years does not recognize death as an irreversible fact. In death it sees life. Between the ages of five and nine death is most often personified and thought of as a contingency. And in general only after the age of nine is it recognized that death is a process happening in us according to certain laws. The frequency of the three degrees in the different age limits is illustrated in Table 2 and Table 3.

First Stage: There Is No Definitive Death

In the first stage the child does not know death as such. He attributes life and consciousness to the dead. There are two variations of this affirmation, which I discuss the one after the other. According to one group, death is a departure, a sleep. This entirely denies death. The other group already recognizes the fact of death but cannot separate it from life. For that reason it considers death either gradual or temporary.

A. Death a departure, a sleep. *B. Jolan* (3, 11):[3] "The dead close their eyes because the sand gets into them."

The child had heard something about the eyes of the dead being closed. It explained this by an exterior cause. The dead person voluntarily, defensively, closes its eyes.

Table 3

What is death? (Discussion)

Age	3 N	3 %	4 N	4 %	5 N	5 %	6 N	6 %	7 N	7 %	8 N	8 %	9 N	9 %	10 N	10 %	Total N	Total %
1st stage	6	85.7	7	50.0	6	33.3	2	7.8	—	—	—	—	—	—	—	—	21	12.9
2nd stage	1	14.3	7	50.0	12	66.7	21	80.7	19	57.6	14	53.8	16	53.3	2	22.8	92	56.4
3rd stage	—	—	—	—	—	—	3	11.5	14	42.4	12	46.2	14	46.7	7	77.8	50	30.7
Total	7	100.0	14	100.0	18	100.0	26	100.0	33	100.0	26	100.0	30	100.0	9	100.0	163	100.0

Sch. Tomy (4, 8): "It can't move because it's in the coffin."

"If it weren't in the coffin, could it?"

"It can eat and drink."

Like the first with the closing of the eyes, here too the immobility is the consequence of exterior compulsive circumstances. It doesn't move because the coffin does not permit it. He considers the dead as still capable of taking nourishment.

Sch. Juliska (5, 10) had already seen a dead person. "Its eyes were closed, it lay there, so dead. No matter what one does to it, it doesn't say a word."

"After ten years will it be the same as when it was buried?"

"It will be older then, it will always be older and older. When it is 100 years old it will be exactly like a piece of wood."

"How will it be like a piece of wood?"

"That I couldn't say. My little sister will be five years old now. I wasn't alive yet when she died. She will be so big by this time. She has a small coffin, but she fits in the small coffin."

"What is she doing now, do you think?"

"Lying down, always just lies there. She's still so small, she can't be like a piece of wood. Only very old people."

In the beginning she sees the matter realistically. The dead person cannot speak. The closed eyes do not necessarily mean the cessation of sight. The dead person is compared to a piece of wood. In all probability she wanted thus to express immobility. Later it comes out that young people grow in the grave. The growth is not great. She says her sister is five years old because she herself is five.

B. Irén (4, 11): "What happens there under the earth?"

"He cries because he is dead."

"But why should he cry?"

"Because he is afraid for himself."

She feels that death is bad. Perhaps she has had the experience of seeing the dead mourned. She transfers this sentiment to the dead themselves. They also mourn for themselves.

V. Juliska (5, 3): "What is your father doing now under the earth?"

"He lies there. Scratches the earth, to come up. To get a little air."

She knows of the reclining state of the dead. She imagines that in the earth it must be difficult to breathe. The dead person scratches the earth away, to get air.

T. Pintvöke (4, 10): "A dead person is just as if he were asleep. Sleeps in the ground, too."

"Sleeps the same as you do at night, or otherwise?"

"Well—closes his eyes. Sleeps like people at night. Sleeps like that, just like that."

"How do you know whether someone is asleep or is dead?"

"I know if they go to bed at night and don't open their eyes. If somebody goes to bed and doesn't get up, he's dead or ill."

"Will he ever wake up?"

"Never. A dead person only knows if somebody goes out to the grave or something. He feels that somebody is there, or is talking."

"Are you certain? You're not mistaken?"

"I don't think so. At funerals you're not allowed to sing, just talk, because otherwise the dead person couldn't sleep peacefully. A dead person feels it if you put something on his grave."

"What is it he feels then?"

"He feels that flowers are put on his grave. The water touches the sand. Slowly, slowly, he hears everything. Auntie, does the dead person feel if it goes deep into the ground?" (i.e. the water.)

"What do you think, wouldn't he like to come away from there?"

"He would like to come out, but the coffin is nailed down."

"If he weren't in the coffin, could he come back?"

"He couldn't root up all that sand."

Death is on the one hand identified with sleep, on the other hand is supposed to be in connection with the outside world. The dead person has knowledge of what goes on in the world. It does not merely think, but also feels.

B. Evi (6, 5): "Between sleeping and death there isn't any difference."

She identifies sleep and death.

J. Mancika (3, 11): "What does he do, since he is in the coffin?"

"Sleeps. Covered with sand. It's dark there."

"Does he sleep as we do at night, or differently?"

"He puts sand there, lies on it. If you die the bed will be sandy, then the sheet will be black."

The dead person lives, as he himself prepares the sleeping place. The grave is a bed, the dead person also has sheets. Death is sleep.

H. Gàspàr (8, 5):[4] "People think dead persons can feel."

"And can't they?"

"No, they can't feel, like sleep. Now, I sleep, I don't feel it, except when I dream."

"Do we dream when we're dead?"

"I think we don't. We never dream when we're dead. Sometimes something flashes out, but not half as long as a dream."

"What flashes out?"

"Some little kind of thought, some little kind of dream. Pictures disappear in front of him. But they're so short, much less than when we're asleep."

This child has at times a quite realistic conception of death. He states definitely that the dead do not feel nor think. Later, however, he thinks that thoughts and pictures flash out before the dead person.

F. Robi (9, 11): "I was six years old. A friend of my father's died. They didn't tell me, but I heard. Then I didn't understand. I felt as when Mother goes traveling somewhere—I don't see her any more."

He feels the same about news of death as about traveling. The dead person resembles the absent, in that he sees neither of them.

Summary.　As we see, in general these children do not accept death. To die means the same as living on, under changed circumstances.

Death is thus a departure. If someone dies no change takes place in him. Our lives change, inasmuch as we see him no longer, he lives with us no longer.

This, however, does not mean that the children have no disagreeable sentiments in relation to death, because for them the most painful thing about death is just the separation itself.[5]

To the child the association Death-Departure exists also in the inverse sense. If anyone goes away it thinks him dead. Jaehner states that his children thought that whenever their father went away they were going to bury him, as they already knew the connection between death and burial.

Most children, however, are not satisfied, when someone dies, that he should merely disappear, but want to know where and how he continues to live. As all the children questioned knew of funerals, they connected the facts of absence and funerals. In the cemetery one lives on. Movement is to a certain degree limited by the coffin, but for all that the dead are still capable of growth. They take nourishment, they breathe. They know what is happening on earth. They feel it, if someone thinks of them, and they even feel sorry for themselves. Thus the dead live in the grave. Most children, however, feel too—and have therefore an aversion for death—that life is limited, not so complete as our life. Some of them consider this diminished life exclusively restricted to sleep. While here they identify death with dreams, from seven years on they liken it to sleep. But as the child's sense of reality increases, the more it feels and knows the difference between the two.

According to psychoanalysis, to the unconscious sleep and death are the same. Both satisfy the desire to return into the mother's womb. In death and in sleep the separation stops and the unity with the mother, which was complete in the intrauterine life, is restored. In the child both are the same, because in him the desire is more openly shown than in adults and the so-called "birth trauma" is still fresh.

In primitive peoples too we find widespread examples of the identification of death and sleep. The natives of West Africa, for example, have no special word for sleep. The verb for sleep is written "to be half dead." If the dead live they think it principally in that in dreams they can return and visit us. And the extent to which death to them is merely a removal is also shown by the fact that in very many places food and drink are put beside the deceased, and even clothing and arms. Servants and wives are buried with them, that there should be someone to look after them in the after-life.

But even within our cultural regions these primitive forms are often found, if not otherwise than in our expressions. If someone dies we say he has "passed on." The deceased returns to his dear "mother-earth." We "take our leave" of the dead, wish him "peaceful repose." And if our feelings were consistent, that there was only a dead body in the grave, our funeral rites would lose much of their meaning.

Finally I must answer the question, what impels the children to the denial of death? What endeavor brings about the identification of death with departure, or with sleep? In early infancy, that is, under five, its desires guide the child even at the price of modifying the reality. Opposition to death is so strong that the child denies death, as emotionally it cannot accept it.

B. Death is gradual, temporary.   There are among children of five and six those who no longer deny death, but who are still unable to accept it as a definitive fact. They acknowledge that death exists but think of it as a temporary thing.

L. Bandika (5, 6): "His eyes were closed."

"Why?"

"Because he was dead."

"What is the difference between sleeping and dying?"

"Then they bring the coffin and put him in it. They put the hands like this when a person is dead."

"What happens to him in the coffin?"

"The worms eat him. They bore into the coffin."

"Why does he let them eat him?"

"He can't get up any longer, because there is sand on him. He can't get out of the coffin."

"If there weren't sand on him, could he get out?"

"Certainly, if he wasn't very badly stabbed. He would get his hand out of the sand and dig. That shows that he still wants to live."

In the beginning the child sees realistically. He does not say, like the previous children, that "he closes his eyes," but that the eyes were closed. He sees only exterior differences between sleep and death. This would again be evidence of a denial of death, if immediately afterwards he had not begun to speak of worms. He does not state that the dead cannot move, merely that the sand hinders them in moving. On the other hand, he attributes a desire for life to the dead person—though only when he is not "very badly killed." Thus there are degrees of death.

T. Dezsö (6, 9): "My sister's godfather died and I took hold of his hand. His hand was so cold. It was green and blue. His face was all wrinkled together. He can't move. He can't clench his hands, because he is dead. And he can't breathe."

"His face?"

"It has goose-flesh, because he is cold. He is cold because he is dead and cold everywhere."

"Does he feel the cold or was it just that his skin was like that?"

"If he is dead he feels too. If he is dead he feels a tiny little bit. When he is quite dead he no longer feels anything."

Again the explanation begins realistically. The dead person cannot move or breathe. Quite cold. He explains the cause of the cold childishly. He is cold because it is chilly. He feels the cold, however, only when not entirely dead. This has no relation to the process of the death agony, as he saw his sister's godfather only at the funeral.

That gradualness in death is not merely a matter of insufficiency of expression and is not related to the processes of death can be seen from the case of a ten year old, to whom this early childish impression remained as an incoherent element in what otherwise was an entirely realistic conception:

"Until he disappears from the earth he knows everything. Until they have thrown three shovelsful, three handsful of earth on him, he knows if they say anything about him."

In the beginning he describes realistically the physical changes which take place in death and then, after all, states that until he is put into the earth the dead person knows everything. Thus the time between dying and being buried is a transitory state between life and death.

Pr. Ibolya (5): "His eyes were shut."

"Why?"

"Because he couldn't open them. Because he is in the coffin. Then, when he wakes up, then they take him out of the coffin. They put somebody else in."

"When they take him out of the coffin what happens to him?"

"If I die my heart doesn't beat."

In death the action of the heart stops. On the other hand, she states too that death is sleep. But not eternal sleep, because the dead person awakens.

Gr. Pityu (6): "He stretched out his arms and lay down. You couldn't push down his arms. He can't speak. He can't move. Can't see. Can't open his eyes. He lies for four days."

"Why for four days?"

"Because the angels don't know yet where he is. The angels dig him out, take him with them. They give him wings and fly away."

"What stays in the cemetery?"

"Only the coffin stays down there. Then people go there and dig it up. They take out the coffin for it to be there if somebody dies. If they couldn't make one quickly it would be there. They clear it up, good and bright."

"What happens to him in Heaven?"

"If it's a woman, she does the cleaning. If it's a man, then he'll be an angel. He brings Xmas trees . . . bakes cakes in the sky and brings toys. It's bad to go to Heaven, because you have to fly. It's a good thing to be in Heaven. You can't get wet, don't get soaked if it rains. It only rains on the earth."

"Well, what are you going to do if you ever get there?"

"I'm going to bake cakes, the whole year. Each angel has got his own stove."

"Won't there be an awful lot of cakes, if you bake the whole year around?"

"Lots of houses. Lots of children. If the cakes are done we can play hide-and-seek. Then the children hide in the clouds. You can hide very well up there. One flies up, the other flies down."

He describes death realistically. The activities of life are missing. He says that one remains only four days in the tomb, then goes to heaven.[6] Thus death lasts four days. He imagines heavenly life in a quite childish way. They play and eat cakes. The question of rain came up because there was a great rainfall at the time of the questioning, he got wet and went home from the kindergarten.

Summary.   As we see, the children of the second group already accept death to a certain extent. The distinction between life and death is, however, not complete. If they think of death as gradual, life and death are in simultaneous relation; if it is temporary, life and death can change with one another repeatedly.

These conceptions are of a higher order than that which entirely denies death. Here, namely, the distinction between the two processes has already begun. Further-

Table 4 Personification of death

		Discussion		Composition	
Distinct person:	the reaper	31 }	67	27 }	49
	original	36 }		22 }	
The dead		31		16	
Total		98		65	

more, beside their desires the feeling for reality also plays a role. Thus occurs the compromise solution, that while death exists it is not definitive.

Rivers tells of similar experiences in the Solomon Islands. There is a word—the "mate"—which they translate as death, though it cannot be used as the contrary of "toa," which is the expression for life. "Mate" is not only the dead person but the dying, even the old and the sick, those who, in the opinion of the natives, should already have died. "Mate"-ness is a state which can last for years. It is not the period before death, because for them there is no death but a transition between the two modes of existence. The person designated as in a state of "mate" is accorded funeral rites. Thus with them the burial is not the burial of the dead body but a festive transposition from the "toa" state into the "mate" state. It is a great turning point in life, one of several, such as for instance pubescence, the founding of a family. As we see, in this conception life and death are confused just as in the children's ideas.

Second Stage: Death—a Man

In the second stage the child personifies death. This conception is to be found in the whole of childhood, but seems characteristic between the ages of five and nine. The personification of death takes place in two ways. Death is imagined as a separate person, or else death is identified with the dead. When death is imagined as a separate person we again find two conceptions. Either "the reaper" idea is accepted, or a quite individual picture is formed of the death—man. The ways of personifying death are shown, in respect to their frequency, in Table 4.

Br. Marta (6, 7): "Carries off bad children. Catches them and takes them away."

"What is he like?"

"White as snow. Death is white everywhere. It's wicked. It doesn't like children."

"Why?"

"Because it's bad-hearted. Death even takes away men and women too."

"Why?"

"Because it doesn't like to see them."

"What is white about it?"

"The skeleton. The bone-skeleton."

"But in reality is it like that, or do they only say so?"

"It really is, too. Once I talked about it and at night the real death came. It has a key to everywhere, so it can open the doors. It came in, messed about everywhere. It came over to the bed and began to pull away the covers. I covered myself up well. It couldn't take them off. Afterwards it went away."

"You only pretend it was there. It really wasn't there."

"I was ill then. I didn't go to the kindergarten. A little girl always came up. I always quarreled with her. One night it came. I always took raisins, though it was forbidden."

"Did you tell your mother?"

"I didn't dare to tell my mother, because she is anyhow afraid of everything."

"And your father?"

"Papa said it was a tale from the benzine tank. I told him it wasn't any fairy-tale."

In the description of the skeleton-man his color is important. He carries people off because he is bad-hearted. So dying is considered a bad thing. Death was seen in feverish dreams. Since then she is convinced that it exists. Talk of death causes its magical advent. Death came too because she had done wrong. So there is a relationship between sin and death.

K. Karoly (7, 8): "Death is a living being and takes people's souls away. Gives them over to God. Death is the king of the dead. Death lives in the cemetery and can be seen only when he carries off some person's soul. There is a soul in death."

"How do you mean that?"

"He can go where he likes."

"What is death like?"

"White. Made of a skeleton. It's covered with a white sheet."

"How do you know it's like that?"

"Because once I saw a play and I saw it there."

"And in reality death is like that?"

"Alive he couldn't be drawn, because there isn't any such man who is made only of a skeleton. Who wants to can't see him and who doesn't want to sees him."

"How do you know it's like that?"

"It has already been experienced."

"People didn't just make it up? It's truly so?"

"It's really like that."

Death is king and in the service of God. Only the dying can see him. The ability to move about derives from the soul. He considers death impossible to draw.

P. Géza (8, 6): "Death comes when somebody dies, and comes with a scythe, cuts him down and takes him away. When death goes away it leaves footprints behind. When the footprints disappeared it came back and cut down more people. And then they wanted to catch it, and it disappeared."

Death is so much a person that it even leaves footprints. Like a child, it teases people. He wants to exterminate death.

B. Tibor (9, 11): "Death is a skeleton. It is so strong it could overturn a ship. Death can't be seen. Death is in a hidden place. It hides in an island."

He thinks of death in fairy-tale style. It hides on an island. Its strength is tremendous. Death is invisible. He doesn't say whether it is invisible of itself or whether it is only that people don't see it.

V. Peter (9, 11): "Death is very dangerous. You never know what minute he is going to carry you off with him. Death is invisible, something nobody has ever seen in all the world. But at night he comes to everybody and carries them off with him. Death is like a skeleton. All the parts are made of bone. But then when it begins to be light, when it's morning, there's not a trace of him. It's that dangerous, death."

"Why does it go about at night?"

"Because then nobody is up and it can come undisturbed."

"Is it afraid of people?"

"No. It doesn't want people to see it."

"Why?"

"Because they would be frightened of it."

Death is invisible because it goes about at night. Others imagine death as ill-intentioned; this child supposes it to have good intentions. It goes about secretly because it does not want to frighten people.

V. Imre (7, 7): "What is death? A ghost. Invisibility. Ugly. Full of skeletons."

"Is the skeleton invisible?"

"The skeleton doesn't show because it is invisible too. When one draws the skeleton then it can be seen."

Death is a person. Why the skeleton is invisible and how the invisibility can be drawn, he doesn't say.

B. Gyuszika (4, 9): "Death does wrong."

"How does it do wrong?"

"Stabs you to death with a knife."

"What is death?"

"A man."

"What sort of a man?"

"Death-man."

"How do you know?"

"I saw him."

"Where?"

"In the grass. I was gathering flowers."

"How did you recognize him?"

"I knew him."

"But how?"

"I was afraid of him."

"What did your mother say?"

"Let us go away from here. Death is here."

He imagines death as a man whom he saw when gathering flowers. He could be recognized by his fearfulness. Afterwards he says he would like to know death's address; he would go and shoot him. Kill the death-man, that we should not die is the children's reiterated desire.

K. Pityu (6, 1): "Puts on a white coat, and a death-face."

"Who?"

"Death. Frightens children."

"Has he frightened you already?"

"I'm not afraid. I know it's just a man who has put on a death-face. He was in the circus once."

"Now don't tell me about that man, but about real death. What is death, really?"

"Real death? I don't know. It has big eyes and white clothes. It has long legs, long arms."

"But that's not really death. That is an 'uncle' dressed up like death."

"No. I went to church. I saw the real death. He went toward the Népliget (a park)."

"You are mistaken. That was a man dressed up like death."

"But death has eyes as big as the squares on this table. Death is also only a man, only it has bigger eyes."

Death is the same as an actual, existing person. He can be recognized by his big eyes.[7] At one time he can distinguish death from that which he sketches, at other times he cannot. The circus plays a large role in the formation of ideas of death of children in the suburbs.

Sz. Daisy (8, 3): "It's like a man."

"How?"

"Well, when its time comes it dies. Then it comes down from Heaven and takes him away."

"Who?"

"Death?"

"It's like a man?"

"Sort of like a man. Lives up in Heaven."

"Is death good?"

"I think it's bad, because it stops people from living."

"In what is it like a man?"

"It's like a man in its body. In its way of thinking it's different. People think that death is bad. Then death thinks now it is going to do good if it takes people up to Heaven."

"Then does it think too that it is doing good when it takes people to Hell?"

"No. People are afraid of death, but death isn't afraid of itself. It certainly takes them up in some kind of carriage. It surely takes a lot of people at a time. So it couldn't take them otherwise than in a carriage."

Death is a man, living in Heaven. In body he resembles mankind, in thought he is different.

B. Ildiko (7, 11): "Death can't be seen, like the angels can't be seen, because they are spirits. I imagine death is a bad man's skeleton brought to life."

"How do you mean?"

"A spirit like that. If you catch him it's like air."

"Is it different somehow from our souls?"

"Once death died. And then it was a bad man's soul. It kills people once they are very old."

"Only old people?"

"If they are ill. Death gives illness, and bacilli, too."

"Why did that man become death.?"

"Because he was a specially, terribly bad man. He did every sort of wickedness. He stole, and everything all his life. God wanted that he should be death."

"Why is death a spirit?"

"Death has to have a soul too, so he can move, because if people hadn't souls they couldn't move."

"How is it different from our souls?"

"I don't know. Somehow I can't express it. Death is a skeleton and a soul. A person is skeleton, soul and skin. There's flesh on him."

Death is temporary, otherwise a dead person could not be brought to life. Death became death as a punishment. The death-man spreads illness. The soul is the principle of motion. Quite an individual idea. A tendency to fabulizing is apparent, but belief in the personal nature of death is a serious conviction.

H. Gabriella (7, 9): "Whoever dies the death angels carry away. The death angels are great enemies of people. Death is the king of the angels. Death commands the angels. The angels work for death."

Death is the angels' king.

T. Stefi (7, 6): "What is death? A ghost. You can't see him, he just comes, like that. Like something that flies in the air."

"What is a ghost?"

"Somebody invisible. An invisible man. In the form of a ghost. Comes in the air."

Death is an invisible man, that is, a ghost.

Szm. Gyula (8, 3): "Death is not a living person, it takes away the souls of the dead. It keeps watch over the dead. Death is like a spirit. Death doesn't go about by day, but by night."

"What is that, a spirit?"

"An invisible person."

"Why invisible?"

"Because he isn't dressed and doesn't go among people."

"Why does he go about only at night?"

"Because by day he can't go among people."

"Why?"

"Because they would be frightened of him."

"Aren't they frightened of him at night?"

"They aren't afraid of him at night because at night people sleep. Death isn't a living person."

"What is it then?"

"Death is alive, too."

Death being a person not living means that it is invisible, as it goes about at night.

M. Imre (9, 9): "They always draw death with a skeleton and a black cloak. In reality you can't see him. In reality he's only a sort of spirit. Comes and takes people away, he doesn't care whether it's a beggar or a king. If he wants to, he makes them die."

"What is that, a sort of spirit?"

"You can't see him."

He makes a distinction between drawing and the reality, but still personifies death. Death is a spirit. In this he understands the same as the others in spirit, or ghost, that is, invisible.

Sz. Marianne (9, 7): "He takes people's lives."

"How?"

"Not the way they always draw it. He comes there."

"What is death?"

"It is a spirit that doesn't exist. It isn't on earth, either, it's in the sky. People don't see it. It is an invisible spirit."

"Spirit?"

"You can't see it. It's air."

She does not accept the usual drawings of death. Death is a spirit and invisible. In the sky. She says it is non-existing because it has no body.

H. Gàspàr (8, 5): "I don't think it's the same as in the picture. The reality is different from the picture. Only people die, there isn't any death itself. I don't know if it's alive, if it is a person. If it is a man it is like the woodcutter. It has a white cloak on, a scythe in its hand, as one imagines it in a picture. It's not something you can see."

"In reality what is it like?"

"I think it is only a picture. But perhaps in reality too it is a sort of invisible person. I'm not sure if there is really any such thing."

"If there is, where is it?"

"Spirit forms haven't any country."

"Haven't angels either?"

"Yes, but they are good spirits. I only mean the bad ones. Bad men haven't any home. They come and go, wander about, loiter around, doing damage."

"Is death a bad spirit?"

"Yes."

"Why?"

"Because somehow it's cold. I imagne it would be terrible if you saw it. You would kneel down, implore it, pray to it, and still death would make you die. I've often imagined I ran away from death."

"How, ran away?"

"In my room, by myself, I imagine it. I don't dare to go out. I shut the door after myself, so he can't catch me. It's as if he were there. I play like that, often."

"Is it a game?"

"I don't know. I often pretend about him."

"Are you afraid, when you are alone?"

"No, I just pretend to myself."

"The whole thing isn't true?"

"No."

"Why are you afraid, if it isn't true?"

"Somehow I'm afraid. Death is the most powerful lord in the world, except the good God. Death is a companion of the devil. Death is like a ghost. If death has servants then the ghosts are its servants. If death dances, then a lot of ghosts come in white cloaks and dance the ghost-dance. It could be so beautiful.''

"What would be beautiful about it?"

"I don't know, but there's something so beautiful about it. Something so suitable. Death and ghosts go together, like fairies and angels. Spirits and the devil go together with death. But the most terrible of all is death."

"Do you often think of death?"

"I often do. But such things as when I fight with death and hit him on the head, and death doesn't die. Death hasn't got wings."

"Why?"

"I imagine somehow that he hasn't. The angels have, and the fairies in the stories, but death hasn't. But he can fly, for all that. He can fly without wings, too. Death has got some kind of invisible wings. In reality they can't be seen.''

In the beginning he denies that death is a personal reality, then after all imagines it. These are characteristic day-fantasies. He runs away from death, hits it on the head, but it doesn't die.

Sz. Jozsef (9, 10): Already accepts death quite realistically. He tells how at home he always plays ghosts with the smaller children. He shakes the bushes and says that death is going about there. On that the small children run away, while he gathers up their toys and the whole playground is his. He stretches cords so the little ones cannot come back. After all, what happened to him once?

"I stayed there, lying on the ground. I fell into the cord myself. I stayed for a quarter of an hour lying on the ground. Only later I dared to get up. I was afraid that death was really there and perhaps I would die too."

He doesn't believe in the death-man, and yet he began to be afraid of him in an evening's play. Fifteen percent of the children questioned stated that they were accustomed to think about death at evening. They supposed, therefore, a relationship between death and darkness. This connects with the examples already mentioned, where the children often imagine that it is "usual" to die at night. The death-man also principally goes about at night.

The third form of personification of death is when death is identified with the dead. This group consequently uses the word for death in place of the word for the dead person. This is the more extraordinary, as in Hungarian the two words are essentially different and even in sound could never be confounded as in other languages (Der Tot — tot; la mort — mort; death — the dead). The word for dead person instead of the word for death occurs in every discussion, every writing.

W. Làszlo (6, 8): "It is superstition about death, because it doesn't go about at night, anywhere. It's in its coffin. Death isn't true. It isn't true that it goes about on earth and cuts people down."

"Then where is it?"

"It's in the coffin, always. Death lies in the coffin."

He doesn't believe in death as a distinct personality. He identifies death and dead people.

A. Carla (7, 11): "Death can't speak, nor move. I was often at the cemetery. It's very sad."

"What is sad?"

"When I see a grave there's a death in it. That's sad."

"Is death in the grave, or a dead person?"

"A dead person . . . I never saw death, only heads and bones."

"What is death?"

"A dead person, who hasn't any flesh any more, only bones."

According to her twin brother, Béla: "Death is a skeleton."

"Is it real, or is it only that one makes an image like that of it?"

"It exists, too. If a person dies, that will be death."

Death as identified with the dead exists for both twins.

B. Miklos (8, 2): "Death can't talk. Death can't talk, because it isn't alive. Death has no mind. Death can't think because there isn't any mind in him. Death can't write because there isn't any soul in him. Death can't read because there is no living soul in him."

"What is the difference between death and the dead?"

No answer.

"What are the dead?"

"The person who dies."

"What is death?"

No reply.

In a childish way he describes in detail all the things the dead cannot do. His ideas of life and soul are confused. He cannot express the difference between death and the dead, nor define death.

E. Laci (8, 8): "What is death? A being, dead of old age or illness."

Complete identification.

M. Mària (9, 6): "What is death? Soul. I, if I die too, I am soul, not a body."

Death is again identified with the dead person. Diverging from the usual, she considers characteristic not the destruction of the body but the endurance of the soul.

Summary.   In the second stage of development, in general between five and nine, the children personify death in some form. Two-thirds of the children belonging to this group imagine death as a distinct personality. Either they believe in the reality of the skeleton-man, or individually create quite their own idea of the death-man. They say the death-man is invisible. This means two things. Either it is invisible in itself, as it is a being without a body or it is only that we do not see him because he goes about in secret, mostly at night. They also state that death can be seen for a moment before, by the person he carries off.

Compared with the first stage, where death is denied, here we find an increase in the sense of reality as contrary to their desires. The child already accepts the existence of death, that is its definitiveness. On the other hand, he has such an aversion to the thought of death that he casts it away. From a process which takes place in us death grows to a reality outside us. It exists but is remote from us. As it is remote our death is not inevitable. Only those die whom the death-man catches and carries off. Whoever can get away does not die.

Of the children in the second stage of development again one-third thought of death as a person and identified it with the dead. These children use the word death for the dead. In this conception, too, is evident a desire to keep death at a distance. Death is still outside us and is also not general.

It is surprising how little the literature on this subject deals with the personification of death, though the tendency to personify is in general well known at certain stages of a child's development. Only E. Stern mentions it concerning ten year olds but does not see its universal significance nor deal with its motives.

Third Stage: Death the Cessation of Corporal Activities

In general it is only after the age of nine that the child reaches the point of recognizing that in death is the cessation of corporal life. When he reaches the point where death is a process operating within us he recognizes its universal nature.

F. Eszter (10): "It means the passing of the body. Death is a great squaring of accounts in our lives. It is a thing from which our bodies cannot be resurrected. It is like the withering of flowers."

Death is the destruction of the body. She mixes the natural explanation with the moral, also considers death a reckoning.

Cz. Gyula (9, 4): "Death is the termination of life. Death is destiny. Then we finish our earthly life. Death is the end of life on earth."

He expresses its regularity by the word destiny.

F. Gábor (9, 11): "A skull portrays death. If somebody dies they bury him and he crumbles to dust in the earth. The bones crumble later, and so the skeleton remains altogether, the way it was. That is why death is portrayed by a skeleton. Death is something that no one can escape. The body dies, the soul lives on."

He knows that the portrayal of death is not death itself. Indeed, he also explains why the skeleton became the symbol of death. Death is universal.

Sz. Tamás (9, 4): "What is death? Well, I think it is a part of a person's life. Like school. Life has many parts. Only one part of it is earthly. As in school we go on to a different class. To die means to begin a new life. Everyone has to die once, but the soul lives on."

It is comprehensible; he sees eternal mystery beyond the physical changes.

SUMMARY

I investigated how children from three to ten think of death. I employed written compositions, drawings, and discussion alike in collecting the data, and 484 protocols from 378 children were at my disposition. In the present study the material has not been fully worked up; I only desired to answer the question of what death is to the child, what theories he constructs as to the nature of death. I found three stages of development. The first is characteristic of children between three and five. They deny death as a regular and final process. Death is a departure, a further existence in changed circumstances. There are ideas too that death is temporary. Indeed distinction is made of degrees of death.

The child knows itself as a living being. In his egocentric way he imagines the outside world after his own fashion, so in the outside world he also imagines everything, lifeless things and dead people alike, as living. Living and lifeless are not yet distinguished. He extends this animism to death too.

In the second stage, in general between the ages of five and nine, death is personified, considered a person. Death exists but the children still try to keep it distant from themselves. Only those die whom the death-man carries off. Death is an eventuality. There also occur fantasies, though less frequently, where death and the dead are considered the same. In these cases they consistently employ the word death for the dead. Here death is still outside us and not universal. The egocentric, otherwise called anthropocentric, view, therefore, plays a role not only in the birth of animism, but in the formation of artificialism too. Every event and change in the world derives from man. If in general death exists, it is a person, the death-man, who "does" it. We get no answer, naturally, as to why, if death is bad for people, he does it.

Finally, in the third stage, in general around nine years, it is recognized that death is a process which takes place in us, the perceptible result of which is the dissolution of bodily life. By then they know that death is inevitable. At this age not only the conception as to death is realistic, but also their general view of the world. Negatively this means that animistic and artificialistic tendencies are not characteristic and egocentrism is also much less.

As we see, the theory the child makes of death faithfully reflects at each stage a general picture of its world. To conceal death from the child is not possible and is also not permissible. Natural behavior in the child's surroundings can greatly diminish the shock of its acquaintance with death.

NOTES

1. In the schools I frequented the most I everywhere got the name "Auntie Death," though the schools had no connection with one another.
2. In the present study I do not give the complete results of the material collected, only that dealing with the nature of death.
3. The age is significant. The child was past 3 years and 11 months old.
4. The age of the children who took part equally in written composition and discussion was reckoned from the time of writing the composition. The discussions took place three months later than the compositions.
5. As control I asked 30 older children what was the most terrible thing about death, and they all answered that it was the separation.
6. This is not belief in a life in the world beyond, but simply living on, because while the former know about the body's dissolution, the latter fantasy does not know it.
7. This child also has remarkably large eyes. Many of them drew the death-person as themselves.

JAMES AGEE

A Death in the Family

In the following selection, two children work to understand the sudden death of their
father, a tragedy that has effectively disordered their universe. The children mull over
the explanations given them by adults and pool their own reflections to conclude that
God, the death-man, has carried off their father. In the discussion between the
children and their Aunt Hannah, Catherine typifies the response of a young child as
she listens to all the explanations and yet denies the finality of death with her question,
"When is Daddy coming home?" Rufus, for his part, moves toward a more mature
understanding of death as physical cessation when he realizes that it was not God but a
concussion that killed his father.

Catherine did not like being buttoned up by Rufus or bossed around by him, and
breakfast wasn't like breakfast either. Aunt Hannah didn't say anything and neither
did Rufus and neither did she, and she felt that even if she wanted to say anything she
oughtn't. Everything was queer, it was so still and it seemed dark. Aunt Hannah sliced
the banana so thin on the Post Toasties it looked cold and wet and slimy. She gave
each of them a little bit of coffee in their milk and she made Rufus' a little bit darker
than hers. She didn't say, "Eat"; "Eat your breakfast, Catherine"; "Don't dawdle,"
like Catherine's mother; she didn't say anything. Catherine did not feel hungry, but
she felt mildly curious because things tasted so different, and she ate slowly ahead,
tasting each mouthful. Everything was so still that it made Catherine feel uneasy and
sad. There were little noises when a fork or spoon touched a dish; the only other noise
was the very thin dry toast Aunt Hannah kept slowly crunching and the fluttering sipping of the steamy coffee with which she wet each mouthful of dry crumbs enough to
swallow it. When Catherine tried to make a similar noise sipping her milk, her Aunt
Hannah glanced at her sharply as if she wondered if Catherine was trying to be a smart
aleck but she did not say anything. Catherine was not trying to be a smart aleck but

Source: From *A Death in the Family* by James Agee. Copyright © 1957 by The James Agee Trust. Used by permission of Grosset & Dunlap, Inc.

she felt she had better not make that noise again. The fried eggs had hardly any pepper and they were so soft the yellow ran out over the white and the white plate and looked so nasty she didn't want to eat it but she ate it because she didn't want to be told to and because she felt there was some special reason, still, why she ought to be a good girl. She felt very uneasy, but there was nothing to do but eat, so she always took care to get a good hold on her tumbler and did not take too much on her spoon, and hardly spilled at all, and when she became aware of how little she was spilling it made her feel like a big girl and yet she did not feel any less uneasy, because she knew there was something wrong. She was not as much interested in eating as she was in the way things were, and listening carefully, looking mostly at her plate, every sound she heard and the whole quietness which was so much stronger than the sounds, meant that things were not good. What it was was that he wasn't here. Her mother wasn't either, but she was upstairs. He wasn't even upstairs. He was coming home last night but he didn't come home and he wasn't coming home now either, and her mother felt so awful she cried, and Aunt Hannah wasn't saying anything, just making all that noise with the toast and big loud sips with the coffee and swallowing, *grrmmp*, and then the same thing over again and over again, and every time she made the noise with the toast it was almost scary, as if she was talking about some awful thing, and every time she sipped it was like crying or like when Granma sucked in air between her teeth when she hurt herself, and every time she swallowed, *crmmp*, it meant it was all over and there was nothing to do about it or say or even ask, and then she would take another bite of toast as hard and shivery as gritting your teeth, and start the whole thing all over again. Her mother said he wasn't coming home ever any more. That was what she said, but why wasn't he home eating breakfast right this minute? Because he was not with them eating breakfast it wasn't fun and everything was so queer. Now maybe in just a minute he would walk right in and grin at her and say, "Good morning, merry sunshine," because her lip was sticking out, and even bend down and rub her cheek with his whiskers and then sit down and eat a big breakfast and then it would be all fun again and she would watch from the window when he went to work and just before he went out of sight he would turn around and she would wave but why wasn't he right here now where she wanted him to be and why didn't he come home? Ever any more. He won't come home again ever any more. Won't come home again ever. But he will, though, because it's home: But why's he not here? He's up seeing Grampa Follet. Grampa Follet is very, very sick. But Mama didn't feel awful then, she feels awful now. But why didn't he come back when she said he would? He went to heaven and now Catherine could remember about heaven, that's where God lives, way up in the sky. Why'd he do that? God took him there. But why'd he go there and not come home like Mama said? Last night Mama said he was coming home last night. We could even wait up a while and when he didn't and we had to go to bed she *promised* he would come if we went to sleep and she promised he'd be here at breakfast time and now it's breakfast time and she says he won't come home ever any more. Now her Aunt Hannah folded her napkin, and folded it again more narrowly, and again still more narrowly, and pressed the butt end of it against her mouth, and laid it beside her plate, where it slowly and slightly unfolded, and, looking first at Rufus and then at

Catherine and then back at Rufus, said quietly, "I think you ought to know about your father. Whatever I can tell you. Because your mother's not feeling well."

Now I'll know when he *is* coming home, Catherine thought.

All through breakfast, Rufus had wanted to ask questions, but now he felt so shy and uneasy that he could hardly speak. "Who hurt him?" he finally asked.

"Why nobody hurt him, Rufus," she said, and she looked shocked. "What on earth made you think so?"

Mama said so, Catherine thought.

"Mama said he got hurt so bad God put him to sleep," Rufus said.

Like the kitties, Catherine thought: she saw a dim, gigantic old man in white take her tiny father by the skin of the neck and put him in a huge slop jar full of water and sit on the lid, and she heard the tiny scratching and the stifled mewing.

"That's true he was hurt, but nobody hurt him," her Aunt Hannah was saying. How could that be, Catherine wondered. "He was driving home by himself. That's all, all by himself, in the auto last night, and he had an accident."

Rufus felt his face get warm and he looked warningly at his sister. He knew it could not be that, not with his father, a grown man, besides, God wouldn't put you to sleep for *that*, and it didn't hurt, anyhow. But Catherine might think so. Sure enough, she was looking at her aunt with astonishment and disbelief that she could say such a thing about her father. Not in his *pants,* you dern fool, Rufus wanted to tell her, but his Aunt Hannah continued: "A *fatal* accident"; and by her voice, as she spoke the strange word, "fatal," they knew she meant something very bad. "That means that, just as your mother told you, that he was hurt so badly that God put him to sleep right away."

Like the rabbits, Rufus remembered, all torn white bloody fur and red insides. He could not imagine his father like that. Poor little things, he remembered his mother's voice comforting his crying, hurt so terribly that God just let them go to sleep.

If it was in the auto, Catherine thought, then he wouldn't be in the slop jar.

They couldn't be happy any more if He hadn't, his mother had said. They could never get well.

Hannah wondered whether they could comprehend it at all and whether she should try to tell them. She doubted it. Deeply uncertain, she tried again.

"He was driving home last night," she said, "about nine, and apparently something was already wrong with the steering mech—with the wheel you guide the machine with. But your father didn't know it. Because there wasn't any way he could know until something went wrong and then it was too late. But one of the wheels struck a loose stone in the road and the wheel turned aside very suddenly, and when . . . " She paused and went on more quietly and slowly: "You see, when your father tried to make the auto go where it should, stay on the road, he found he couldn't, he didn't have any control. Because something was wrong with the steering gear. So, instead of doing as he tried to make it, the auto twisted aside because of the loose stone and ran off the road into a deep ditch." She paused again. "Do you understand?"

They kept looking at her.

"Your father was thrown from the auto," she said. Then the auto went on without him up the other side of the ditch. It went up an eight-foot embankment and then it fell down backward, turned over and landed just beside him.

"They're pretty sure he was dead even before he was thrown out. Because the only mark on his whole body," and now they began to hear in her voice a troubling intensity and resentment, "was right—here!" She pressed the front of her forefinger to the point of her chin, and looked at them almost as if she were accusing them.

They said nothing.

I suppose I've got to finish, Hannah thought; I've gone this far.

"They're pretty sure how it happened," she said. "The auto gave such a sudden terrible jerk"—she jerked so violently that both children jumped, and startled her; she demonstrated what she saw next more gently: "that your father was thrown forward and struck his chin, very hard, against the wheel, the steering wheel, and from that instant he never knew anything more.

She looked at Rufus, at Catherine, and again at Rufus. "Do you understand?" They looked at her.

After a while Catherine said, "He hurt his chin."

"Yes, Catherine. He did," she replied. "They believe he was *instantly* killed, with that one single blow, because it happened to strike just exactly where it did. Because if you're struck very hard in just that place, it jars your whole head, your brain so hard that—sometimes people die in that very instant." She drew a deep breath and let it out long and shaky. "Concussion of the brain, that is called," she said with most careful distinctness, and bowed her head for a moment; they saw her thumb make a small cross on her chest.

She looked up. "Now do you understand, children?" she asked earnestly. "I know it's very hard to understand. You please tell me if there's anything you want to know and I'll do my best to expl—tell you better."

Rufus and Catherine looked at each other and looked away. After a while Rufus said, "Did it hurt him bad?"

"He could never have felt it. That's the one great mercy" (or is it, she wondered); "the doctor is sure of that."

Catherine wondered whether she could ask one question. She thought she'd better not.

"What's an eight-foot embackmut?" asked Rufus.

"Em-bank-ment," she replied. "Just a bank. A steep little hill, eight feet high. Bout's high's the ceiling."

He and Catherine saw the auto climb it and fall backward rolling and come to rest beside their father. Umbackmut, Catherine thought; em-*bank*-ment, Rufus said to himself.

"What's instintly?"

"Instantly is—quick's that"; she snapped her fingers, more loudly than she had expected to; Catherine flinched and kept her eyes on the fingers. "Like snapping off an electric light.'' Rufus nodded. ''So you can be very sure, both of you, he never felt a moment's pain. Not one moment.''

''When's . . . '' Catherine began.

''What's . . . '' Rufus began at the same moment; they glared at each other.

''What is it, Catherine?''

''When's Daddy coming home?''

''Why good *golly*, Catherine,'' Rufus began; ''Hold your tongue!'' his Aunt Hannah said fiercely, and he listened, scared, and ashamed of himself.

''Catherine, he *can't* come home,'' she said very kindly. ''That's just what all this means, child.'' She put her hand over Catherine's hand and Rufus could see that her chin was trembling. ''He died, Catherine,'' she said. ''That's what your mother means. God put him to sleep and took him, took his soul away with Him. So he can't come home . . .'' She stopped, and began again. ''We'll see him once more,'' she said, ''tomorrow or day after; that I promise you,'' she said, wishing she was sure of Mary's views about this. ''But he'll be asleep then. And after that we won't see him any more in this world. Not until God takes us away too.

''Do you see, child?'' Catherine was looking at her very seriously. ''Of course you don't, God bless you''; she squeezed her hand. ''Don't ever try too hard to understand, child. Just try to understand it's so. He'd come if he could but he simply can't because God wants him with Him. That's all.'' She kept her hand over Catherine's a little while more, while Rufus realized much more clearly than before that he really could not and would not come home again: because of God.

''He would if he could but he can't,'' Catherine finally said, remembering a joking phrase of her mother's.

Hannah, who knew the joking phrase too, was startled, but quickly realized that the child meant it in earnest. ''That's it,'' she said gratefully.

But he'll come once more, anyway, Rufus realized, looking forward to it. Even if he *is* asleep.

''What was it you wanted to ask, Rufus?'' he heard his aunt say.

He tried to remember and remembered. ''What's kuh, kuh-kush, kuh . . . ?''

''Con-cus-sion, Rufus. Concus-sion of the brain. That's the doctor's name for what happened. It means, it's as if the brain were hit very hard and suddenly, and joggled loose. The instant that happens, your father was—he . . .''

''Instantly killed.''

She nodded.

''Then it was that, that put him to sleep.''

''Hyess.''

''*Not* God.''

Catherine looked at him, bewildered.

JOAN FASSLER

My Grandpa Died Today

In recent years, however, death has returned to children's literature as a subject for
realistic presentation and open consideration. Often in works such as *Charlotte's Web,*
it is an animal that dies, but the following piece by Joan Fassler demonstrates that even
the death of a family member can be presented to children so as to allay rather than
arouse fears. In *My Grandpa Died Today,* the child who serves as the narrator
describes his feelings of loss and grief as well as his personal means of honoring his
grandfather's memory.

My grandpa was very, very old. He was much,
much older than me. He was much older than
my mother and father. He was much older
than all my aunts and uncles. He was even a
little bit older than the white haired
bakery-man down the block.

My grandpa taught me how to play checkers.
And he read stories to me. And he helped me
build my first model. And he showed me how
to reach out with my bat and hit a curve ball.
And he always rooted for my team.

One day, grandpa and I took a long slow walk
together. Grandpa stopped to rest awhile.
"David," he said, "I am getting very old now.
And surely I cannot live forever." Then
grandpa put his arm around my shoulders and

258

Source: Joan Fassler. *My Grandpa Died Today.* New York: Human Sciences Press, 1971.

went on talking in a soft voice. "But I am not afraid to die," he said, "because I know that you are not afraid to live." And I nodded my head in a thoughtful way, even though I did not understand what grandpa meant.

Just two days later grandpa sat down in our big white rocking chair. And he rocked himself for a little while. Then, very softly, very quietly, grandpa closed his eyes.

And he stopped rocking.
And he didn't move any more.
And he didn't talk any more.
And he didn't breathe any more.
And the grownups said that grandpa died.

My mother cried and cried. And my father cried and cried. And many people came to our house. And they cried, too. And they took grandpa away and buried him.

More people kept coming to our house. And they pulled down all the window shades. And they covered all the mirrors. And our whole house looked as if it was going to cry. Even the red shingles on the roof. Even the white shutters at the windows. Even the flagstone steps going up to the door. And everyone was very sad.

I was sad, too. I thought about my grandpa and about all the things we used to do together. And, in a little while, I discovered a funny, empty, scary, rumbly kind of feeling at the bottom of my stomach. And some tears streaming down my cheeks.

Somehow, I didn't feel like sitting in the living room with all the gloomy grown-ups. So I walked quietly into my own room, and I took out some of my favorite toys. Then I did two jig-saw puzzles and colored three pictures. And I rolled a few marbles very slowly across the floor.

The grownups didn't mind at all. They came
in and smiled at me. And someone patted me
gently on my head. It was almost as if they all
knew that grandpa and I must have had some
very special talks together.

The next day was still a very sad day at our
house. Late in the afternoon, I heard a soft
knock at the door. My best friend, Bobby,
wanted to know if I could play ball. And
again the grownups didn't seem to mind. So I
left our sad, sorry house. And Bobby and I
walked slowly down to the park.

Almost too soon, it was my turn at bat. I
looked around and saw that the bases were
loaded. Then I took a deep breath, and tried
to forget about the rumbly feeling at the
bottom of my stomach. I planted my feet
firmly on the ground. I grasped the bat with
two steady hands. I watched the ball whizz
towards me. And, SMACK, I hit it high and
far.

And then I ran. I ran with every bit of
strength and power and speed inside my
whole body.

And it was a grand slam home run!

And somehow, right there on the field, in the
middle of all the cheers and shouts of joy, I
could *almost* see my grandpa's face breaking
into a happy smile. And that made me feel so
good inside that the rumbles in my stomach
disappeared.

And the solid hardness of the ground under
my feet made me feel good inside, too. And
the warm touch of the sun on my cheeks
made me feel good inside, too.

And, it was at that very moment, that I first
began to understand why my grandpa was not

afraid to die. It was because he knew that there would be many more hits and many more home runs for me. It was because he knew that I would go right on playing, and reading, and running, and laughing, and growing up.

Without really knowing why, I took off my cap. I stood very still. I looked far, far away into the clear blue sky. And I thought to myself, "Grandpa must feel good inside, too."

Then I heard the umpire calling, "Batter-up!" And we went on with the game.

IRVING and BLU GREENBERG

Telling Your
Children about
the Holocaust

The desire to present facts truthfully to children may be at odds with protective
instincts. But the historical reality of the Holocaust is so much a part of contemporary
Jewish identity that the Greenbergs argue for continued observance of its impact even
for children. Though the Greenbergs present a specialized example, every parent or
teacher is, at some time, confronted with the conflicting values of knowledge and
protection.

On Wednesday morning, November 15, 1978, the *New York Times* front page
featured an aerial photo of a large open-deck sea transport filled to capacity with
human cargo. These were Vietnamese refugees, 2,500 men, women, and children
waiting to gain entry to any country that would offer a temporary haven.

I have always felt that to be a Jew is to see the world with Jewish eyes, to hear the
world with Jewish ears, and to do it effortlessly, unconsciously, sometimes almost
against one's will. Like many other Jews who read the paper that morning, I was
reminded of another picture, another story — 1939: the *Struma,* the *St. Louis,* 100
other refugee ships laden with Jews shunted from one country to another, confirming
the darkest suspicions of their passengers that no one in the whole world cared about
or wanted Jews. My memory recalled distant, deeply embedded descriptions of
month-long voyages, crowded, unsanitary conditions, passengers who carried
unbelievable tales of terror, trauma, loss, and separation.

I did not summon these images; they were simply there. Nor did I share them with
our children, who also read the article that Wednesday morning. I was convinced that

Source: Irving and Blu Greenberg, "Telling Your Children About the Holocaust." *Kosher Home's Jewish Living,* March/April, 1979, © 1979,
Adar Communications Company, New York, New York.

they had read it without all the layers of associated memories that I had, and on one level I was relieved.

On another level, however, I felt that I should use the opportunity to get across one more "Jewish connection." But I let it pass. Almost perfunctorily I said, "We should do something about it; we should write a letter to Carter telling him to help these Vietnamese." But I did not give voice to the feelings that I felt and feel, the anger at the world that did nothing while Jews' lives were at stake. Why burden the children with this pain?

On the following Monday morning it was snowing. A beautiful pristine snow, not yet turned to slush. The children were elated. Our daughter Goody was ahead of the rest of us and was standing at the window with her nose pressed against the cold pane. She stared dreamily outside at the falling flakes. Talking to no one in particular, she prattled on about how she was going to go sledding after school, that she would bring some friends home, was there hot chocolate in the house, and maybe (dream of dreams) school would have to close early. After a moment of silence I heard her say, "I wonder how Renee Ostry feels when it starts snowing." (Renee, our good friend, is a survivor of Auschwitz.)

"What do you mean, Goody?" I asked.

"Well," she said, "the snow must remind her of Gehenna [hell], and for me it's fun and play." For a moment, the sight of emaciated prisoners dressed in rags in the freezing snow shivered through my mind, as it did through hers. I gave her a little hug and said, "You're right, Goody," and pursued it no further. But it took my breath away, the incredible sensitivity of an 11-year-old.

Three days after that, our daughter Deborah was writing a letter to President Carter protesting the U.N.'s backing of the P.L.O. As she read it over to us, we heard these words: ". . . and I see by your act of taking in the Vietnamese refugees that you learned your lesson from the Holocaust." This time, I couldn't resist pursuing it further. "Did you discuss that in school, Deb?" "No," she answered. "Then what made you think of that?" "Well, I just thought about it when I saw the boats in the *New York Times* and it reminded me of the *St. Louis.*"—*Blu Greenberg*

We share these incidents with you because we have learned from them that our children have a deeper sense of the Holocaust then we ever imagined, and that they have the ability to make sophisticated connections and associations and draw certain inferences on their own.

The Holocaust is a central event in our lives. It comes up naturally in our conversation—sometimes daily, sometimes not for long periods of time. It has never seemed to us that we were doing a hard-sell job on the subject. Rather, our children have learned about the Holocaust almost by osmosis—from their relationships with people, from their home and school environments, and from communal events.

There are many events in the Jewish community that seem to be unrelated to the Holocaust, yet are, in fact, intimately connected. The underlying sense of all those rallies for Soviet Jewry to which we take our children is that never again will anyone do to us what Hitler did. The birth of Israel conveys a similar message. We have never been to a Yom Haatzmaut parade or celebration where the theme of nationalism was half as important as the theme of rebirth. As we pushed strollers and bought balloons and sang with the marchers, or later took pictures as our children marched past us in the parades, we gradually began to realize that these celebrations were another facet of our children's Holocaust education. Here they were learning not facts, but rather the basic lesson: We are one people, we are responsible for each other, we will not stand idly by as the world once did.

Another important factor in our children's understanding of the Holocaust has been our friendship with many survivors. The Holocaust does not automatically come up in our conversations together. In fact, many survivors feel that no one wants to hear about the Holocaust and are reluctant to discuss their experiences. But each and every survivor's life is a miraculous gift and a precious resource to the Jewish community. They have suffered for all of us, and we must be ready to hear the whole story each witness has locked up inside him. At times, our children have seen us, our eyes glistening, in quiet conversation with our friends. Sometimes they would overhear; sometimes they would ask later; sometimes we offered without their asking. We have always told them the tales we felt they could bear to hear.

The personal stories of people they know are certainly the most potent means of conveying to our children the essence of the Holocaust. And in a certain unspoken way, a survivor who has managed to put together a normal second life, despite the memories and nightmares, must surely represent to our children, as to us, a symbol of hope. Perhaps, too, our children will become sensitive to the special needs and problems of survivors' children and grandchildren, and to their emotional wounds, which the rest of the community must help to heal.

Every year, our synagogue, the Riverdale Jewish Center, marks Yom Ha-Sho'ah, a day of remembrance of the Holocaust. When it first began, some 15 years ago, only a handful came, all adults. Ironically, most of them were survivors.

Now the children come. They even take part in the program. Two years ago, the fourth-grade class of SAR (Salanter Akiba Riverdale) Academy was asked to participate in the synagogue memorial. Several students spoke of family members who had died in the Holocaust. We listened as Sharon Moerdler, a fair-skinned, freckle-faced, ten-year-old redhead, spoke of her family. Up until that moment, we did not know that her father, Charles Moerdler, a one-time New York City Commissioner of Housing, had escaped Germany as a boy. But he had paid a terrible price. His father, who had arranged for the wife's and son's escape, had to stay behind. "We still don't know what happened to my grandfather," said Sharon.

Another ten-year-old, Pamela Shamir of Israel, talked about her great-grandmother, dead at age 45 in Auschwitz. As Pamela spoke, she fingered a small silver brooch and said, "This is all that I have of hers." Everyone in the synagogue was moved to tears.

Through a subtle process, Yom Ha-Sho'ah has become increasingly child-oriented. The genius of the rabbis of ancient times is that they structured many of the holiday mitzvot as pedagogic devices for the young. The Passover seder and the Chanukah lights are perfect examples. It seems as if, almost instinctively, we are moving in that direction today with Yom Ha-Sho'ah.

While we have tried to do many things as a family and with the community, we have to say that a major part of the children's knowledge of the Holocaust has come through the yeshiva day school they all attended. The SAR Academy places great emphasis on both the Holocaust and Israel in its curriculum. Not only the facts are taught, but also their implications for Judaism and human relations. And for our three older children, this process has been continued at the Manhattan Hebrew High School.

In addition to an extensive Yom Ha-Sho'ah program, SAR also marks the anniversaries of the Warsaw Ghetto uprising and Kristallnacht [The Night of Shattered Glass, November 10, 1938: the beginning of a massive pogrom against the Jews of Germany] with special activities. This year, for Kristallnacht, a parent who had lived through it described the event to the students of grades four through eight.

But it is not only at these special times that the connection is made. In their final term the eighth-graders work on an independent research paper. They may choose any topic relating to the Holocaust. And recently, in response to the Guyana tragedy, the school showed a film on mind control to the seventh and eighth grades. In the discussion that followed, the issue was raised as to whether or not the German people had been subjected to mind control—as in fact had been the plea of many Nazi war criminals.

Thus, the school has made our task as parents infinitely easier. Even more important, the fact that our children have experienced some of the trauma alongside their friends and peers has made it that much easier for them. But what if your children's school doesn't have such a program? We believe that almost any school or youth-centered program can duplicate the SAR model. Parents who want their children to come to grips with Sho'ah, yet are unsure of how to approach it themselves, would be wise to prod their schools—parochial and public—to institute Holocaust teaching as part of the standard curriculum.

Fieldston, a private school in New York City, has inaugurated such a program. It all began with Sondra Wald, a 17-year-old senior. Sondra's young grandmother, a still stunning blue-eyed blonde, barely escaped Germany in 1939 along with her new husband, who had just been released from a concentration camp. They spent the next six years desperately trying to bring to America some of the large family they had left behind. But they had little success — only five of five score survived. Two years ago, Sondra approached the social studies teacher at Fieldston about scheduling a Holocaust program. Many of the students and faculty were unaware even of the meaning of the word.

As Sondra and her teacher talked, the idea developed from having a single hour-long assembly into setting aside a Holocaust commemoration week. Sondra's mother and grandmother were called upon as resource people, as were many others in the area. The local newspapers covered it, and it was an educational experience for the entire community.

Programs like this can be—and are being—duplicated across the country with but a little initiative from interested parents. And how valuable it would be to have, along with these school programs, a Holocaust memorial in every major U.S. city, for Jewish and non-Jewish children alike. The Holocaust should no longer be the private, painful secret of the Jewish people.

In contrast to barely a decade ago, there is now a large body of Holocaust books and films available, geared to children at different levels. The most widely used and most powerful literary encounter for children, as well as for adults, still remains Elie Wiesel's *Night*. Wiesel manages to convey a sense of the enormity of the catastrophe in a manner that even the young mind can grasp. Each of our children read this work at a different age (the youngest was ten); for each it was a very powerful experience. They all read Anne Frank's *The Diary of a Young Girl,* another classic text. There are certain weaknesses in the diary; in particular; the Holocaust is kept rather distant. But one cannot be a purist here. The fact that the book is readily available—and very moving—makes it a most useful text. A more direct account of the ruptures in a young child's life, and of the losses in the Holocaust, can be found in Marietta Moskin's *I am Rosemarie.*

Two years ago, a publisher sent us a review copy of Milton Meltzer's book, *Never to Forget*. The book lay around for a while unreviewed. Several weeks later, as we came to tuck in Goody, we noticed she was reading it. She had been reading a few pages every night before falling asleep. It's not exactly what we would have prescribed as bedtime reading for a nine-year-old. But this was what she had done on her own, and we simply observed how she handled it. Several times, she had to read through her tears; but every night she would once again pick up the book. *Never to Forget* gives an accurate, factual account with hardly any rhetoric. It is history, not a novel; yet it held our daughter's interest until she finished it. Since that time, another historical work accessible to children has appeared: *Hitler's War Against the Jews,* an adaptation of Lucy Dawidowicz's prize-winning *The War Against the Jews.*

Other material has caught the children's eye—the collections of poetry of children in the camps, such as *I Never Saw Another Butterfly,* or Hannah Senesh's *Diary.* We never push specific books on them, but we have noticed the power of environmental learning: what is around, and appropriate for their level, has a fairly good chance of being looked at; even if they don't read it, they know such a work exists.

Many Holocaust documentaries have been shown on television. These include *Night and Fog*, a 30-minute presentation; *The 81st Blow,* a devastating hour-long documentary; *Genocide,* a unit of the BBC's history of World War II; and *Let My People Go,* a description of the Holocaust and the emigration to Israel that followed. Having the family view these films together is an effective way of sharing the experience. Afterward, there is a natural opportunity to talk over and assimilate the film.

After watching a television program on the Holocaust last spring, Goody and J.J. had the following conversation:
Goody: "If Grandpa hadn't come to America when he did, that would have been us."
J.J.: "You're wrong, Goody [his favorite phrase]. If Grandpa hadn't come to America, we would never have been born."

One of the ways in which we thought that our children's perception would differ from ours is that they would never say, "There but for the grace of God go I," that they would never feel that their very lives were intertwined with the events of the Holocaust. We thought that even with all they had learned at school and at home, they would never be able to bridge the gulf of time. It took the power of the visual media to bring to them a new and deeper level of understanding. Now, for the first time, we knew that they understood that the Holocaust meant that whole family lines were cut off, that there but for the grace of God. . . .

Many questions have been posed to us about teaching the Holocaust to children. What we have found to be true for our family may not be true for another. Still, we can offer some reassurance. Children are not as fragile or as vulnerable as we often think they are. They can feel pain, and they can overcome.

At what age to begin? The Holocaust is so horrifying an event that if one could, one would postpone indefinitely telling one's children about it. But the Holocaust is fact; it is our heritage; we can't make it go away by ignoring it.

Each of our children encountered the Holocaust at a different age and in a different way. When Moshe was five, he spent a Shabbat with his grandparents in Far Rockaway. On Sunday, he returned home, the same old Moshe, full of fun and mischief. After he had been home several hours, he paused in the middle of his usual high jinks and asked, "Is it true what Saba [grandfather] said—that there was an enemy worse than Pharoah, worse than Haman, that he killed all the Jews, that his name was Hitler?" "Yes," we said. Back came Moshe, who had obviously mulled over the question in his five-year-old mind, "Then why wasn't there a Moshe Rabbeinu (Moses our teacher) to save the Jews?"

David and Deborah were probably closer to nine or ten. For David, it was learning about the great-uncle after whom he was named and reading Wiesel's *Night* that brought forth the questions. For Deborah, it was her fascination with Hannah Senesh. By the time she was ten, she had already read five different books on or by this heroine. J.J. and Goody, while they had heard a good deal of the word Holocaust, and had associated it with a tragedy, did not really begin to comprehend the event until the family visited Yad Vashem, the Holocaust memorial in Jerusalem. J.J. was then nine and a half, Goody, eight.

When Moshe and David were quite young (seven and eight), we took them to a Yom Ha-Sho'ah service at the synagogue. The film they showed that year was *Camps of the Dead,* a stark documentary. In retrospect, we had made a mistake in bringing them. But no harm was done. They immediately tuned out and started to fool around. We simply took them right out. They had let us know indirectly, but in no uncertain terms, that the film was not for them at that stage of their lives.

One thing we have learned is that there are no hard and fixed rules. At about the time a child begins to comprehend evil in the world, he can begin to understand the Holocaust. Common sense dictates that a parent start with the bearable—not with the Mengele medical experiments, for example. But when dealing with the Holocaust, one soon runs out of bearable facts.

We rather suspect that those of our children who now seem to be less sensitive to the Holocaust will later do what many Jewish college students and adults do—go through a period of intense encounter, reading Holocaust literature voraciously for months on end—and then go through a period of distancing, of disengagement, a period of healing emotional wounds, until their Holocaust consciousness stabilizes and becomes a natural component of their lives as Jews. This, in fact, is what happened to both of us.

How will our children be affected? Will they have nightmares? Will they feel threatened and disturbed by the sheer horror? We have always been caught in this dilemma—between the feeling that our children must be told and the problem of how to tell them effectively without scarring them emotionally.

Last year, when our son David balked at going to a Yom Ha-Sho'ah program because he had a big test the next day, we simply said to him, "This comes first. This is what we do as a family. Change out of those sloppy jeans. You are coming." Our big compromise was that he could wear his old sneakers and flannel shirt to the synagogue. We have often suspected that David resists because he cannot bear the pain of the Holocaust. Are we wrong in forcing him to come? We will never know, since he certainly manages to cope. At the least, he understands how important it is to us to have him share this experience.

When Goody saw the rape scene on NBC's "Holocaust," she burst into tears. Yet she did not become morbid or withdrawn. In fact, the next day she and her friend discussed the scene and their fright—probably a much healthier way of handling it than that of most grown women, who no doubt felt equally threatened by the scene.

Some psychologists have suggested that if children are exposed to morbid material during certain stages of development, it can retard their emotional growth. Our general impression is that the chance of this happening is quite small. The response to the Holocaust is itself developmental; it is a gradual process. Children will be guided by their own level of emotional and psychological maturation; they generally know how to protect themselves.

And are not some of the responses that we fear—tears, anger, nightmares—in fact protective devices? How many times have we ourselves put down a book after only a few pages, unable to withstand any more pain? How many nights have we, as adults, awakened with Holocaust nightmares? Perhaps it is these nightmares that allow some catharsis and enable us to function normally, happily, during our waking hours.

The absorptive capacity of young children is quite amazing. If a child is not otherwise emotionally disturbed, he will manage to absorb what he can handle—and then some—and still remain psychologically intact. Children, while highly impressionable, seem to be as capable as adults of assimilating the horrors of the Holocaust. Our children know quite a lot about the Holocaust, a thousand times more than we knew at their ages, yet they are all as happy and fun loving as any other normal child. The difference is that they have this little pocket of consciousness that can be summoned forth when necessary.

How can a child handle it as a Jew? If Passover, Sukkot, Chanukah, and Purim all teach us of God's special love for the Jewish people, what can we answer the child who asks why God let the Holocaust happen? Or worse, what can we say to the child who does not ask but who privately wonders: perhaps God does not exist; perhaps God no longer loves His people.

We personally reject the notion that the Holocaust was God's punishment of the Jews for their sins. We feel that within the framework of the Holocaust this classic response is inappropriate.

A child can intuitively understand that one can be Jew of faith and commitment, with love for God and the Jewish people, even while wrestling with questions that have no answers, questions that trouble parents as much as their children. Equally important, a child can gain from the Holocaust a new sense of the unity of the Jewish people, of love for all its members and of the primacy of ethical responsibility.

Children experience all the redemptive joy of Passover, Purim, and Chanukah. They can travel to Israel—the modern Exodus experience. Thus feeling God's presence in their lives and experiences, they are better able to struggle with God's silence at Auschwitz.

Paradoxically, a child's knowledge of the Holocaust can lead to a feeling of hope and pride and even to a sense of great security as a Jew. We have survived such terrible destruction. We are alive and creative, we have a restored homeland and a hopeful future. What greater testimony can there be to the original promise that we would survive into eternity? The incredible resurgence of life spirit with which the Jewish people responded to the Holocaust has led to a reborn Israel and to the rebuilding of hundreds of yeshivot. Our daughter Deborah wants to learn Yiddish. Moshe and David stayed up all night on Yom Ha-Sho'ah last year to study Torah.

Two years ago on a B'nai Akiva Simchat Torah retreat, after a discussion of the Holocaust, the children began to sing and dance to the song "Am Yisrael Chai"—the people of Israel lives! Then they went into the chant: Mi Anachnu? Israel! Who are we? Israel!

When his turn came, our son began to chant: After Auschwitz? Israel! After Hitler? Israel! We will never forget his final words: Until the Messiah? Israel!

The fundamental statement of the Jewish people, that hope is not lost and that the promise will be kept, will surely find its place in the fertile, searching minds and souls of our young.

AT WHAT AGE

JEWISH LIVING recently asked Yael Danieli, a clinical psychologist and founder and director of the Group Project for Holocaust Survivors and Their Children, to discuss her views on teaching the Holocaust to children. Following is an excerpt from the interview, which was conducted by Jacob Helfman, himself a child of survivors.

Jewish Living: At what age do you think it's appropriate to teach a child about the Holocaust?

Yael Danieli: *I think children of three, four, and five don't have the equipment to* *comprehend or make sense of the Holocaust in terms of their own world. A child should be at least seven, eight, or nine. However, the way you convey the material to children is really more important than whether you convey it. If you want real learning to take place, you have to address yourself to the age group. I think eleven is a very important age to teach it because that's also the age of identity crisis.*

JL: What are the roles of the school and home in teaching the Holocaust?

YD: *Ideally, knowledge of the Holocaust should start at home, like most intimate and important teaching. It should be done while everybody in the family is together. Then the child won't feel totally lonely with the stories. The parent shouldn't just hand the child a book to read. Parents should be available to discuss it, to talk about the feelings.*

But there are also great advantages in school teaching, especially if there's a curriculum, because the school can cover many more aspects than a parent is competent to cover. However, the teacher doesn't replace the parent. When the child has a nightmare, it's Mommy who will take him in her arms, not the teacher.

JL: What would you tell parents who want to start talking about the Holocaust with their seven-year-old?

YD: *You know your child best. If you listen to your child, are intimate with him, you will know how to talk about the Holocaust better than any expert. Better than I. I don't know your child.*

Be responsible about learning the Holocaust for yourself; so when your child asks a question, you can answer knowledgeably. If you can't handle talking about the Holocaust, then don't, because you'll just confuse the child. Don't share only fantasies and fears with the child, because then he's faced with having to take care of you.

C.M. BINGER, A.R. ABLIN, R.C. FEUERSTEIN,
J.H. KUSHNER, S. ZOGER and C. MIKKELSEN

Childhood Leukemia:
Emotional Impact
on Patient and Family

If the discussion of death is always a sensitive task, how much more difficult it is when the discussion is conducted with a child about to die. Given the progress of medicine, the death of a child sends shock waves through the entire family structure. To investigate ways of assisting the families of terminal children, the research team conducted a retrospective study of twenty families in which a child had died of leukemia. The following selection reports the responses of the families to the medical staff and the impact of the child's illness and death on the parents, siblings, and grandparents.

Terminal illness makes a heavy impact upon all concerned, family and professionals. Particular effects of terminal illness and loss have been the subject of numerous studies.[1-14]

Lindemann points out that among adults the grief reaction is a syndrome with psychologic and somatic symptomatology, including somatic distress, a preoccupation with the image of the deceased, feelings of guilt, hostile reactions and the loss of previous patterns of conduct. How long the acute symptoms last seems to depend upon how quickly a person breaks his bonds with the one who has died, returns himself to his diminished human environment and forms new relationships. Lindemann also described the "anticipatory grief reaction" that occurs upon the initial diagnosis of a fatal disease.

Source: Reprinted with permission from *The New England Journal of Medicine*, Vol. 280, pages 414-418, Feb. 20, 1969.

271

A child's concept of death varies with his age; so, too, does his anxiety about his illness. Whether he grieves and how he grieves is also related to his maturation and point of development. Whatever the age of a patient whose illness is terminal, honesty and truthfulness are important from those who work with him. The workers, too, must maintain the patient in hope and reassure him that there will be relief from pain. The patient must be assured that he will not be isolated and that those upon whom he depends will not desert him.

To prepare themselves more fully to support families who face the crisis of a child's death, four pediatric hematologists, a child psychiatrist and a social worker undertook a retrospective study of families who had lost a child from acute leukemia. This paper summarizes the findings of the group, indicates how these findings have been used in their ongoing work with such families and describes their application by other professionals who face this problem.

THE STUDY

The pediatric hematology records revealed that 23 children had died of leukemia between January, 1964 and December, 1966. The parents of these children were asked to come to be interviewed by the child psychiatrist regarding the impact of the crisis and its after-effects upon their lives. Twenty families agreed to come. The interview, which lasted for two to three hours, elicited information including the following: limited family data; details surrounding the diagnosis; short-term and long-term effects upon patient, parents, siblings, and family constellation; relation with doctors and other professional personnel; sources of support during stress; terminal phase and death; the funeral; and after-effects. The structure and the content of the interviews were managed with considerable freedom in an effort to make this interview a helpful or even therapeutic experience for these families. The interviews were transcribed and analyzed, and the results compiled.

THE CLINIC

Inpatient and outpatient care was carried out through the Department of Pediatrics house staff at the medical center with supervision by us. History, physical findings and laboratory data were included in the discussion of the findings and recommendations at the end of each visit.

In the past two years, supportive efforts have been enriched by the regular presence of a child psychiatrist and a psychiatric social worker at the initial conference and in the hematology clinic. Families are also invited to return two or three months after the child's death to discuss their reactions to the crisis, the autopsy report and current stresses.

FINDINGS

Learning the Diagnosis

In the 16 cases the diagnosis of leukemia had already been revealed to the parents or was strongly suspected by them at the time they were referred. In eight families, one or both parents thought their child might have had leukemia before any mention of it by a physician. Most of the parents had sensed something seriously wrong with the child before the diagnosis was discussed or confirmed.

Reactions immediately upon diagnosis ranged from loss of control to outward calm and resignation. Many parents described this as the hardest blow they had to bear throughout the course of illness. During the first days or weeks after hearing the diagnosis, most parents experienced symptoms and feelings of physical distress, depression, inability to function, anger, hostility and self-blame (the "anticipatory grief reaction"). These gradually subsided and were followed by acceptance and resolution to meet all the special needs of the child. Persistent overt denial of the diagnosis or "shopping around" was not encountered. There was denial of the diagnosis by relatives (especially grandparents) and friends rather than among the parents themselves.

The Initial Conference

Whether or not the diagnosis had been known before referral, members of the team discussed many aspects of both diagnosis and disease with the parents. Specific topics included what was known about etiology, heredity, therapy, ultimate prognosis, problems to be anticipated, possible sources of help, means to support the affected child and his siblings, the function of the clinic, current research and reasons for hope. All families expressed appreciation for the frankness and honesty of this initial discussion, and eight specifically singled it out as one of the major sources of help. Several parents who had received their information piecemeal elsewhere made reference to the anxieties specifically provoked by unanswered questions.

Attitudes Toward Professional Personnel

In general, most parents were well satisfied with the clinic and the professional team: nine families specifically mentioned the "panel" of specialists as a source of reassurance.

When parents complained, the discontent was far more frequent with inpatient than with outpatient care. Usually, this was not for any recurrent or basic shortcoming in care but upon a specific situation, whether real or imagined: a doctor's "choking" a child while trying to stop a nosebleed; a nurse's slowness in lending a mother a dime to call her husband for what she considered to be an emergency; a doctor who was "too busy" caring for another child to answer a question; and the premature discharge of a child who had to be rehospitalized on the following day.

Even good intentions and scrupulous care cannot wholly eliminate such situations. When the child is in relapse and ill enough to require hospitalization, parents and physicians experience a significant increase in strain and tension, and the grief reaction becomes more manifest. Professional personnel, when they understand the attitudes of parents and are prepared to respond to their needs, become a valuable source of help instead of becoming enmeshed in a pattern of mutual hostility and recrimination.

Six of the 20 families believed that, as death approached, the professional staff became more remote. The child seemed to become progressively isolated both in a physical sense (because of leukopenia and infections, most of the children were on isolation precautions terminally) and in the sense that he was "avoided" (a word used by several parents) by the staff.

The professional has his own problems in coping with the imminent death of a child. He is distressed and often feels guilty about the failure of therapy. Simultaneously, he is troubled by his own fears and anxieties about death and feels inadequate to support the dying child and his parents. Faced with these conflicts, he often avoids the patient or family or makes himself unapproachable by presenting a facade of busyness, impatience or formality. Thus, at a time when most needed, the professional often assumes a neutral or even negative role in contacts with the family of the dying child.

The parents with the most negative attitudes toward the professional staff were those whose children had had the shortest course of illness. These children were usually the sickest, did not have remissions and were constantly a source of distress to parents and staff.

In contrast with negative attitudes toward inpatient care were the many positive remarks on the support received from the professional staff. In particular, parents appreciated being allowed to participate in the care of the child and being granted complete freedom of visiting privileges.

Impact on Patients

Most children above four years of age, although not told directly of the diagnosis, presented evidence to their parents that they were aware of the seriousness of their disease and even anticipated their premature death. The parents of 14 children tried to shield them from the diagnosis; during the course of the illness 11 of these children indicated their sense of impending death. Younger children, though not expressing fear of death per se, manifested concern about separation, disfigurement or hurt.

Only two of the teenagers were told that they had leukemia for which there was currently no known cure. There was no evidence during the course of the illness or in the interview with the family after death that they had greater difficulty coping than their counterparts to whom nothing had been said directly. Both these families reported a more meaningful relation with their child than they had ever experienced before. They thought this change was due largely to their frank discussion of the diagnosis and the open communication within their families.

As parents attempted to protect their children from the concerns of the illness, older leukemic children attempted similarly to protect their parents; the children who were perhaps the loneliest of all were those who were aware of their diagnosis but at the same time recognized that their parents did not wish them to know. As a result, there was little or no meaningful communication. No one was left to whom the child could openly express his feelings of sadness, fear or anxiety.

Impact on Parents

From the initial diagnosis through the illness of a child and his subsequent death, parents manifested all aspects of "anticipatory" as well as subsequent grief reactions, such as intellectualization, irritability, depression, somatization, denial and frenzied activity. We had not previously been aware of the silent, intense worry of some parents about the circumstances under which their child might die.

The circumstances surrounding a child's terminal illness should be discussed with parents early in the course of the treatment, for parental fantasies are often much worse than actual fact. At first thought, to discuss death might seem needlessly cruel, but parents are troubled by the specific circumstances of this eventuality. A frank discussion does much to relieve months of anxiety. It becomes obvious to all when the child is in a preterminal or, finally, a terminal state, so that the family and professionals will not be left unprepared.

The fathers found many ways to absent themselves from painful involvement with their troubled families. This type of behavior is a coping mechanism, and often indicates the father's need for additional support. Although others may look upon such behavior as expressing a lack of interest or concern, it is a way of avoiding the pain of an ongoing involvement with the dying child. Such avoidance, however, often leaves the mother bereft of much needed support. Fathers who manifest this type of behavior should be helped to express their painful feelings and to look at the effect on their families of this method of coping.

Impact on Siblings

In approximately half the families one or more previously well siblings showed significant behavioral patterns that indicated difficulty in coping. Problems described by parents included an onset of severe enuresis, headaches, poor school performance, school phobia, depression, severe separation anxieties and persistent abdominal pains. Several siblings complained of the preoccupation of parents and friends with the ill child. Often, siblings had feelings of guilt and fear that they too might suffer a fatal illness; they misinterpreted their parents' preoccupation with the sick child as rejection of themselves. In their own way, they had "anticipatory grief reactions." Supportive therapy and counseling for parents and siblings should be considered an essential aspect of total care.

Impact on Grandparents

Ten families stated that one or both sets of grandparents were a burden or hindrance during the course of the child's fatal illness. In many other families the grandparents offered considerable support. Negative interactions reflected to a considerable extent past relations between parents and grandparents. Grief reactions or the grandparents' lack of knowledge also contributed to the ineffectiveness in helping the parents of the child. Grandparents are welcomed to the clinic to discuss concerns with us; like parents, they grieve and need help in coping with their feelings.

Sources of Support to Parents

The physician was only one of a number of sources for simultaneous support.

In 15 families, *parents* turned to each other. The quality of this support seemed to be related to the previous state of the marriage. In others, each parent in handling his own grief was unable to be helpful to the spouse.

If there was a meaningful relation with the *clergy* before the illness, it seemed to continue throughout; de novo introduction of clergy at this time seemed to be of little help. Although only a small number of families received help from clergy, personal religion and religious concepts seemed to be of considerable help. Three families made no comment about the role of religion; 10 expressed negative feelings and disappointment in religion as a source of support during this time.

The *referring physician* was a source of help in nine families and in six of minimal or no help; in one the parents were openly antagonistic. Sometimes, the referring physician seemed to lose contact with the parents and left patient management to the hospital specialists, or in other ways provided only minimal support to the family. Often, the parents of a leukemic child resented the person who first made the diagnosis.

This feeling may be a factor in the parents' resentment toward the referring physician; another may be that the parents of a child with a serious or terminal illness leave the referring physician to seek the "best" or "most specialized" medical service, and since criticism of their choice is a criticism of their own judgment, it is easier to criticize the referring physician than the "superspecialist." Sometimes, a close relation between the referring physician and parents can be inadvertently impaired by the university physician, who takes over the entire management.

The *social worker* was of considerable help to many parents by offering practical assistance in solving financial, housing and transportation problems and as someone who was always available to listen to parental worries, anxieties and other painful feelings. She was introduced at the initial interview as a member of the "leukemia team" and helped greatly in subsequent contacts with the parents and family of the leukemic child.

Parents of other leukemic children, as they waited in the clinic, often discussed common problems and gave significant support to one another. They often formed strong bonds, which continued long after their children expired—despite extreme differences in background, residence, race or economic status. Of 15 families who mentioned the possible role of parents of other leukemic children, 11 expressed positive feelings toward these relations. Although the Oncology-Hematology Clinic makes communication possible among people with similar problems, burdens are sometimes increased by inappropriate sharing of sorrows. Efforts are now made to introduce families to each other if a need seems to be present.

The hospital physician, house officer and nursing staff were a major source of support to most families. Often, the parents became dependent upon a senior physician or house staff member and called on him during times of need. The private telephone number of one of the staff hematologists is now given so that someone whom the family members know will always be available to them.

Fifteen families expressed positive feelings toward the *mortician or funeral director.* Their experience with grief reactions makes them skilled in offering solace to grieving families.

The Child's Death

The actual death was not always the most important event in the *parents'* recollection of the child's illness. Often, the time of the initial diagnosis was equated with death, and it was then that grieving began. The parents of 10 children expressed a sense of relief as well as grief at the time of the child's death. Some were relieved that the child's suffering was at an end; others felt released from long standing worry over when and how the child would die. Four couples recalled intense anger concerning circumstances surrounding their child's death, which was directed against medical personnel, house staff, nurses, physicians or religious personnel. Such reactions should be taken as expressions of grief, not as personal insults.

Siblings' reactions to the death were manifested in varying ways. Some of the children cried and verbalized their grief directly. Others seemed to work out their grief through play activities. Another group of children seemed on the surface to be unconcerned at the time of death only to overreact to a subsequent loss (delayed grief reaction) some months later. Still another group tended to contain their grief only to show marked behavioral changes subsequently. Siblings often felt responsible in some way for the death, or thought they would also die of leukemia. During this period of general confusion and turmoil, the parents may not be able to deal effectively with these feelings, but professionals should be sensitive to them and offer assistance.

Aftereffects

In 11 families, one or more members had emotional disturbances that were severe enough to interfere with adequate functioning and required psychiatric help. None had required such help before. These emotional disturbances included several cases of severe depression requiring admission to a psychiatric hospital, a conversion reaction wherein a man was temporarily unable to talk, divorce, severe psychosomatic symptoms and the behavioral changes in siblings mentioned above. In other families, milder disturbances occurred in both the adults and the children.

Physicians should be alert to the families that might be particularly vulnerable so as to help them through this period.

Suggestions by Parents

All parents considered it important to treat the child "normally" during the illness. They advised that the family "live day to day," "enjoy the child," "not give special privileges" and "not be overprotective." They also expressed a need for more time to talk to doctors about matters other than medical management of the disease. Nineteen families thought that more specific information about the terminal events should have been given to them.

Parents made no clear-cut recommendations about whether a child under nine years of age should be told the diagnosis. In retrospect, all three families with an affected child over this age would have told the child the diagnosis early in the course of the illness. Most families would have told the older siblings of the diagnosis and prognosis.

DISCUSSION

A crisis of this kind is admittedly a major challenge for any family. Still, the fact that in 50 percent of the families at least one member reacted so strongly to the crisis as to need psychiatric help was somewhat startling. From the point of view of preventive mental health the question remains how these untoward reactions could have been anticipated and prevented.

It is a grave error to think that a child over four or five years of age who is dying of a terminal illness does not realize its seriousness and probable fatality. Repeatedly, experience has shown us otherwise. We have seen the pathetic consequence of the loneliness of a fatally ill child who has no one with whom he may talk over his serious concerns because his parents are frequently trying to shield him from the diagnosis. His siblings or contemporaries also almost never act as a sounding board for release of his tensions. Whereas dying adults can express some of their feelings to their spouses, to mature and respected friends, to the clergy or to doctors, the dying child may have to deal alone with his fears, concerns and apprehensions and also cope with his own inner scheme of fantasies and "white lies" developed by his parents so that meaningful communication between the child and adults is prevented. The question is not whether to talk about the diagnosis and prognosis (the child usually senses it), but rather how to let the child know that his concerns are shared and understood and that there is willingness to talk about them with him. Reassuring him that everything possible will be done, that each discomfort that can be alleviated will be, and that all are ready to help in every possible way will allay many apprehensions.

Hope rests not only on life or death. Recognizing with the child what he already knows (that he has a fatal illness) opens up communication without which hope cannot be conveyed. Though he knows the worst that can happen, hope can yet be imparted. He knows that lies will not be told to him, that he will not be deserted physically or emotionally, and that he can voice aloud his feelings of sadness, fear, helplessness, loss and anxiety. Older ill children can be told about current research and prognosis, and their cooperation can be enlisted in medical efforts to help them. Adults can give them the support they so clearly need.

Each parent and sibling reacts to a fatal illness individually, in a manner consistent with his own personality structure, past experience, current crises, and the particular meaning or special circumstances associated with the loss threatening him. To help them, one must know each one and his relation to his or her family, how they react to the initial diagnosis, how their grief process begins and how they cope. One should know, too, something of their beliefs about life, death and religion, their response to previous crises, and their current burdens and sources of support.

Our own efforts to help parents and siblings begin with a team approach at the initial conference conducted by one of the pediatric hematologists and with the house officer, child psychiatrist and social worker participating. Most often the diagnosis has already been shared with the family by the house officer directly responsible for care of the child. The conference occurs in the hospital when the family has had the opportunity to adjust to this initial impact. This meeting is open-ended and sets the stage for help to the family throughout the course of the child's illness. During it we attempt to anticipate questions and to elucidate diagnoses, prognoses and methods of treatment. The conference also provides an opportunity for us to know the family and for them to know us. They are not told how to manage their lives but are helped to arrive at the solution most adequate for them and encouraged to express feelings. We expect to leave the conference with greater sensitivity toward the family. They, in turn, learn that we are not only concerned about the medical aspects of the illness, but are engaged with them as human beings who are facing a crisis, and that our efforts to help will be steady and continuous.

As a result of our study, we have become aware of the importance of inviting families to return to the clinic after the child's death. At this follow-up interview, a summary of the autopsy report is given to them, their reactions to the child's death are reviewed, current stresses are discussed, and all the family members are encouraged to express their thoughts and feelings. Such interviews seem to lead to healthful resolutions of grief.

Who, however, provides help for the professional personnel? They are dedicated and accustomed to making young patients well. When they cannot do so, they feel intense frustration, and their own anxieties concerning death and dying are exacerbated. Anxiety, depression and irritability sometimes ensue. As a child nears death, many professional personnel tend to cope with their own anxieties by avoiding the patient and family when both need support most. For the professional staff to talk with one another periodically about their own emotions and reactions to the work is necessary and useful. They should examine and discuss their own emotional reactions continually, as they affect their interaction with the child and his family. Thus, the professional enables himself to undertake the comprehensive approach to the dying child.

NOTES

1. A.G. Bergman and C.J.A. Schulte. "Care of Child with Cancer," *Pediatrics* 40 (1967): 492-546.
2. A.C. Cain, I. Fast and M.E. Erickson. "Children's Disturbed Reactions to Death of Sibling," *Am. J. Orthopsychiat.* 34 (1964): 741-752.
3. S.B. Friedman, P. Chodoff, J.W. Mason and D.A. Hamburg. "Behavioral Observations on Parents Anticipating Death of Child," *Pediatrics* 32 (1963): 610-625.
4. R. Furman. "Death and the Young Child: Some Preliminary Considerations," *Psychoanalyt. Stud. child* 19 (1964): 321-333.
5. M.B. Hamovitch. *The Parent and the Fatally Ill Child* (Albany, N.Y.: Delmar, 1964).
6. S.I. Harrison. C.W. Davenport and J.F. McDermott. "Children's Reactions to Bereavement: Adult Confusions and Misperceptions," *Arch. Gen. Psychiat.* 17 (1967): 593-597.
7. M. Karon and J. Vernick. "Approach to Emotional Support of Fatally Ill Children," *Clin. Pediat.* 7 (1968): 274-280.
8. E. Lindemann. "Symptomatology and Management of Acute Grief," *Am. J. Psychiat.* 101 (1944): 141-148.
9. J.R. Morissey. "Death Anxiety in Children with Fatal Illness," in *Crisis Intervention*, ed. E. Parad (New York: Family Service Association of America, 1965), pp. 324-338.
10. Idem. Note on interview with children facing imminent death. *Social Case Work* 44 (1963): 208.
11. L.D. Siggins. "Mourning: Critical Survey of Literature," *Internat. J. Psycho-Analysis* 47 (1966): 14-25.
12. A.J. Solnit and M. Green. "Psychologic Considerations in Management of Deaths on Pediatric Hospital Services, I, Doctor and Child's Family," *Pediatrics* 24 (1959): 106-112.
13. Idem. "Pediatric Management of Dying Child, II, Child's Reaction to Fear of Dying," in *Modern Perspectives in Child Development*, ed. A.J. Solnit and S.A. Provence (New York: International University Press, 1963), pp. 217-228.
14. J. Vernick and M. Karon. "Who's Afraid of Death on Leukemia Ward?" *Am. J. Dis. Child.* 109 (1965): 393-397.

EUGENIA H. WAECHTER

Children's Awareness of Fatal Illness

We can no longer accept the rationalization that since children do not understand the meaning of death they are unaware of its approach. In order to determine the extent of terminally ill children's awareness, Eugenia Waechter administered a standardized anxiety scale to sixty-four hospitalized children between the ages of six and ten. Her findings indicate that despite efforts to shield a child from knowledge of the seriousness of his illness, the anxiety of those close to him is likely to alter the emotional climate in the family to such a degree that the child will develop suspicions and fears about his condition. Often the child will feel that his awareness of his condition is knowledge that he is not supposed to have, so the silence of those around him isolates him from needed support. Waechter dismisses the much debated question of whether a child should be told if his condition is terminal, as she argues that the seriously ill child should be able to discuss any concerns or questions he has.

No one's emotions are left untouched by the death of a patient, but the death of the very young is particularly poignant because it speaks silently of unfulfilled promise and destroyed hopes. To defend ourselves, we may unconsciously avoid children with fatal illness and leave them largely alone to deal with their fears and anxieties at a time when comfort, nearness, and sympathetic understanding are most important to them.

Researchers have been reporting that fatally ill children do not, as a rule, experience or express anxiety about death until after the age of ten. And they infer that until then, children are not aware of what is happening to them.[1-4]

I didn't believe them.

To test my own hypothesis I set up a study based on the assumption that, despite widespread efforts in our society to shield children with fatal illness from awareness of their diagnoses or prognoses, the anxiety of meaningful adults is conveyed to them through the false cheerfulness or evasiveness of those around them. The child might believe that if he expresses fear of death openly, he may risk loss of human contact. Therefore, research that relies on a child's overt expression of anxiety or fears about death, mutilation, or separation might get an incomplete or distorted picture of the actual concerns of the seriously ill child.

The subjects for my study were 64 children between the ages of six and ten, divided into four groups matched for age, race, social class and family background. In one group were three children with leukemia, six with neoplastic diseases, six with cystic fibrosis, and one with progressive septic granulomatosis. In the second group were children with a chronic disease, but good prognosis; in the third, children with a brief illness. These groups were tested in the hospital. Testing of the fourth group, non-hospitalized children, was carried out at an elementary school selected after the data had been completed for the three groups of hospitalized children.

A General Anxiety Scale for Children that measured concerns in many areas of living was administered to each hospitalized child.[5] Each child was also shown a set of eight pictures and asked for stories about the pictures to elicit indirect and fantasy expression of the child's concerns related to present and future body integrity. Four of the pictures were selected from the Thematic Apperception Test and four were specifically designed for the study.[6]

In one of the projective tests to elicit the fantasies of dying children ages six to ten the author asked them to tell stories about these pictures. They often gave the characters their own diagnosis and symptoms, and 63 percent related their stories to death.

Interviews with the parents of each hospitalized child were tape recorded to gather data on the variables that I believed would influence the quality and quantity of fatally ill children's concerns related to death. These were the child's previous experience with death, the religious devoutness within the family, the quality of maternal warmth toward the child and the opportunities the child had had to discuss his concerns or the nature of his illness with his parents, professional personnel, or other meaningful adults.

Analysis of the results of the General Anxiety Scale showed that the total scores of the children with fatal illness were twice as high as the scores of the other hospitalized children, supporting the prediction that although only two of the 16 children had been told their prognoses, the generalized anxiety was extremely high in all cases.

Children with poor prognoses told substantially more stories relating to threat to body integrity than did the comparison groups, indicating that they were more preoccupied with death, and suggesting that the denial may not be an effective or complete defense in blocking awareness and in minimizing fear and anxiety in such an extreme situation.

Those children who were threatened with death discussed loneliness, separation, and death much more frequently in their fantasy stories, although none of them did so directly either to me or to other hospital personnel.

A most striking finding was the dichotomy between the child's degree of awareness of his prognosis, as inferred from his imaginative stories, and the parent's belief about the child's awareness. As mentioned previously, only two of the 16 subjects in the fatally ill group had discussed their concerns about death with their parents, yet the proportion of stories related to death told by these children was 63 percent. The children often gave the characters in the stories their own diagnoses and symptoms; they frequently depicted death in their drawings; and occasionally they would express awareness of their prognoses to persons outside their immediate family. This dichotomy suggests that knowledge is communicated to the child by the change in affect which he encounters in his total environment after the diagnosis is made and by his perceptiveness of other nonverbal clues. It also implies a deepening of isolation when the child becomes aware of the evasiveness which meets expression of his concern.

I found a highly significant correlation between the total score on the projective test and the degree to which the child had been given an opportunity to discuss his fears and prognosis. This supports the prediction that giving the child such opportunity does not heighten death anxiety; on the contrary, understanding acceptance and conveyance of permission to discuss any aspect of his illness may decrease feelings of isolation, alienation, and the sense that his illness is too terrible to discuss completely.

The degree of awareness, as influenced by the opportunities the child has had to discuss his illness with his parents, is influenced by the immediacy of the threat of death, or the chronicity of the disease, and by the extent to which the cooperation of the child is necessary in the treatment regimen. The immediacy to parents of the threat of the child's death affects both the intensity of anxiety communicated to the child and the quality of his particular concerns. Children with illnesses which run a fairly rapid course are not often allowed to learn of their diagnoses (adults consider this a protective measure), whereas children with cystic fibrosis or other chronic handicapping conditions may become more aware of and knowledgeable about both their medical regimens and their ultimate prognoses.

Many parents are deeply troubled about the best procedure to follow with their child. Frank discussion with their child about the possibility of imminent death would arouse, they believe, feelings they couldn't cope with. Although my purpose in the interview with the parents was to elicit specific information, it also gave parents an opening to discuss their feelings and concerns about their child's prognosis. Many parents asked for further interviews. They needed to discuss these questions with an empathetic counselor.

The data about religious instruction and previous experience with death lacked a variability suitable for drawing conclusions about specific effects of either. Trends, however, indicated that both influences do affect the response of children with fatal illness. The religious devoutness of parents does not seem to affect the quantity of anxiety as expressed by children, but does influence the quality of their concerns and the manner in which they cope with their fears. Previous experience with death may also influence children's fantasy about their own future, depending on the manner in which they were supported during the former incidents.

Some illustrations from the data may highlight these children's awareness of their diagnoses and prognoses and their fears of the future.

One six-year-old boy in the terminal stages of leukemia had discussed his illness with his parents in terms of "tired blood." He told me the following story after looking at a picture of a woman entering a room with her face in her hands:

> This is about a woman. She's somebody's mother. She's crying because her son was in the hospital, and he died. He had leukemia. He finally had a heart attack. It just happened . . . he died. Then they took him away to a cemetery to bury him, and his soul went up to heaven.
>
> This woman is crying. But she forgets about it when she goes to bed. Because she relaxes and her brain relaxes. She's very sad. But she sees her little boy again when she goes up to heaven. She's looking forward to that. She won't find anybody else in heaven—just her little boy that she knows.

This story illustrates this boy's awareness of the present and probable future, the influence of religious instruction on this fantasy and ways of dealing with his concerns, and the quality of loneliness and separation he is experiencing. His sense of helplessness to alter events and certainty about an inevitable future are apparent.

One eight-year-old girl with cystic fibrosis told the following story after examining a picture of a small child in bed with a nurse standing nearby:

> One girl was reading a book in the hospital. The nurse was over by the bed. The girl's name was Becky. She had the bad coughing. She had trouble with her lungs. She had lung congestion. The nurse is looking at her chart. Becky is thinking they're going to do an operation. Becky is only eight years old. She thinks they're going to hurt her and she

doesn't want it. And they did give the operation. They gave her a sleeping shot. She didn't like shots. The same nurse always came in, because she knew what to do. Becky died. Then her mother came to see her and they told her she died. But the mother didn't like to hear that.

This story illustrates further the identification which was apparent as the children viewed the pictures, and in this case, the child's projection of her feelings onto the mother. In many instances, though the clues were purposely vague, the children attributed their own diagnoses and symptoms to the characters in their story and thus communicated their concerns and fears. Again, a sense of helplessness is apparent in this story—of inability to alter events, fear of mutilation and pain, certainty about an inevitable future, sadness and separation, yet reliance on those in her environment as giving the only assistance available to her.

Some comments in the stories not only indicated the helplessness a child may feel, but also reflected the view of an environment which is nonsupportive and on some occasions actively hostile, punishing, and impeding anxiety reduction and recovery of a sense of body integrity. A seven-year-old boy with cystic fibrosis commented in a story:

> The little boy had to stay in the hospital because the doctor wanted it. He got a shot in the back; a big needle. He was scared of shots, and didn't want it. And the doctor did it hard. His lungs are gone—he can't breathe. His lungs got worse and he didn't get well. He died and he was buried with a big shovel.

These statements also communicate the child's fear, his perspective regarding treatment procedures, his sensing that body integrity and intactness cannot be regained, and his feeling of incompleteness in body image. Despondency regarding the future is poignant and loneliness is apparent in the concluding sentence.

In other stories, this boy made statements such as "They [hospital personnel] put a tent on him and freeze him, too," "The nurse turned off the lights and the door was closed, and he was lonesome and scared," "The little boy's very sick—he's mad too, because he wanted to go home." Statements like these illustrate some children's real concern about what they see as unsupportiveness in an environment they are incapable of escaping. They may not appreciate the therapeutic intent of hospital personnel and are preoccupied with fear, loneliness, and anger. Other statements this boy made, such as, "The boy is thinking he hopes he gets well—he's thinking he might not get well and die," highlight very real anxiety about nonbeing, though he had never discussed this overtly with anyone. When coupled with the loneliness he also expressed, it is possible to imagine his fear that he might die in an alien and hostile environment, separated from all those who care about him.

The sense of loneliness is accentuated because of the young child's sense of time as stretching interminably between parental visits. One six-year girl commented, "She has to be in the hospital for long days and never gets to see her Mommy and Daddy. She's very lonesome." She also said in one of her stories that the child character "got sick by not coughing up the mucus," which tells us not only that she has received instruction about her condition (cystic fibrosis), but also that young children often assume responsibility for the causality of their illness whether warranted or unwarranted and may feel guilt in addition to their fears.

Strong feelings of anger and hostility may also accompany the loneliness associated with the question, "Why did this have to happen?" And these feelings may be accentuated by sensed prohibitions against revealing suspicion or knowledge of the diagnosis. An eight-year-old girl who had very recently been diagnosed as having a malignant tumor of the femur and whose mother was determined that she should never be told the diagnosis, nevertheless indicated preoccupation with death in all eight of her stories, angrily concluding almost every story with the death of the main character and remarking, "And nobody cared—not even her mother!" Another story ended with the statement, "She was very lonesome before she died because nobody cared." Such statements give us insight into the manner in which evasiveness or uneasy cheerfulness may be interpreted by children. That this girl was aware of the meaning of the alterations in the emotional climate surrounding her can be seen in this story:

> She's in the hospital, and the doctor is talking to her mother and father. She's sick—she's got cancer. She's very, very sick. She's thinking she wishes she could go home. She had an operation at the hospital, but she didn't want it because she wanted to get out of the hospital. This little girl dies—she doesn't get better. Poor little girl. This girl at the hospital—she has cancer. Her hip is swollen and her bone's broken. This little girl in the picture died, and then they buried her. And then she went up to heaven. She didn't like it there—because God wasn't there.

CONCLUSION

It seems clear that frequently denial or the protectiveness of adults may not be entirely effective in preventing children with fatal illness from experiencing anxiety or in keeping awareness of their diagnoses and probable prognoses from them. The question of whether a child should be told that his illness is fatal is meaningless; rather questions and concerns which are conscious to the child threatened with death should be dealt with in such a way that the child does not feel further isolated and alienated from his parents and other meaningful adults. There should be no curtain of silence around his most intense fears. These feelings of isolation may also be relieved by efforts designed to keep the child closer, both spatially and emotionally, to others on pediatric wards.

Support must also be made available for them during and following actual encounters with death on pediatric wards. They need support that allows introspective examination of attitudes and fears related to death in general and to the death of children in particular.

THE GENERAL ANXIETY SCALE FOR CHILDREN

1. When you are away from home, do you worry about what might be happening at home?

2. Do you sometimes worry about whether your body is growing the way it should?

3. Are you afraid of mice or rats?

4. Do you ever worry about knowing your lessons?

5. If you were to climb a ladder, would you worry about falling off it?

6. Do you worry about whether your mother is going to get sick?

7. Do you get scared when you have to walk home alone at night?

8. Do you ever worry about what other people think of you?

9. Do you get a funny feeling when you see blood?

10. When your father is away from home, do you worry about whether he is going to come back?

11. Are you frightened by lightning and thunderstorms?

12. Do you ever worry that you won't be able to do something you want to do?

13. When you go to the dentist, do you worry that he may hurt you?

14. Are you afraid of things like snakes?

15. When you are in bed at night trying to go to sleep, do you often find that you are worrying about something?

16. When you were younger, were you ever scared of anything?

17. Are you sometimes frightened when looking down from a high place?

18. Do you ever worry when you have to go to the doctor's office?

19. Do some of the stories on radio or television scare you?

20. Have you ever been afraid of getting hurt?

21. When you are home alone and someone knocks on the door, do you get a worried feeling?

22. Do you get a scary feeling when you see a dead animal?

23. Do you think you worry more than older boys and girls?

24. Do you worry that you might get hurt in some accident?

25. Has anyone ever been able to scare you?

26. Are you afraid of things like guns?

27. Without knowing why, do you sometimes get a funny feeling in your stomach?

28. Are you afraid of being bitten or hurt by a dog?

29. Do you ever worry about something bad happening to someone you know?

30. Do you worry when you are home alone at night?

31. Are you afraid of being too near fireworks because of their exploding?

32. Do you worry that you are going to get sick?

33. Are you ever unhappy?

34. When your mother is away from home, do you worry about whether she is going to come back?

35. Are you afraid to dive into the water because you might get hurt?

36. Do you get a funny feeling when you touch something that has a real sharp edge?

37. Do you ever worry about what is going to happen?

38. Do you get scared when you have to go into a dark room?

39. Do you dislike getting in fights because you worry about getting hurt in them?

40. Do you worry about whether your father is going to get sick?

41. Have you ever had a scary dream?

42. Are you afraid of spiders?

43. Do you sometimes get the feeling that something bad is going to happen to you?

44. When you are alone in a room and you hear a strange noise, do you get a frightened feeling?

45. Do you ever worry?

The author marked the "yes's," counted them, and compared the scores of dying children with two control groups of hospitalized children. Dying children showed twice as much anxiety.

Source: Adapted from Sarason, S. B., and Others. *Anxiety in Elementary School Children.* New York, John Wiley and Sons, 1960.

NOTES

1. A.G. Knudson and J.M. Natterson. "Participation of Parents in the Hospital Care of Their Fatally Ill Children," *Pediatrics* 26 (Sept. 1960): 482-490.
2. J.R. Morrissey. "Death Anxiety in Children with a Fatal Illness," in *Crisis Intervention,* ed. H.J. Parad (New York: Family Service Association of America, 1965), pp. 324-338.
3. J.M. Natterson and A.G. Knudson. "Observations Concerning Fear of Death in Fatally Ill Children and Their Mothers," *Psychosom. Med.* 22 (Nov.-Dec. 1960): 456-465.
4. J.B. Richmond and H.A. Waisman. "Psychologic Aspects of Management of Children with Malignant Diseases," *Am. J. Dis. Child.* 89 (Jan. 1955): 42-47.
5. S.B. Sarason et al., *Anxiety in Elementary School Children* (New York: Wiley, 1960).
6. H.A. Murray. *Thematic Apperception Test* (Cambridge, Mass., Harvard University Press, 1943).

Questions

1. Define the following terms. Those marked with an asterisk are terms the authors expect the reader to know already. If you are not familiar with them, consult a dictionary.

   *statistical distribution   *hematology
   death-man   *anxiety scale
   *concussion   *thematic apperception test
   *egocentric   *projective test
   holocaust

2. The children's statements, "The First Time Somebody I Knew Died," which appear at the beginning of this chapter, represent individual attempts to make sense of death. Examine each selection, separating accurate from inaccurate information, and hypothesize how the ideas were formed.

3. In each of the three developmental stages that Maria Nagy outlines, the child is likely to hold some beliefs that will be carried into adult life either as factual errors or, more subtly, as attitudes. List euphemisms that parallel the child's notion of death as (1) reversible, as (2) sleep, and as (3) a person.

4. a. *A Death in the Family* and *My Grandpa Died Today* both portray a young boy faced with the death of a close family member, a father in the former and a grandfather in the latter. Though this chapter presents only a small section of *A Death in the Family* much of the mourning process is depicted. Compare and contrast the grief reactions of the boys in the two works. Consider the degree of loss, the practical implications of the loss, the "appropriateness" of the death, the information the boy has been given about the death, as well as each boy's efforts to cope with his loss.

    b. Using the information from this chapter, write a brief explanation to (a) Rufus and (b) Catherine explaining that their father has died.

5. Recalling the discussion of grief and mourning by Lindemann in Chapter Three, list the factors in the symptomatology of grief that you would expect to differ in the case of a child mourner. What systems of support would you suggest?

6. Many of the professionals represented in this chapter (Binger, et al., Waechter) advocate honesty in communications with children who are fatally ill. Yet they do not necessarily equate that honesty with a decision to inform a child of his terminal diagnosis. Outline the factors to be considered and the kind of information to be given if a child is to be informed of a terminal diagnosis.

7. In the retrospective study conducted by the Binger research team, most families indicated that they had accepted the terminal diagnosis for their child as his "death." But with continued medical advances in the treatment of leukemia, extended remission is a more likely possibility, and the impact of this "Lazarus syndrome" is often difficult for families. Outline the possible difficulties for the family when a child who had been diagnosed as terminal continues in an unexpected and extended remission. In your outline, consider the impact on the patient (his social development, peer relationships, academic pursuits), his siblings, and his parents.

8. Eugenia Waechter discusses a number of reactions that terminally ill children express either verbally or nonverbally. List these reactions and compare them to the reactions of a dying adult as outlined by Kübler-Ross in Chapter Two.

Projects for Further Study

1. Interview three children on the subject of the death of a favorite pet. Allow their discussion to range freely, and ask questions only when necessary to continue the discussion. Analyze each set of interview responses in terms of the developmental stages outlined by Maria Nagy.

2. Using the card catalog of your local children's library, compile a bibliography of children's literature in which the primary subject is death. Expand the bibliography through annotation: include such details as date of publication, developmental level of audience, point of view from which the story is told, conceptualization of death, religious or cultural setting, object of death, portrayal of the mourning reaction.

3. Much as attitudes about death and dying are rooted in childhood, so are attitudes towards the aging process and the aged shaped at an early age. To explore children's attitudes towards aging, ask five or six children, "Who is the oldest person you know?" and "What do they most like to do?" Then have each child draw a picture of that person involved in his or her favorite activity. Ask each child to tell you about the picture. Compare the pictures and the oral reports that you gather from the children. Note both the similarities and the differences in their accounts and suggest possible reasons for each.

Structured Exercises

Before beginning these exercises, please read "Note to the Instructor" on page xiii.

1. Set aside a class session for a study group on children's literature. Bring a large selection of children's books which deal with death or have students each bring two books they have read. Divide the class into groups of five. Circulate the books within each group so each person can read all the books in the group. Allow twenty minutes for reading them, and have the groups discuss their reactions to the books. Did they find them enjoyable? realistic? Was the dialogue realistic? Were the characters credible? How threatening was the death? Was there any resolution for the grief? Would the student read the book to a child? Why or why not? Did they agree with the conception of death?

2. Select five members of the class to role-play the following situation before the rest of the class:

    The parents of a seven year-old leukemic boy are meeting with a health care team consisting of the child's physician, nurse and social worker. The child has reentered the hospital in the terminal phase of his painful illness; he has previously experienced three spontaneous remissions and returned home, only to fall dangerously ill and return to the hospital each time. A fourth remission is not expected. The group must decide whether to begin the child on an expensive new experimental treatment. Although the treatment is not expected to be able to control the disease for the child, it might keep him alive for up to six months longer, and its use in this case would add to medical knowledge and possibly improve the survival rate of other sick children. However, the parents and the two younger brothers of the child have prepared themselves for his death at each return to the hospital. The emotional strain of the dramatic recoveries is reflected in the worsening relationship between the parents and in behavior problems in the children. The father is working a second job to help pay the medical bills. The mother alternates between wanting to keep her child alive at all costs and wanting to release him from pain. The doctor is committed to saving and prolonging life if at all possible, especially in the case of a child.

The nurse has cared for the child during each hospitalization and considers herself to have the primary responsibility for caring for the child. The social worker has given the parents financial counseling and has tried to give them psychological support during the long illness.

The five students are to reach a group decision as to whether to prolong the child's life. After the decision has been made, each should describe to the class how he felt about his role as the discussion progressed. Then the class as a whole should discuss their reactions, answering the following questions:

a. What criteria did the group use to reach the final decision?
b. What additional information would you have liked to have had?
c. Should anyone else have been included in the decision making?
d. What factors contributed most to the difficulties in making the decision?

For Further Reading

The following books provide in-depth coverage of the topics introduced in this chapter.

Anthony, E. J. and Koupernik, C., eds. *The Child in His Family,* Vol. II: *The Impact of Disease and Death.* New York: Wiley, 1973.

Anthony, S. *The Discovery of Death in Childhood and After.* New York: Basic Books, 1972.

Bowlby, John. *Attachment and Loss,* Vol. I: *Attachment,* Vol. II: *Separation.* New York: Basic Books, 1973.

Coerr, E. *Sadako and the Thousand Paper Cranes.* New York: Putnam, 1977.

Furman, E. A. *A Child's Parent Dies: Studies in Childhood Bereavement.* New Haven, Conn.: Yale University Press, 1974.

Grollman, E. A., ed. *Explaining Death to Children.* Boston: Beacon Press, 1967.

Lindgren, A. *The Brothers Lionheart.* Leicester: Brockhampton, 1975.

Miles, M. *Annie and the Old One.* New York: Little, Brown, 1971.

Mills, G. C., Reisler, R., Jr., Robinson, A. E., and Vermilye, G. *Discussing Death: A Guide to Death Education.* Homewood, Ill.: ETC Publications, 1976.

The School Counselor, 24, No. 5, 1977: ("Special Issue on Death"), 305-384.

Smith, D. B. *A Taste of Blackberries.* New York: Thomas Y. Crowell, 1973.

Stein, S. B. *About Dying.* New York: Walker and Company, 1974.

Wolf, A. *Helping Your Child to Understand Death.* New York: Child Study Press, 1973.

Wolfenstein, M. and Kliman, G., eds. *Children and the Death of a President.* Garden City, N.Y.: Doubleday, 1965.

Chapter Five

Choices and Decisions in Death

Given an extended period of dying, would you prefer to be at home or in a hospital? Would you want to be maintained on life-extending machinery? To what extent? What do you want to happen to your body after death? Can you imagine any cause that might motivate you to sacrifice your life in martyrdom or that would motivate you to sacrifice your life in an altruistic act? Are there any conditions under which you might choose to end your own life? How would you like to spend your last decade?

The discovery of the role of decision in death is not recent, but the range of possible choices is continually expanding, as is the range of choices for improving the quality of life. Treatments of the element of personal decision in death in earlier centuries occasionally included references to martyrdom, but most often they were limited to a discussion of suicide, an option that was rarely considered responsible.

SUICIDE

Apart from isolated accounts of honorable death, as in battle, both Greek and Roman culture generally opposed suicide on ethical grounds. In Athens, for instance, those who attempted suicide were punished with the removal of one hand, generally the hand that had been instrumental in the attempt.

297

The milder Roman censure of suicide was strengthened with the influx of the Christian tradition which judged suicide an offense against the commandment "Thou shalt not kill."

From the Middle Ages through the eighteenth century, penalties against suicide continued in the form of confiscation of property, degradation of the corpse, and prohibition against burial in consecrated ground. Though the legal sanctions against suicide have fallen into disuse, the social censure against a suicide attempter or the bereaved "survivor" of a suicide continues.

Not until the nineteenth century was suicide studied as a medical problem, often as a form of insanity. In 1897, Emile Durkheim began to study suicide within the context of societal disorganization and alienation. More recently, psychology has taken the study of suicide into an investigation of the nature of personal motivation and levels of intention, thereby expanding the study of self-murder into one of self-destructive behaviors.

ELECTIVE DEATH

The debate over the role of decision in death extends far beyond the issue and frequently centers on the right of the dying patient to determine the manner of his own death. Euthanasia, which once meant simply "the good death," is now associated with elective death in the face of imminent natural death. In this context, the ethical dilemmas that were posed with the issue of suicide are multiplied; with euthanasia, in the sense of voluntary death, the responsibility for decision usually extends beyond the dying person to those around him.

IMPLICIT CHOICE

Choices related to death are made regularly both in the social context and in the personal realm. In the larger framework of society, the decision to enter a war, no matter how just the cause, to impose the death penalty on a convicted criminal, or even to accelerate the progress of environmental pollution is an exercise of choice. Likewise, the personal decision to undertake a rescue operation in spite of personal hazard or even to persist in a life-endangering behavior challenges mortality.

REVERENCE FOR LIFE

Decisions in death, and their counterpart, reverence for life, force a reexamination of ethical principles. The abilities to create living organisms under laboratory conditions, on the one hand, and to terminate prenatal life through abortion, on the other, call for an evaluation of responsibility in the generation and termination of life. Ethical issues which once may have been reserved for the philosopher have entered the domain of the scientist and press with immediacy on the common man. Confronted with the intubation of the helpless who, if conscious at all, seem aware only of pain and hopelessness, how is one to weigh the relative merits of the quality of life against its quantity, or, as some have suggested, against its costs—both psychological and financial? Any study of elective death must draw freely on the best available information in all disciplines. In the future, the number of choices associated with death is destined to increase, and a continued study of death and dying can make implicit choices *explicit*. Continued examination is not without its hazards, however. We might ask what the effects of an intellectual familiarity with death will be. Will the study of death and dying be popularized to the point of defeating its purpose by exploiting innate fears? Or, in taming death, will we regularize decisions with mundane practicality and rob death of its mystery? And, finally, will the study of death enrich living?

OVERVIEW OF THE CHAPTER

Chapter Five brings together readings from moral philosophy, psychology, and literature (many of which have implications for public policy) in a review of the range of choices an individual is likely to encounter. Joseph Fletcher, a medical ethicist, begins, in "Elective Death," with the question, "If we have a right to initiate a life deliberately, may we not terminate one?" He develops his case in the context of temporal existence, warning that his results may be at odds with those who begin with the conviction of an objective reality or the conviction of life as the gift of a Creator rather than as a human right. As he articulates his views clearly, noting qualifications at each step, he provides a framework for a discussion of *chosen dying.* To set the conflict, the reader may find it useful to return to Paul Ramsey's "The Indignity of 'Death with Dignity' " in Chapter One.

Philosopher Michael Bayles expands the discussion in "The Price of Life" by moving a conflict developed in individual terms to the generalized terms of ethics in society. Additionally, he moves the discussion from the hypothetical mode back to the experiential world as he extracts implicit value statements from common practices where life is priced, for example, in the building of a skyscraper, the purchase of life-saving equipment, the budgeting for additional medical facilities. Bayles argues that it is not only rational and morally permissible to place a price on one's own life but that there is also a morally acceptable method of using this pricing to determine some social policies. His work provokes much needed discussion as the contemporary individual recasts enduring values in a form responsive to the potential afforded by new technologies.

Anne Sexton, a modern American poet, narrows the focus of the discussion to a particular form of elective death—suicide. In "Suicide Note," the persona explores from the inside the decision to die, questioning the purity of motives, trying, at all costs, to evade narcissism.

It is not clear that the choice of death can ever be entirely objective. Edwin Shneidman, a thanatologist known for his work in suicide prevention, argues against the romanticization of death and suicide. In "The Enemy," expanding his consideration from the conscious choice of suicide, Shneidman examines a range of subintentioned deaths in which unconscious motivation may result in the truncation of life. Shneidman questions not only the choice made but the basis on which it is made.

Choices in death imply a range of alternatives. This chapter closes with two approaches to living and dying, each offering a contrast to the study in earlier chapters. Concern over the quality of life in the final stages has led to the rapid development of the hospice movement. In "Hospice: A Caring Community," hospital administrator Kenneth P. Cohen describes the growth of alternative models for terminal care. Although the original British Hospice was a separate demonstration facility, Cohen shows how the hospice philosophy has penetrated mainstream medical care to the point that hospice units are now being frequently established within acute care hospitals, the very institutions the hospice movement was designed to counterpose. Finally, in "Exits and Existence: Alternative Scenarios," psychologist Robert Kastenbaum examines society's unwritten script for old age and death. He traces two scenarios, extrapolating from the ways society has answered this question: "What value is there in being an old, dying, or dead person?"

Encounter

SUICIDE PACT

Dr. and Mrs. Henry P. Van Dusen, leaders in American theological life, swallowed overdoses of sleeping pills last month in the bedroom of their Princeton, N.J., home in an effort to carry out a suicide pact.

Mrs. Van Dusen died. Dr. Van Dusen vomited up the pills and died 15 days later on Feb. 13, apparently of a heart ailment, in the Carrier Clinic in Belle Meade, N.J.

Dr. Van Dusen, the former president of Union Theological Seminary, and his wife—both members of the Euthanasia Society and advocates of an individual's right to terminate his or her own life—had entered into the pact rather than face the prospect of debilitating old age.

Mrs. Van Dusen was 80 years old when she died on Jan. 28. Her husband was 77. Although reportedly depressed, the Van Dusens were convinced that their suicide attempt carried no burden of sin but rather the promise of after-life.

Friends and associates had known of the couple's suicide effort, but details about the incident did not become widely known until yesterday.

In a letter they left behind, the Van Dusens said there were many old people who would die of natural causes if not kept alive medically and expressed the resolve not to "die in a nursing home."

The Van Dusens, whose prominence peaked while Dr. Van Dusen served as president of the seminary from 1945 until his retirement in 1963, said that they had led "happy lives" but that poor health no longer permitted them to "do what we want to do."

A worsening arthritic condition had made Mrs. Van Dusen lame. Five years ago, Dr. Van Dusen suffered a severe stroke which limited his physical activity and prevented him from speaking normally. For the vigorous, articulate Presbyterian scholar and his active wife, the setbacks were serious impediments to living the kind of useful, productive lives to which they had become accustomed.

Source: Kenneth A. Briggs. "Suicide Pact Preceded Deaths of Dr. Van Dusen and His Wife." *New York Times,* February 25, 1975. ©1975 by the New York Times Company. Reprinted by permission.

1. The Van Dusens' act highlights the issue of the individual's right to choose death. Do you believe that this right exists? Under what circumstances?

2. Had you been in circumstances similar to the Van Dusens' would you have made the same choice?

3. Consider the person discovering the Van Dusens within a reasonable period after they had taken the sleeping pills. Would that person have a moral obligation to revive them? Would the obligation be any different for a friend, relative, or family doctor?

JOSEPH FLETCHER

Elective Death

In choosing their time of death, the Van Dusens took a stand on a long-debated issue: whether an individual has the right to terminate his life. Though some major writers (Epicurus, Thomas More, John Donne, and Montaigne among them) have presented arguments in favor of the individual's right to choose his dying, the main current of Western thought has held that the proprietary right over human life rests with divine authority or with the state (often viewed as the earthly representative of the divine order) rather than with the individual.

In the following article, Fletcher argues that human needs validate human rights, so that in certain situations, a person has the right to end his own life. Fletcher bases his views on what he terms a "pragmatic situation ethic" and urges that the issue of when to terminate life be examined in the context of changing conditions.

> Vex not his ghost: O, let him pass! He
>   hates him
> That would upon the wrack of this
>   tough world
> Stretch him out longer.
>
> *Shakespeare*

Since we shoulder our responsibility for birth control, a feature of every civilized culture, can death control be far behind? If we have a right to initiate a life deliberately, may we not terminate one? Depending, of course, upon the circumstances?

There are really two questions here, one factual and one moral. In what follows, the thrust is toward answering both of them in the affirmative. To a certain extent these questions are mutually penetrating. In actual fact the practice of death control is

Source: Joseph Fletcher, "Elective Death." *Ethical Issues in Medicine.* Edited by E. Fuller Torey. Boston: Little, Brown and Company, 1968.

303

increasing, due to medical pressures and human needs so great that they provide their own moral justification. And as the practice is further justified by the situation, it is more easily and sensibly encouraged and disinhibited. It is exactly in this sense that I use the term *right*—as something justified pragmatically by the situation. Those who entertain any notion that there are some rights which are simply given in the very nature of things, above and beyond circumstances or human needs, will not be happy about everything I am about to say, and they ought to be alerted.

What is to be said to a nurse who is upset and suffers an acute anxiety reaction, unable to carry out her duty, because an intern, on instructions from a staff surgeon and a resident, has told her that a patient in the recovery room is to be "let go," and that she is to turn off the intravenous fluids and the oxygen? (Often only the slower strategy of starvation is used, without suffocation.) What is a man to do whose father has been lying virtually unconscious for four years in a hospital bed, following a massive cerebral hemorrhage? The patient cannot eat or speak; is incontinent, shows no neurological evidence of interpersonal communication and is kept going with tube feeding by around-the-clock private nurses. The patient's son would feel guilt about suggesting that the doctors bring it to a close, yet he also feels guilty about the expense ($40,000 a year), the wasted resources that other things and people need, and his father's distressingly subhuman status. After all, is the patient anymore his father?

Years ago, in 1954, I wrote that there is a logical contradiction in the Hippocratic Oath, subscribed to by the medical profession. As I saw it then, the Oath illogically promises two incompatible things, both to relieve suffering and, as I put it, to "Prolong and protect life."[1] But I was mistaken. Actually, there is not a word in that pious old apprenticeship agreement about either relieving suffering or prolonging life. Instead, the promise is to seek the "benefit of the sick," leaving the meaning of "benefit" unstipulated. The vitalistic idea that preserving life is the *summum bonum* of medicine appears nowhere in the Oath, except eisegetically (i.e., when read into it). On the contrary, making life sacrosanct was more likely a Pythagorean taboo, different from the empirical temper of Hippocrates and his case-minded approach. In place of such moral metaphysics, he said, in a famous maxim, "Life is short and art is long, the occasion fleeting, experience fallacious and judgment difficult." He knew the relativity of ethical decision. In fact, some of his disciples engaged in direct euthanasia on the same grounds that Plato, Socrates, Epicurus, and the Stoics approved it.[2]

In any case, what appeared to be ethical to whomever it was who wrote the Oath is not an eternal verity. Almost certainly it was not Hippocrates, as Edelstein has now made abundantly clear.[3] There is no reason to take that unknown moralist's understanding of right and wrong or good and evil as a permanent model of conscience for all times and all conditions. What is right or good does not transcend changing circumstances; it arises out of them.

When biologists predict that by, let us say the year 2100, men will be free of hunger and infectious diseases, able to enjoy physical and mental life to the age of 90 or 100, replacing defective parts of the body as need develops, cyborg fashion, we can hope that the frequency of treatment situations posing the question of elective death will be cut down. But sooner or later it will arise for many patients, no matter what the longevity norm may become. Paradoxically, modern medicine's success in prolonging life has itself directly increased the incidence of death control decisions in the chronic and terminal ills of the American people. Those over 65 are expected to increase from 18.5 million in 1966 to 24.5 million in 1980—something in the order of one out of every eight persons.

Novels in the classic tradition have drawn a picture of the deathbed scene where the elderly "pass on," surrounded by their families and friends, making their farewell speeches and *meeting* death instead of being overtaken or snatched by it. This model of death has become almost archaic. Nowadays, most of the time, death comes to people (even the young and middle aged) in a sedated and comatose state; betubed nasally, abdominally, and intravenously; and far more like manipulated objects than like moral subjects. A whole fascinating array of devices—surgical, pharmacological, and mechanical—is brought into play to stave death off clinically and biologically. Yet ironically, by their dehumanizing effects these things actually hasten personal death, i.e., loss of self-possession and conscious integrity. They raise in a new form the whole question of "life" itself, of how we are to understand it and whether the mere minimum presence of vital functions is what we mean by it.

For many people contemplating modern medicine's ability to prolong life (or, perhaps, to prolong death), death itself is welcome compared to the terrors of senility and protracted terminal treatment. Patients actually look for doctors who will promise not to allow them to "go through what mother did" or "lie there as Uncle John was made to." They are beginning to ponder ways of *escaping* medical ministrations; the white coats of our doctors and their paramedical attendants are taking on a grimmer hue, a new and less benign image. This is bound to increase as medicine's victories continue. It is a success problem, not a failure problem! The predominant illnesses become degenerative and chronic, not acute or infectious. Disorders in the metabolic group, cardiovascular ills, renal problems, and malignancies—these fill our hospital beds.

DEATH: ENEMY AND FRIEND

In all talk of elective death—that is, chosen or moral dying rather than fatal or amoral dying (*moral* always means the voluntary as against the involuntary or helpless)—the basic issue is whether human beings are always to regard death as an enemy, never as a friend. Is death never to be welcomed? May we never choose to go out and meet it? Dr. Logan Clendenning years ago, in his popularizing effort to make knowledge a part of the public's weaponry against illness, thought of it as being sometimes a friend. He wrote, "As I think it over, death seems to me one of the few evidences in nature of the operation of a creative intelligence exhibiting qualities which I recognize as mind stuff. To have blundered onto the form of energy called life showed a sort of malignant power. After having blundered on life to have conceived of death was a real stroke of genius."[4]

The logic of this is to either fight off or make an ally of *mortis,* as it happens to suit human needs. This is exactly what all medicine does; it either uses or outwits all biological forces for the sake of humanly chosen ends. Medicine is, at bottom, an interference with blind, brute nature. Three hundred years ago Thomas Sydenham called it "the support of enfeebled and the coercion of outrageous nature." Medicine refuses to "leave in God's (nature's) hands what must be" in everything else but death. Why should it stop there? Maurice Maeterlinck was sure that "there will come a day when science will protest its errors and will shorten our sufferings."⁵ And that day is at hand, precisely because of the achievements of medical science and the pressures such achievements create to rethink our values and our view of man.

Medicine's primary *raison d'être* is, in Albert Schweitzer's phrase, "reverence for life." Life is its business. This, however, is very far from absolutizing the vital spark regardless of human personality and its claims. To subordinate every other consideration to bare sentience is to make biological life, as such, an idol. It is the vitalistic error. Respiration, circulation, reflexes, and the like, are not ends in themselves. Can it not be that life in its fullest meaning includes death, and that, since death is certain to come whether it does so constructively or willy-nilly, the only real question open to us is how it comes, as a good death ("euthanasia") or a bad death ("dysthanasia")?

Dr. David Karnofsky, who did so much for the Sloan-Kettering Institute, put the point of view of radical vitalism very clearly, at a meeting of the American Cancer Society in 1961. He opposed letting the patient go under any circumstances, arguing that the practice of keeping the patient alive is endorsed by "state planners, efficiency experts, social workers, philosophers, theologians, economists and humanitarians." Apart from this being a pretty wild *omnium gatherum* (practically everybody in the helping professions), the accusation is symptomatic of the embattled, almost paranoid mentality of many physicians. Karnofsky's main professed reason for preserving life by any and all means as long as possible was the old statistical absurdity about "something might turn up at the last minute, some new discovery or an inexplicable remission." But what is more irresponsible than to hide from decision-making behind a logical possibility that is without antecedent probability?

As an example of "ethical" medicine, Dr. Karnofsky cited a patient with cancer of the large bowel. After a colostomy followed by recurrence, x-ray treatment was used; radioactive phosphorus checked abdominal fluids, and an antibiotic stopped broncho-pneumonia. Metastases ended liver function in spite of innumerable delaying actions, stupifying or traumatic, until the end "came." The patient was kept alive for ten months, but might otherwise have died in a matter of days or weeks. Was it right or wrong to add ten months? Was it more life or more death that was added? Who was benefited? What were the benefits? For Dr. Karnofsky, the obligation to maintain biological function or "life" was not a question of weighing benefits and forfeits. For him what is right or good was intrinsic; and life, as such, per se, was precious—of greater value than anything else. This is the fundamental question in all cases of ethical concern, not only in life and death. Is the worth or desirability of thing or action inherent and intrinsic, regardless of the situation; or do right and good depend contingently and extrinsically upon the situation? If you take the intrinsic position, then some if not all obligations are absolute and universal; if you take the extrinsic view, all are relative. Karnofsky, like many others, was an absolutist. I am not. On the absolutist view some things are never open to responsible decision and choice; in "situation ethics" everything is.

IMPORTANT DISTINCTIONS

It is at this point that we need to pause to make distinctions of some practical importance. In the management of terminal illness there are two distinct moral problems, closely related but by no means the same. One is the classic issue over *euthanasia;* the other, and by far the more pressing in its frequency, is "letting the patient go" or, as I have called it, *antidysthanasia.*[6] The classic debate was about "mercy killing," i.e., doing something directly to end a life graciously when it would otherwise go on (active euthanasia, it is sometimes called). The more pressing and more common issue is whether one may graciously refrain from procedures, not *doing* something but *omitting* to do something, so that death will come (in some circles this is called *passive euthanasia*). This second problem is the one that our success with prolongation and resuscitation forces upon us daily in hospitals all around the world. Possibly the best way to put the distinction with its various sides is to speak of euthanasia in four terms:

1. *Direct voluntary,* as when a patient consciously chooses to end it all, with or without medical intervention. Such is the case of the patient who sneaks an overdose or is left one within reach, or who swallows a Kleenex or pulls out a tube. It is deliberately done and consciously willed by the patient.
2. *Indirect voluntary,* as when a patient before reaching an unconscious or comatose state (while still competent and with a *mens sana* even if not *in corpore sano*) gives leave to his medical servants to use discretion about letting death come. This, too, the patient has willed, yet his death is not directly done but indirectly by ceasing opposition to it. Such is the case of those who, after consultation, "pull the plug" at some point of diminishing returns.
3. *Indirect involuntary,* as when a patient's wishes are not known and yet doctors and/or family and friends *choose for him* to stop fighting off death. Such is the case when the pain, subhuman condition, irreversibility, cost, injustice to others, and the like, combine to outweigh the benefits of keeping him alive. This third form is far and away the most typical and frequent situation—indirect euthanasia, without the patient's past or present opinion in the account, except as it might be presumed.
4. *Direct involuntary,* as when a patient's wishes are not known, yet in the judgment of physicians, family, or friends it seems better to them to end his life by a "mercy killing" than to let it go on, as it will. Such a case would be a decerebrated person, perhaps one whose cerebral cortex has been shattered in an auto accident, in "excellent health" biophysically, fed by indwelling nasal tubes, unable to move a muscle, suffers no pain but only reacts by reflex to a needle

prick. I know one such, a young man (who now looks like a little child), and his mother says, "My son is dead." Another case would be an obstetrician's decision not to respirate a monster at birth, or a "blue baby" deoxygenated beyond tolerable limits of cyanosis or brain suffocation.

Some moralists have tended to put great store by the distinction between "direct" and "indirect" actions, Roman Catholics, for example. They argue that it is one thing morally to *do* an act such as ending a life by "bare bodkin" (as Shakespeare put it), and another thing altogether to *permit* a life to end by starvation, as when an intravenous therapy is discontinued. To others this seems a cloudy and tenuous distinction. Either way the intention is the same, the same end is willed and sought. And the means used do not justify the end in one case if not the other, nor are the means used anything that *can* be justified or "made sense of" except in relation to the gracious purpose in view. Kant said, as part of his practical reason, that if we will the end, we will the means. Whether euthanasia is direct or indirect, voluntary or involuntary, is ethically something that *depends upon the facts in the situation,* not upon some intrinsic principle regardless of the realities. This is the shape of the tension between empirical and metaphysical moralities.

Curiously enough, in view of the religious and philosophical differences which divide moralists and ethicists, this matter of an alleged obligation to make the maintenance of a patient's life the supreme obligation is one around which moralists are pretty well united against the publicly professed opinion of the medical profession. (Note, I say "publicly.") That is, we find that Catholic, Protestant, Jewish, and humanist teachings all have a place for euthanasia in one form or another. Archbishop Temple,[7] the Anglican theologian, once said of pacifism what can be said of Karnofsky's radical vitalism, that it "can only rest upon a belief that life, physiological life, is sacrosanct. That is not a Christian idea at all; for, if it were, the martyrs would be wrong. If the sanctity is *in* life, it must be wrong to give your life in a noble cause as well as to take another's . . . Of course, this implies that, *as compared to some things*, the loss of life is a small evil; and, if so, then, *as compared to some other things*, the taking of life is a small injury."

Catholic moralists, and most orthodox Jews and most orthodox Protestants, are opposed to euthanasia in forms #1 and #4 (see previous list); i.e., they rule out as immoral any direct methods of ending a life in order to end suffering and waste. But they allow forms #2 and #3, the indirect strategies. Catholic theologians refuse to call the indirect forms "euthanasia," and they add a further *caveat* or limitation. Pius XII[8] and his interpreters have restricted even the indirect forms (both of which they justify) to permission to cease and desist from the use of "extraordinary" treatments only, where there is no reasonable hope of benefit. All ordinary treatments must continue without letup. Usually, *extraordinary* procedures are taken to be those that are expensive, painful, or inconvenient.[9]

The difficulty with this is, like so much else, due to the rapid advance of medical science and of the medical arts. Ordinary and extraordinary are very relative terms as the weaponry of health and control of nature's pathologies sweeps on. Look at how quickly penicillin ceased to be extraordinary, and also sulpha drugs and electronic cardiac devices such as the pacemakers. In no time prosthetic implants will be old hat. There is no way to establish a consensus (even if desirable) as to the defining features of an extraordinary treatment. Is it mortality rate, pain, inconvenience, expense, effectiveness, competence, subject's life expectancy (a lung removed in a child is not the same as in an old person), frequency, or what? And so it goes.

Those who live by situation ethics, and this includes many liberal Jews and Protestants and humanists (this writer being one), are ethically prepared to employ euthanasia in all four forms, depending in every actual case upon the circumstances. Nevertheless, no matter what rhetoric and doctrine are used at the theoretical level, there can be no doubt that in practice there is an increase of responsible situational decision making in proportion to the increase of the problem's occurrence in our hospitals. By now, due to greater longevity and medical know-how, it is an everyday, almost routine thing. Considerations of income and experience, especially in teaching hospitals, may tend to soft-pedal the issue and discourage it, but profit, training, and research are only brakes; they do not stop the trend to elective death. The frightening pressures of population only add to it. Sooner or later we shall be forced back on "statistical" morality. Speaking of a situation not unlike ours in America, the British medical journal *Lancet*[10] says: "If the average length of a patient's stay in a hospital is two weeks, a bed in that hospital occupied for a year could have been used by 26 other patients . . . In a country without a surplus of hospital beds, an irrevocably unconscious patient may sometimes be kept alive at the cost of other people's lives."

OBJECTIONS

In *Morals and Medicine* I have identified and thoroughly discussed ten different objections to euthanasia. I will not attempt to retrace all that ground but there are some elements in the traditional opposition to euthanasia (we can call it *elective death,* if we prefer) that keep cropping up. The objection that it is suicide is only an epithet which is not really in question. The objection that it is murder only begs the question, since the problem is precisely whether a *felo de se* for medical cause is to be held an unlawful killing or not. When people cite the Ten Commandments they often fail to note that the decalogue prohibits murder, not killing as such, and this too ties in with the whole question of licit and illicit dying and killing. Obviously the Jews, as well as their Christian cousins, have not been in any significant numbers vegetarians or pacifists or opposed to capital punishment.

Once a bishop castigated me for saying that by wanting to release those caught in a painful and incurable condition I was ignoring the theologically alleged benefit spiritually ("the redemptive effect") of suffering, as in Jesus' crucifixion. The bishop himself ignored the fact that sacrificial suffering is voluntary and chosen and conscious. There is nothing redemptive going on *in most instances* of terminal misery and loss of human functions. And when it is said that given the right to choose death too many would do it impulsively or connive and encourage it in others for selfish reasons (e.g., "to get the deed to the old home place"), what reply is needed other than *abusus non tollit usum,* the abuse of a thing does not rule out its use? Otherwise we should always have to repress any research, innovation, and development which enlarges our human control over the conditions of life, since all such power can be used for ill as for good.

Some say that if our society and culture tolerated suicide in such cases as we have mentioned the result would be a cheapening of life and weakening of our moral fiber.[11] They seem to think that all interest would be lost, for example, in intensive care units, and nobody would respond to emergency Code 90 calls! If there is danger of becoming hardened by the practice of death control, by the same token there is danger of becoming hardened by the constant practice of prolonging life beyond any personal or human state. Pope's lines on vice cut two ways: "Yet seen too oft, familiar with her face, We first endure, then pity, then embrace." It is at least possible that euthanasia could not have half the demoralizing influence of stockpiling and planning to use weapons of mass extermination, even "tactical" bombs, and the total war of modern military technology. Besides, not every human being cries, *Timor Mortis conturbat me* (the fear of death confounds me): there are the pure in heart who fear not. "It is safe," said C.S. Lewis, "to tell the pure in heart that they shall see God, for only the pure in heart want to."[12] The fear of the hereafter, among religious believers and skeptics alike, is nearly gone except for primitives and a few doctrinaire incorrigibles.

Perhaps the most anomalous stance in the whole developing discussion is the official or formal position of the medical fraternity, as taken in the American Medical Association and similar groups, that what they are opposed to only is making euthanasia *legal.* That is, they want to use their own discretion, as they are already doing, but they do not want any public acknowledgment that they have any such discretion or ever use it. The fact is, of course, that even in the case of euthanasia in form #3, doctors are vulnerable to malpractice suits ("failure to do what is of average competence and practice"). Hence the essentially scared and "phony" discussion in medical circles, and a tightly bound fraternal refusal to testify in court adversely to a fellow physcian no matter what the charge or the facts. In this matter as in so many others, the law, and the conventional wisdom, are hopelessly antediluvian when seen in the light of medicine's progress. But the day is coming when doctors will recognize that just as they are slowly accepting the morality of terminating some lives at the beginning (abortion) for therapeutic reasons of mental, emotional, and social well-being, so they should be terminating for these reasons some lives at the ending, i.e., therapeutic euthanasia.

It would be unfair to the morally muscle-bound and false to the facts to urge the case for euthanasia in any of its forms as if there were no difficulties. The finest diagnosticians and prognosticians are sometimes baffled. At best the safest way to describe a professional person, whatever his field, is as an educated guesser. We cannot be "sure" that the "hopeless" case is really hopeless. Resuscitation procedures now have greatly increased our chances of reviving drowned people or frozen people who not long ago were beyond help. So also with cardiac arrests, anoxia, some cerebral vascular lesions, spontaneous hypoglycemia, and the like. The exciting thing about medicine is that even though it magnifies the problem of medical initiative in death for the aged and the chronic, it reduces it for the young and the acute. Yet there is no escape from the necessity of decision, case by case. This is as true for "ending it all" or "letting him go" as for whether to operate or not. Nothing is certain but death itself, on its own terms or ours. But if in the face of man's finite knowledge and understanding of health, life, and death, even our physicians cannot make good *"guesstimates,"* then we are indeed trapped in a merely fatalistic web. But if they have a truly creative competence, as I believe they have, then why refuse them the initiative late and not early? What does it mean to "have" a doctor?

WHAT IS DEATH AND WHEN?

Back and behind this very human and crucial question of when death is to be accepted lies the question, "When *is* death?" And, in a way, *what* is death? Even the most pragmatic value problems presuppose profound philosophical or theological commitments. The outmoded legal definition of death nearly completely misses the mark in these days of biochemistry and death control, and of genetic control. Almost certainly the heart-and-lungs definition, by which life is supposed to be present if there is clinically detectable breathing or heartbeat, will have to go. We cannot use mad Lear's test of Cordelia's corpse: "Lend me a looking glass; If that her breath will mist or stain the stone, Why then, she lives."

The philosophy of elective death turns its advocates in the direction of determining death as present, or life gone, when a patient's EEG (electroencephalographic tracing) has remained flat for say 24 hours, regardless of other criteria such as respiration or heartbeat.[13] This is certainly a long enough anoxia or cessation of the bioelectric activity of the brain to establish cerebral death, *and cerebral death is death.* This is reported to have been adopted by the French Academy of Medicine, and neurologists everywhere (e.g., Clarence Carfoord of Sweden) advocate it.

The point to note is that modern medical thinking, using a conceptual apparatus drawn from scientific method, no longer regards life and death as *events.* They are seen and understood now as points along a biological continuum. This makes nonsense of much of the old-fashioned abortion debate about when conception occurs, at insemination or fertilization or development of the embryo to certain stages, and so on along the pregnancy line. In the same way it undercuts the argument about when death "occurs," because death is a *process,* not an event. And the core of it is not sentience of the body or some arbitrary minimum of vital functions; *it is the person, and mental function.* When mind is gone, in the degenerative process, and with it the homeostasis of the organism, then life is gone: death has come. Then, at least, if not before, let the battle stop.

It is this problematic character of both life and death, medically regarded, that lends so much interest to a suggestion from Dr. Charles K. Holling[14] of the College of Medicine in the University of Cincinnati: "Hospitals of the future may well have 'death boards.' Applications for permission to discontinue the artificial measures by which life is being maintained might be made to such boards either by the patient who is in possession of his mental faculties or by his next-of-kin." Such review boards could well have an ombudsman, an intelligent lay participant. Dr. Holling is using a model from the "TA" boards of hospitals, those that make decisions in cases of therapeutic abortion.

Bernard Shaw has Sir Patrick say, in *The Doctor's Dilemma,* "All professions are conspiracies against the laity." The old gambit of writing prescriptions in Latin to keep patients from knowing what they say will not work any longer. Medicine is not a "mystery" any more, and its practitioners no longer have a craft of which everybody else is totally ignorant. This is the age of science, and that means a unity of knowledge and freedom of exchange. Repressed knowledge does not stay repressed, as the growing membership of the Nuclear Nations Club attests. Among other things this means that the doctors are no longer alone or isolated in their decision making. In situation problems about terminal cases the physician does not have to cast his own vote alone and uncounted with others. Nor, given medicine's great gains, is the range of decisions as narrow as it once was. When we have to reckon with death, we need not always only glimpse it over our shoulder as we run. Indeed, if we run we are lost.

FATALITY OR INTEGRITY

There are deep-rooted psychic inhibitions which prevent us from seeing our problem in a rational and responsible perspective. There is, or has been, too much *mystique* and superstitious metaphysics about it. But now it presents itself as a challenge to human control, as distinguished from supernatural or natural and fatalistic control. It is a question of responsible control of life, not merely of health and wellbeing but of being itself. It is time we confronted theology's blanket denunciation of suicide and medicine's uncritical opposition to death.[15]

In the final analysis there are three postures we can assume. The one with the most tradition is absolutist. In its theological form it has been expressed in terms of a divine monopoly theory of life and death. It says that God is the creator of each person ("soul") and reserves to himself the right to decide when life shall come (as against birth control) and when death shall come (as against euthanasia). A much studied treatise in this old tradition says death control is "a violation of the property rights of Jesus Christ."[16] If the absolutist posture takes a nontheological shape it becomes radical vitalism or a sort of naturalistic mystique about life as the highest good and death the worst evil, regardless of the situation. It is the first posture, the absolutist one, which lends itself to accusations of "playing God" when elective death is discussed.

The second posture is the one of stoic indifference or anomie. Because it finds no meaning in existence, it assigns no real value to it and can as easily embrace endurance of life at its worst as repudiation of life at its best.

In between these two extremes of absolutism and adiaphorism lies the pragmatic situation ethic. It finds life good sometimes, and death good sometimes, depending upon the case, the circumstances, the total context. In this view life, no more than any other good thing or value, is good in itself but only by reason of the situation; and death, no more than any other evil, is evil in itself but only by reason of the situation. This is the method by which medicine makes decisions, and there is every reason why it should do so from first to last.

NOTES

1. J. Fletcher, *Morals and Medicine* (Princeton: Princeton University Press, 1954).
2. G. Williams, *The Sanctity of Life and the Criminal Law* (New York: Knopf, 1957).
3. L. Edelstein, *The Hippocratic Oath* (Baltimore: Johns Hopkins University Press, 1943).
4. L. Clendenning, *The Human Body,* 3rd ed. (New York: Knopf, 1941).
5. G.W. Jacoby, *Physician, Pastor and Patient* (New York: Hoeber, 1936).
6. J. Fletcher, "Death and Medical Initiative," *Folia Medica* (Tufts University) 7 (1962): 30.
7. W. Temple, *Thoughts in War Time* (London: Macmillan, 1940).
8. Pope Pius XII, *Acta Apostolicae Sedis* 49 (1957): 1027.
9. G. Kelly, *Medico-Moral Problems* (St. Louis: Catholic Hospital Association, 1958).
10. "The Prolongation of Dying." Editorial, *Lancet* 2 (December 8, 1962): 205.
11. E. Shils, "The Sanctity of Life," *Encounter* 28 (1967): 39.
12. P.S. Rhoads, "Management of the Patient with Terminal Illness," *J.A.M.A.* 192 (1965): 611.
13. H. Hamlin, "Life or Death by EEG," *J.A.M.A.* 190 (1964): 112.
14. C.K. Hofling, "Terminal Decisions," *Medical Opinion and Review* 2 (1966): 1.
15. J. Hillman, *Suicide of the Soul* (New York: Harper and Row, 1964).
16. A. Koch and A. Preuss, *Handbook of Moral Theology* (St. Louis: Herder, 1924).

MICHAEL D. BAYLES

The Price of Life

Fletcher places his argument of whether to terminate life between the extremes of absolutism and stoic indifference, claiming that the value of a decision is dependent upon its context. In the following article, Michael Bayles pushes the argument further, suggesting that it is both rational and morally justifiable to put a price on life. Focusing his discussion with the question "Is there a price for which one might reasonably sell one's last year of life?" he continues by demonstrating the numerous occasions on which society quite regularly puts a price on life. He then defends a willingness-to-pay method for making some social policy decisions.

It is often said that human life is priceless. No amount of money or other goods equals the value of a human life. The only justification for not preventing the loss of a human life when one can do so is that it would result in the loss of even more lives. In short, only human lives can be balanced against human lives.

The philosophical *locus classicus* for this view is Immanuel Kant's claim that human beings have a dignity but not a price. By 'price' he did not mean a merely monetary value but an equivalence. "Whatever has a price can be replaced by something else as its equivalent."[1] Thus, the claim that human lives are priceless is not merely that no monetary value can ethically be placed upon them, but that no exchange value of other goods can be placed upon them.

A distinct but correlated claim is that all human lives are of equal value. The pricelessness of human life does not imply that all lives are of equal value. Some lives might be more priceless than others just as some infinities are greater than others. However, it does make plausible their having equal value. If no price or value can be assigned to lives, there is no obvious basis for comparative judgments of their value, and they should be treated equally. Contrarily, if human lives do have a price, it is a priori unlikely that all have the same value or price.

Source: Reprinted from *Ethics* 89:1 (October, 1978): 20–34 by permission of the University of Chicago Press, ©1978 by the University of Chicago Press.

The issues of whether human lives have a price, and if so, what it is, constantly recur in bioethics and social policy generally. The distinction between ordinary and extraordinary lifesaving treatment as used by some authors partially depends on the cost of the treatment.[2] If it is permissible to forgo lifesaving treatment because of its cost, life has a monetary price. Issues about the investment of money in research on lifesaving technologies may frequently involve prices of lives. If there are economic limits on the amount of money that should be invested in lifesaving technologies, prices are appropriately placed on lives. Moreover, questions about the purchase or use of lifesaving technologies involve the pricing of life. For example, because of the cost involved, New York City recently considered not acquiring a burn center even though its acquisition would save about a dozen lives a year.

The corollary of the equal value of human lives also frequently arises in bioethics. Questions about which research programs on lifesaving technologies should be funded—those aimed at diseases of the young, the middle aged, or the elderly—raise the issue of whether all lives are of equal value. It is also involved in determining criteria for selecting patients for scarce lifesaving treatments, such as kidney transplants. Different criteria or methods of selection will be used, depending on whether all lives are judged to be of equal value. If they are not, random or first-come selection methods are less plausible.

This paper argues that (1) it is rational and morally permissible to place a price on one's own life, and (2) there is a morally acceptable method of using this pricing to determine some social policies. The argument for the first claim also provides reasons for lives having different values or prices. The argument for the second claim does not establish a method for assigning a price to the life of an individual human being. Such a method is often not directly needed. If one can price lives so that policies and rules may be established, individual cases will often be decided by the application of such rules and policies. If a burn center is not worth having, then the fate of individual burn patients is determined. There will still be some occasions when decisions must be made between individuals—for example, which of two patients will receive an organ for transplantation. This paper does not attempt to provide principles for making those decisions.

In the next section the issues are clarified, and some preliminary observations are made which cast doubt upon the claim of pricelessness. The second section then argues that people can rationally and morally place a price upon their own lives. The third section defends a version of the willingness-to-pay method for making some social policy decisions about investment in lifesaving technologies.

1. PROPAEDEUTIC

Three important distinctions should be made with respect to price-of-life issues. First, one should distinguish issues of amount and of distribution. This distinction is especially important at the level of government health policy. One question is, How much money should be invested in research on, or provision of, lifesaving technologies? Should the U.S. government invest 3 billion dollars in lifesaving health research, or only 200 million, or perhaps none? In short, how much is it worth to prevent deaths? The other question is, How should funds be distributed? Should allocations emphasize research to prevent deaths of infants, the elderly, or members of specific minorities? Some proposed principles pertain only to the distribution issue, while others pertain to both the distribution and amount issues. A distribution principle need not be based on the price of human life, although if lives do have varying prices this will affect judgments about distribution.

Second, one should distinguish between the price of life per se and the price of the lives of existing people. Some people claim life itself, whether human or nonhuman, has value and should be respected. One version of this claim even supports producing human lives. Yet one may deny that life itself is valuable and still hold that the lives of existing people are priceless. So put, the issue is not whether there is a price of a person's entire life, but whether there is a price of a segment of it—at most, the rest of his potential life.

Third, one should distinguish between what may be called personal and social price. Personal price is that which an individual places on his own life, its value to him. Social price is the value of an individual's life to others. One may also distinguish between descriptive and normative social price. The descriptive social price of an individual's life is that which others in fact place upon it, while the normative social price is that which others should place upon it. The claim that human lives are priceless partially stems from the fears that if human lives are priced the descriptive rather than the normative social price will be used, and personal price will be completely ignored.

While it does not prove that morally human life has a price, it is worth noting that society does price human lives. Descriptive social prices are used to make decisions. In building skyscrapers, a predictable number of construction workers will be killed. Yet the building is thought to be worth the expected loss. However, one may say that the workers knowingly and voluntarily assume the risk of losing their lives. In highway construction, lives are also calculated against costs. There are known costs and accident rates for various types of highway construction. It is less plausible that those killed on highways knowingly and voluntarily assumed the risk. People do not know the risks of accident on various highways and hence do not choose their travel routes accordingly. At best, they voluntarily assume a range of risk in using highways. Similarly, various products, from electric toasters to snowmobiles, have associated risks of death in their use, risks which could be minimized if not eliminated, but at such a cost that those making and buying them do not think it is worth doing.

It is sometimes objected that such examples are merely pricing statistical risks. They do not price the life of a known individual who will certainly die if one alternative is chosen. However, this objection is not satisfactory.[3] First, statistics are composed of what happens to real individuals. Statistical lives are not imaginary ones but those of living, breathing human beings. Second, while it may be psychologically more difficult to condemn known individuals, rather than indeterminate ones, to death because it is too expensive to save them, that fact does not show anything about the morality of doing so.

One may reply that people do in fact think human lives are priceless and that only the anonymity of statistics allows them to price human lives. However, this claim may be reversed. Knowing the particular individuals involved may provide a psychological bar to doing what one thinks is morally permissible. For example, there are those of us who believe it morally permissible to kill and eat chickens but find it psychologically difficult to wring a chicken's neck, cut out its guts, and then cook and eat it. That does not show we believe it wrong to eat chickens, only that we have weak wills or stomachs—a luxury afforded only in modern industrialized societies.

These cases of statistical pricing of human lives present a challenge to those who claim that lives are priceless. It is incumbent on them to suggest alternative practices. It will not do to say that there are no alternatives, that these practices must be accepted as part of the human tragedy, for there are alternatives. Products could be required to be completely harmless before their use is permitted; funds could be invested in highway construction to make highways as safe as technically possible. The human tragedy, if there is one, is that it is impossible to make all products and technologies absolutely safe.

2. THE PRICE OF ONE'S OWN LIFE

If human lives are priceless, then it is irrational or immoral to place a price on one's own life. Kant consistently held that one cannot rationally place a price on one's own life. He held that suicide to avoid misery and pain is irrational and immoral. However, he did accept risking one's life in moral actions—for example, to save the lives of others. Ultimately, Kant believed that only the rational self, as opposed to the animal self, has absolute value. In suicide, he thought, one sacrifices the rational self for an end of inclination, for the animal self. Without Kant's metaphysical dualism which ultimately places the source of all moral value outside the phenomenal world, his argument for the pricelessness of human life collapses. Although I cannot argue it here, I shall assume that Kant's metaphysical dualism is untenable.

Is there a way to argue for the pricelessness of human life without adopting Kant's metaphysical dualism? In a recent paper, Kenneth Henley has suggested an alternative.[4] He is concerned to show that individuals are irreplaceable. If they are, then by Kant's definition there is nothing of equivalent value, and they are priceless. He concedes that if they are irreplaceable, then they cannot be valued for their qualities and characteristics. If they were valued for characteristics, then there could, logically, be another individual with these characteristics who would serve as a replacement. However, he asks whether it is irrational to value oneself, as an individual, as irreplaceable. While no reasons can be given for so valuing oneself, he concludes that although egotistic concern for self is unreasoned it is not irrational.

However, showing that it is not irrational to value oneself as irreplaceable does not show that one values oneself as priceless. The Kantian definition of pricelessness as irreplaceability breaks down because the concepts are not the same. I may consider myself irreplaceable in the sense that if "I" die, there will never be another "me." No matter how like me, another being would not be "me." Nevertheless, my continued existence might have a price to me. Even though "I" cannot be replaced, something of equivalent or greater value might be exchanged for "me."

Suppose it were possible to accurately predict how long a person would live. One could always know, say, to the day, how much longer one would live. Further suppose that for some reason another person were willing to pay one to die a year earlier than otherwise. For example, he might want to receive one's heart in a transplant and need it a year before one would die. Is there a price for which one might reasonably sell one's last year of life? Would one sell it for a quarter of a million dollars now? Whether one would be willing to sell, and the price one might demand, depends on a number of factors. For example, a person's present financial condition would obviously affect the price and even the willingness to sell at all. Likewise, the predictable quality of life one would have the last year may also make a difference. If one would be physically or mentally incapacitated and in considerable pain, one might sell for less. While there are many variables, the basic question is whether, on the most favorable assumptions one may make, it would ever be rational to be willing to sell the last year.

Certainly it would not be irrational for some people to do so on some terms in some circumstances. Their last year of life may rationally have a price to them. Indeed, one can imagine circumstances in which one might rationally assign a negative price to one's last year of life. One would be so incapacitated and suffer so much that it would be worth paying a certain amount of money now to be sure that one died a year early. One might be willing to hire a "euthanasist" to ensure that one did not live it. Generally, negative prices will be much smaller than positive ones, because it is comparatively easy to bring about one's early demise.

Some people may not be willing to sell a year of their life for any amount of money. It does not follow that a year of life does not have a price to them. They might exchange it for some nonmonetary benefit—for example, a year of private tutoring by Willard Quine or writing the most significant philosophical work of the century. These prices are not significantly different from money. Except perhaps by misers, money is not valued for its own sake but for the things it buys. A monetary price merely indicates that there are purchasable goods or services of an equivalent value. There is no more reason to disparage a monetary price than there is anything which money can buy. While there are things money cannot buy—love, true friends, and happiness—that they are not in the market is no indication of their value. Hatred and enemies are also not in the market, but they are not thereby valuable. The difference is merely one of production technique, and it may be possible to develop techniques such as drugs or brain implants which produce happiness or love.

It may be objected that this argument merely shows that people may rationally put a price on their lives, not that it is morally permissible for them to do so. In particular, one may object that it is rational for them to do so only because unjust social conditions might force them to sell. However, one must distinguish the questions whether it is immoral to offer to buy a person's life and whether it is immoral for him to sell it. Even if buyers immorally exploit sellers, it does not follow that the sellers are immoral. Moreover, even if one assumes a morally just society, it does not follow that there might not be things for which one would be willing to sell the last year of one's life. A morally just society does not guarantee that all one's desires will be satisfied. Consequently, there may still be good reasons for being willing to sell the last year of one's life.

It may be further objected that, even if the argument shows that part of one's life may rationally have a price, that is different from showing that the rest of one's life may rationally have a price. The structure of the argument is that one be willing to forgo the last year of one's life in exchange for benefits now. As one progressively sells more and more of one's remaining life, one has less and less time to enjoy the benefits derived from selling it. At the point of selling the rest of one's life, one has run out of time in which to enjoy the benefits for which one has sold it. That means, in effect, that there can be no benefits from selling it, and so it has become priceless.

This counterargument takes too narrow a view of what might count as benefits, what might be the price. One can distinguish between the satisfaction and the fulfillment of a desire. The satisfaction of a desire is the psychological state of a person who knows (or believes) that a desired state of affairs obtains (or will certainly obtain). The fulfillment of a desire is the obtaining of the desired state of affairs.

The state of affairs one desires need not include oneself in any way. My desire for the experience of sexual intercourse can be fulfilled only if I exist, but my desire for peace in the world may be fulfilled even if I do not exist. The preceding objection mistakenly assumes that the price of life must always be, at least indirectly, the fulfillment of a desire for a state of affairs including oneself. Since desires are not so limited, one may "sell" the rest of one's life provided the price is some state of affairs not involving oneself. Obviously, there are many such prices. Moreover, they need not involve saving the lives of other persons. For example, the price might be the happiness of one's children while they live but not extra life for them. Or it might be the continued existence of condors for two centuries. Moreover, many of these prices have monetary equivalents—for example, the rest of one's life for a million-dollar contribution to the Salvation Army. The price may even be rather "selfish," for example, a monument commemorating one's selling of one's life. At best, the price of the rest of one's life must not depend on one's personal existence.

Pricing part of one's remaining life may be viewed as a willingness to exchange the length of one's life for its quality in the sense of fulfillment of desires. At this point, it may be useful to classify technologies with respect to their impact upon length and quality of life. Some technologies shift the incidence of death but involve a net extension of lives in society. For example, the introduction of railroads shortened the lives of many people but may have increased overall life expectancy in society by providing faster transportation of food, medical supplies, etc. If those who lived longer gained more life years than those who died earlier lost, railroads were a life-extending technology. There are also some merely life-shortening technologies—nuclear weapons, biochemical-warfare materials, etc.

Other technologies may be both life shortening and life enhancing. Electric toasters have probably not saved any lives and have caused some to be lost, but they provide convenience. Motorcycles and cigarettes may also be in this category. Technologies that shorten but enhance life decrease expectable life yet provide benefits which improve its quality (or at least are thought to do so by those who use them). The use of such technologies involves placing a price on part of one's life. One exchanges part of one's life for something of equivalent or greater value. Nonsmokers have difficulty understanding the attitude of smokers who are willing to accept a lower life expectancy for what they consider to be the benefits of smoking, but many nonsmokers use other shortening but enhancing technologies or engage in activities which are such—climbing mountains or eating high-cholesterol foods.

It may be objected that these cases differ from the earlier one about selling part of one's life. In these latter cases, there is no certainty that one will die early, only a risk of doing so. This objection is similar to the one about statistically predictable deaths from highway construction. Some, maybe even many, people take risks because they discount them psychologically. They may well know the risk, say, of lung cancer from smoking cigarettes. However, they may think that it will not happen to them, only to others, or they may ignore it because it will occur many years hence. Nonetheless, while some people delude themselves, not everyone does. People have differing values and desires; some like cigarettes, others fatty foods, others mountain climbing, and some all three. The logical structure of the valuing is the same in risk taking as in selling part of one's life. One trades expectable quantity of life for quality of life.

One can thus explain why individuals may rationally be unwilling to invest in some lifesaving technologies. They have a price on the extra life they might gain from the investment. The cost of the investment is higher than that price. Thus, they prefer money to obtain benefits now to life later. The benefits are of greater value to them than the possibility of longer life.

A further question is whether the price of life may vary. First, one might claim that life has a uniform price, that each year of life is of equal value. However, this view does not allow for positive and negative pricing. On it, one cannot claim that life with great incapacities and suffering is not worth living—for all life is of equal value. In short, this view does not allow differences in the quality of life to affect its price.

Second, some views allow for a distinction between lives of positive and negative prices but not among those with a positive price. There is some standard or capacity or whatever which makes life have positive as opposed to negative value, but all life of positive value is of equal value. For example, some views claim that certain capacities are necessary for being a person and having a right to life. Such a standard is plausible for distinguishing between beings which have a right to life and those which do not. However, it is not plausible if taken to mean that all lives are of equal value to those who live them.

If the price of life is a judgment of quality against length, equal price of life must mean equal quality of life. If quality of life may vary, different periods of one's life may have different prices. If old age involves a lower quality of life, the price per year of life then will be lower than the price per year of life during youth or middle age when quality is higher. Exactly how these prices vary depends on what a person takes to be the qualities which give life value and his expectations of these qualities at different times of life. Moreover, if people's personal prices of life may vary over time, then different people's lives may have different personal prices. Even at the same age, people's prices will vary depending on the quality of life they have. Thus, there is no reason to expect the same price structure for all people. Moreover, one cannot get around these variations by ascribing them to social injustice. Differential pricing of lives is not solely due to differences in income, etc., but also to differences in desires and values. Only if all people had precisely the same desires and values would their prices be the same.

3. LIFESAVING AS A COLLECTIVE GOOD

Even if it is rational and morally permissible for an individual to place a price on part of his life, it does not follow that there is a rational and morally permissible method for pricing lives for social policy decisions. There are "scientific" problems, such as construction and timing of surveys, in using all of the proposed methods. The discussion here is confined to moral problems. Before developing the moral grounds for a modified willingness-to-pay method, it is useful to look briefly at problems with the other commonly suggested methods—the maximum life-years-saved and human-capital methods.

The maximum life-years-saved method is to invest in those lifesaving technologies which will save the most years of life for a given investment. In short, one saves those lives which one can at least cost. However, this method ignores differences in personal prices; that is, it mistakenly assumes that life is of equal quality and price at all stages for all people.

One could, to some extent, account for quality of life by using a more complex measurement of quality-adjusted life-years.[5] However, even so adjusted, this method still does not do the job that needs to be done. Maximizing life-years or quality-adjusted life-years saved is basically a method for distributing funds. While it does permit cost-effective analyses to determine in which lifesaving technologies to invest a given sum of money, it does not help determine how much money, if any, ought to be invested. In short, it determines only distribution, not amounts, of investment. It does not permit one to judge that the cost of saving a life is simply too great.

The human-capital or livelihood approach, which is the oldest and most widely used method,[6] does enable one to determine both amount and distribution of investment. By this method, the price of a life is the discounted value of the potential earnings of a person for the rest of his expectable life. Others have presented detailed criticisms of this approach which need not be repeated here.[7] One major flaw is that it allows for vast differences in the price of lives depending upon people's expectable incomes. High-income earners receive preference for lifesaving technologies. Given the present economic structure of the United States, lives of males are thus usually preferable to those of females (except in old age), and those of whites to those of blacks. It also supports a prime-of-life subprinciple, with emphasis on saving lives of young adults, since peak discounted earnings occur around the age of thirty.

The human-capital approach does not satisfactorily account for the personal prices of lives. It primarily uses the social price of life, monetary earnings. Personal pricing is accounted for only to the limited extent that personal price is proportional to expectable income. Moreover, discounted expectable income is not even a good index of social price. The value of one spouse to another does not depend solely on the first spouse's expected earnings. Factors such as love and companionship are also relevant to the value one spouse has for another.

It is useful to back off and examine the sort of problem involved in the provision of lifesaving technologies. Both the life-years-saved and human-capital methods view the problem as one of production. On the human-capital approach, it is one of rational economic production. Lives are priced by their contribution to the gross national product, with all the inadequacies of the GNP as a social measurement. Thus, one saves a life if its economic value is greater than the cost of saving it. The life-years or quality-adjusted life-years-saved method also has a production perspective, although it has a more humane notion of what is being produced. As a variant of the total version of utilitarianism, it essentially adopts what has been called the "milk production model." The more milk of better quality produced the better.

Instead of the perspective of a producer, one may adopt that of a taxpayer-consumer or simply a citizen. From this perspective, the development or distribution of many lifesaving technologies is a collective-good problem. By a collective good is here meant something from which many people may benefit but which individuals cannot feasibly provide for themselves. The cost of developing or distributing many lifesaving technologies is too great for any one person to bear for his own benefit. Yet many people perceive these lifesaving technologies as a benefit or good for them. They are not benefits to most people in that their lives will actually be saved by better highways, a burn center, or a cure for cancer. Instead, they are benefits in that the availability of the technologies, should they need them, is valued by most people. Since most people desire the technologies but cannot afford the total cost of providing them, the problem is one of getting everyone (or nearly everyone) to contribute a portion of the cost of their provision. Often this contribution is made by taxes for government funding of research or of distribution of the technologies. The subsequent discussion is limited to those lifesaving technologies which are collective goods to be provided by governments. Extension of the method developed to other technologies, or those not provided by the government, requires a more complex analysis.

Viewing lifesaving technologies as collective goods to be provided by governments leads naturally to use of the willingness-to-pay method for social decisions about investment in them. The simple model is that each person is asked how much he would be willing to pay for a technology which would have a probability P of saving his life or x number of lives. One then totals the amounts individuals are willing to pay. If the total amount people are willing to pay exceeds the cost of the technology, then it is worthwhile. One can then rank technologies by the differences between the total amount people are willing to pay and their costs. The more the amount people are willing to pay exceeds the cost, the higher the priority of the technology. If the total amount people are willing to pay is less than the cost of the technology, then it is not worthwhile.

One major virtue of this method is that it uses people's own pricing of their lives at different times. The human-capital approach essentially operates on a social price system. However, what a person is willing to pay largely depends on the chance of saving his life and its value to him. The method thus avoids making decisions solely on the basis of social price. To the extent people object to pricing lives because personal prices are ignored, it avoids the objection. However, there are number of moral objections to the willingness-to-pay method. Avoiding them requires modifying it.

The most serious objections to the willingness-to-pay method are those of justice and equality. How much one would be willing to pay is usually a function of how much one has. A person who earns $50,000 a year would be willing to pay more for a given technology than would a person who desires it as much but earns only $5,000 a year. Thus, there would be a greater total willingness to pay for cures of diseases affecting the rich than of those afflicting the poor. Since the government is to provide the technologies, the method supports a plutocracy rather than a democracy in which people's desires count equally.

However, one can modify the model to make it more democratic. Each person's "vote" for investment in lifesaving technology may be made as equal as possible. Instead of asking how many dollars a person would be willing to pay, one might ask how large a percentage tax increase he would be willing to pay. However, if there is a diminishing marginal utility of income, then wealthier people may be willing to pay a larger percentage of their income than the poor. The goods they thereby forgo are of lesser value to them than those purchased at lower incomes. Hence, there would still be a plutocratic slant to the voting.

Progressive income taxes are widely thought to be designed to avoid this problem. With a progressive income tax, the question may be put in terms of a percentage surcharge on taxes paid. Thus, a 1 percent surcharge for a technology would be five dollars for a person paying $500 in taxes, while it would be fifty dollars for someone paying $5,000. If a majority of people would be willing to pay a 1 percent surcharge and that would fund a technology, then it would be worth doing.

By considering differences between the surcharge needed to pay for a program and that which people would be willing to pay, one can account for strength of desire. Suppose funding a technology would require a 3 percent surcharge. Further, suppose 40 percent of the population would be willing to pay a 5 percent surcharge, but 60 percent would be willing to pay only a 2 percent surcharge. On a straight equal-"voting" method, the technology would not be justified. However, the feelings of the 60 percent who would be opposed to the technology at 3 percent are not as strong as those of the 40 percent who would favor it. The 60 percent opposed have a strength of aversion of one (3 percent minus 2 percent), while the 40 percent in favor have a strength of desire of two (5 percent minus 3 percent). If one weighs "votes" by strength of desire and aversion, then the technology is favored by a factor of four to three (forty times two to sixty times one).

Another objection based on equality is that certain causes of death are confined to relatively specific groups. For example, Tay-Sachs disease primarily affects

Ashkenazic Jews. Since those at risk are a very small proportion of the population, most people would know they were not at risk and would be unwilling to pay to save lives from Tay-Sachs. In short, since many people know that they are not at risk of certain causes of death, they are not willing to pay to prevent them. Thus, lifesaving technologies to prevent deaths confined to clearly defined subpopulations would rarely be supported, but this is unjust.

This objection is not as serious as it seems. First, the method to take account of strength of desire partially alleviates this problem. If a minority has a stronger desire for a technology than a majority has aversion to paying for it, then it might be supported. Second, even those not at risk might be willing to pay some money to save the lives of others. The extent to which they would be willing to do so depends upon their benevolence and the contributions they believe people saved might make to society. Those not at risk may have purely self-interested reasons for saving the lives of some people; that is, they can vote the social price of others to them. Moreover, to the extent that people are benevolent, they will pay for lifesaving technologies even when they cannot expect to benefit personally from them in any way.

It may plausibly be argued that since social prices reflect judgments about the worth of other people, they should not be permitted in calculations for government decisions. Only personal preferences—those for one's own enjoyment of goods and opportunities—not external preferences—those for the allocation of goods and opportunities to others—should count.[8] However, external preferences are primarily objectionable when they are used to override others' personal preferences. In the present case, they only support fulfillment of others' personal preferences. People may be willing to pay for a technology from which they will not directly benefit and thus help fulfill others' personal preferences. However, as the most negative vote possible is merely not to help, they cannot express negative judgments on saving others' lives. In short, the method allows for benevolence but not malevolence. Moreover, in the absence of sufficient benevolence to justify governmental provision of a technology benefiting a minority, it is still open to those who desire it to combine together to obtain it.

Still, with the willingness-to-pay method, the fewer people at risk, the less likely it is that investment in a lifesaving technology will be justified. But is this implication wrong? Would there not be alternative investments which would be more worthwhile? The modified willingness-to-pay method places highest priority on those technologies saving the lives most desired, with descending priority as fewer people are involved (or strength of desire is less). Eventually there is a point, depending upon the prevalence and strength of desires—including those of benevolence—at which a lifesaving technology is not worth its cost. Any view which takes pricing lives seriously will conclude that some lives are not worth saving at the required price.

Finally, it may be objected that some people are used as means only, because they are required to pay more for the benefit of others than they are willing to do voluntarily. Theoretically, no one need be compelled to pay involuntarily. With the willingness-to-pay method, if technologies are purchased only at prices everyone is willing to pay, then no one is being used as a means to the benefit of others. Everyone would desire the technology at that price; it would be an end each sought. However, this criterior would amount to unanimous-consent democracy and is unrealistic.

Given that this theoretical ideal will not always be achieved, how frequently and how many people will have to pay amounts they are unwilling to pay depends upon how much support is required before a program is adopted. However, no matter what method is used, in any government program some people will be required to pay for lifesaving technologies when they do not want to. With the modified willingness-to-pay method, fewer people would be so used, or they would be used to a lesser extent, than with any other common method, since the other methods do not even consider people's willingness to pay. The more they support providing lifesaving technologies, which the modified willingness-to-pay method does not, the more people will be forced to make unwilling sacrifices for others.

In conclusion, the modified willingness-to-pay method is a morally acceptable one for government decisions for investing in lifesavying technologies which are collective goods. It takes account of people's personal pricing of their lives more than the other methods. Social prices primarily enter as benevolent contributions to other. By using a surcharge on income taxes, it avoids plutocratic skewing of decisions due to possibly unjust distributions of wealth. By giving weight to the strength of desire for lifesaving technologies, it is more reflective of people's desires than a simple voting procedure. Based on people's willingness to pay, it minimizes the frustration of involuntary payments more than any other feasible method. Not all possible lifesaving technologies will be justified by this method, but that is simply the ultimate price of life.

NOTES

1. Immanuel Kant, *Foundations of the Metaphysics of Morals with Critical Essays,* trans. Lewis White Beck, ed. Robert Paul Wolff (Indianapolis: Bobbs-Merrill, 1969), p. 60 (Akademie pagination 434).
2. See, e.g., Edwin F. Healey, S.J., *Medical Ethics* (Chicago: Loyola University Press, 1956), p. 67.
3. I assume that no special relationship, such as doctor-patient or parent-child, exists. Some arguments for distinguishing between the morality of risking statistical lives and risking lives of known individuals only pertain to special relationships (see, e.g., Charles Fried, *Medical Experimentation: Personal Integrity and Social Policy,* Clinical Studies, vol. 5 [New York: American Elsevier, 1974], pp. 67–78, 133, 156).
4. Kenneth Henley, "The Value of Individuals," *Philosophy and Phenomenological Research* 37 (1977): 345–352.
5. Richard Zeckhauser and Donald Shepard, "Where Now for Saving Lives?" *Law and Contemporary Problems* 40, no. 3 (Autumn 1976): 5–45.
6. Rashi Fein, "On Measuring Economic Benefits of Health Programs," in *Ethics and Health Policy,* ed. Robert M. Veatch and Roy Branson (Cambridge, Mass.: Ballinger, 1976), pp. 262–63; generally, pp. 262–69.
7. Jan Paul Acton, "Measuring the Monetary Value of Lifesaving Programs," *Law and Contemporary Problems* 40, no. 3 (Autumn 1976): 46–72.
8. Ronald Dworkin, *Taking Rights Seriously* (Cambridge, Mass.: Harvard University Press, 1977), pp. 234–38, 275–76.

ANNE SEXTON

Suicide Note

While Michael Bayles raised the question of the price of life in the hypothetical or philosophic mode, Anne Sexton's poem reminds the reader that the answer is given in terms of personal experience. The speaker in the following work asserts that "everyone has a death/ his own death/ waiting for him." The right of the individual to choose the best route is proclaimed amidst a tense struggle that provides the central dynamic of the poem.

Suicide notes are typically unrevealing, perhaps because the act of ending one's life requires such concentrated psychic effort. Sylvia Plath's final note, for instance, was stark in its brevity: "Please call Dr. ———," with a phone number following. Yet, the poetry preceding her death stands as an articulate testimony to her increasing preoccupation with self-destruction. In like manner, the final poems of Anne Sexton analyze the decision to die.

You speak to me of narcissism but I reply that it is a matter of my life.

Artaud

At this time let me somehow bequeath all the leftovers to my daughters
and their daughters.

Anonymous

> Better,
> despite the worms talking to
> the mare's hoof in the field;
> better,
> despite the season of young girls
> dropping their blood;
> better somehow
> to drop myself quickly
> into an old room.
> Better (someone said)
> not to be born

326

Source: Anne Sexton. "Suicide Note." *Live or Die*. Boston: Houghton Mifflin Company, 1966.

and far better
not to be born twice
at thirteen
where the boardinghouse,
each year a bedroom,
caught fire.

Dear friend,
I will have to sink with hundreds of others
on a dumbwaiter into hell.
I will be a light thing.
I will enter death
like someone's lost optical lens.
Life is half enlarged.
The fish and owls are fierce today.
Life tilts backward and forward.
Even the wasps cannot find my eyes.

Yes,
eyes that were immediate once,
Eyes that have been truly awake,
eyes that told the whole story—
poor dumb animals.
Eyes that were pierced,
little nail heads,
light blue gunshots.

And once with
a mouth like a cup,
clay colored or blood colored,
open like the breakwater
for the lost ocean
and open like the noose
for the first head.

Once upon a time
my hunger was for Jesus.
O my hunger! My hunger!
Before he grew old
he rode calmly into Jerusalem
in search of death.

This time
I certainly
do not ask for understanding
and yet I hope everyone else

will turn their heads when an unrehearsed fish
    jumps
on the surface of Echo Lake;
when moonlight,
its bass note turned up loud,
hurts some building in Boston,
when the truly beautiful lie together.
I think of this, surely,
and would think of it far longer
if I were not . . . if I were not
at that old fire.

I could admit
that I am only a coward
crying *me me me*
and not mention the little gnats, the moths,
forced by circumstance
to suck on the electric bulb.
But surely you know that everyone has a death,
his own death,
waiting for him.
So I will go now
without old age or disease,
wildly but accurately,
knowing my best route,
carried by that toy donkey I rode all these years,
never asking, "Where are we going?"
We were riding (if I'd only known)
to this.

Dear friend,
please do not think
that I visualize guitars playing
or my father arching his bone.
I do not even expect my mother's mouth.
I know that I have died before—
once in November, once in June.
How strange to choose June again,
so concrete with its green breasts and bellies.
Of course guitars will not play!
The snakes will certainly not notice.
New York City will not mind.
At night the bats will beat on the trees,
knowing it all,
seeing what they sensed all day.

June 1965

EDWIN S. SHNEIDMAN

The Enemy

"Individuals who are actively suicidal suffer—among their other burdens—from a temporary loss of the view of death-as-enemy," according to Edwin Shneidman. Shneidman claims that in most life-destructive acts there is at least a degree of ambivalence. Noting that it is possible to make the choice to die in many different ways, he explains that it is important to consider the degree of conscious and unconscious intentions in bringing about one's death. In his analysis of intentionality in death-related behaviors, Shneidman counters the notion that our age is one of denial with his claim that the prospect of "megadeath in the nuclear age" has instead produced a death-oriented society. Yet, he concludes, the consequences of such an orientation are more often romanticization than acceptance of death.

This may be an age of youth but it is also an age of death. Death is in the air; none of us is more than minutes away from death by nuclear incineration. Life has become both more dear and more cheap. And if it can be taken by others it can also be thrown away by oneself. Senseless killing and the wanton destruction of one's own mind reflect the same debasement of man's basic coin: life itself. In the Western world we are probably more death-oriented today than we have been since the days of the black plague in the 14th century.

The young reveal an acute sensitivity to life-and-death issues. I believe that they can best be seen as children of The Bomb. At Harvard last year my course on death was scheduled in a room with 20 chairs. Having been for over 20 years one of the few researchers who concentrated on death phenomena—my original focus was on suicide prevention—I had come to assume that only a few would want to deal with the subject. To my surprise more than 200 undergraduates from Radcliffe and Harvard showed up for the first session. Much of my recent work grew out of the introspective reports and papers completed by the participants in that course. The students' painful awareness of death, long before the season regarded as appropriate, has helped me to grasp the difference between individual death as it has long been perceived and the prospect of megadeath in the nuclear age.

At first thought, "death" is one of those patently self-evident terms, the definition of which need not detain a thoughtful mind for even a moment. Every mature person knows instinctively what he means by it. A dictionary defines death as the act or event or occasion of dying; the end of life. As far as the person himself is concerned death is his end—the cessation of his consciousness.

In spite of death's seemingly self-evident character, reflection tells us that it might take a lifetime fully to understand the word "death." As Percy Bridgman pointed out, where either consciousness or loss of consciousness (including death) is involved, we must distinguish between *your* private experiences and *my* private experiences. You (privately) can experience my (public) death; we can both (privately) experience someone else's (public) death; but neither of us can experience his own (inexperienceable) death. You can never see yourself unconscious, hear yourself snore or experience your own being dead, for if you were in a position to have these experiences you would not, in fact, be unconscious, asleep or dead.

If you can never experience your own death, it follows logically that you can never experience your own *dying*. "Now, wait a minute," you might say. "Granted that I cannot experience my being dead but obviously I am still alive while I am dying and, unless I am unconscious, I can experience that." The fact is that you can never be *certain* that you are dying. "Dying" takes its only legitimate meaning from the fact that it immediately precedes death. You may think that you are dying—and survive, in which case you were not dying at that time. You can of course at the present moment keenly experience your *belief* that you are dying, and the experience can be deathly real. You can also in the present anticipate what will happen after you are dead. But these anticipations are at the time they occur always present-moment live experiences.

All this is not to gainsay the fact that people are often correct in thinking that they are dying because they do then die. During an extended period of dying (or supposed dying), a person, unless he is massively drugged or in a coma, is very much alive. The interval of dying is a psychologically consistent, often exaggerated extension of the individual's personality and life-style. His idiosyncratic ways of coping, defending, adjusting and interacting remain with him, coloring his inner life and characterizing his behavior. A standard textbook on clinical medicine succinctly states: "Each man dies in a notably personal way."

Termination is the universal and ubiquitous ending of all living things, but only man, because he can talk about his introspective life, can conceptualize his own cessation. Death is the absence of life—and life, *human* life, is the life of the self, the life of mind. Your life is the full accounting of your personal diary, your memory bank, including your experience of the present moment. It is the life of your mind as you look out on the world and reflect upon yourself. Of course by "the life of the mind" I do not mean to limit the notion only to those aspects of mind amenable to immediate or conscious recall.

Death is the stopping of this life. Bridgman said that ". . . my own death is such a different thing that it well might have a different word." I propose that we use the word *cessation*. Cessation ends the potentiality of any (further) conscious experience. It is essentially synonymous with the conclusion of conscious life.

In order to have a full appreciation of the role of cessation, we must understand a few additional terms:

Termination is the stopping of vital physiological function, including such gross measure as the heartbeat or the exchanges of gases between the person and his environment and such refined measures as what we now call "brain death." Physiological termination is always followed shortly by psychological cessation. The converse however is not always true: it is possible for (private) cessation to occur hours or even days before (public) termination. For example when a person's skull is crushed in an accident, cessation occurs at the instant he loses consciousness for the last time, but he might be kept alive in a hospital as long as he breathes and brainwave patterns are traced on the EEG. But his life ended the instant his mind was destroyed. Loved ones and hospital personnel saw him "alive" in the hospital but that could be an experience only for them. Because the moment of "death" is socially defined by termination, we need that concept even in a psychological approach to death.

Interruption is the stopping of consciousness with the expectation of further conscious experience. It is, to use two contradictory terms, a kind of temporary cessation. Sleep—dreamless sleep—is perhaps the best example of an interruption. Other interruptions include unconsciousness, stupor, coma, fainting, seizures and anesthetic states, and can last from seconds to weeks. By definition the last interruption of a man's life is cessation.

Continuation is the experiencing of the stream of temporally contiguous events. Our lives are thus made up of one series of alternating states of continuation and interruption.

As one would imagine, *altered continuation* implies the continuation of consciousness in a way that is different from an individual's usual or modal style of functioning. Examples would be intoxication, drugged states, hypnotic states, malingering, role-playing, spying, feigning and even "unplugging." "Unplugging"—a term suggested to me by Professor Erving Goffman—is getting out of one's ordinary track of life by drifting, seceding or uncorking, such as burying yourself in a book, going on a *Wanderjahr*, watching a Western or, more actively, going on an escapade, a binge or an orgy—in short, escaping, as opposed to sweating it out.

A neglected aspect of death is the role of the individual in his own demise. The current traditional (and in my view, erroneous) conceptualization that views death as an experience—noble, religious, frightening, beneficent, malign—makes too much of the individual's role in his own death. We have already decided that for the chief protagonist, death is not an experience at all. But there is still another traditional view of death that, curiously enough, makes too little of man's role in his own demise. That view can be seen in the way we conceptualize death in our official records.

In the Western world "death" is given its operational meaning by the death certificate. The death certificate can be divided into three parts, reflecting the three basic kinds of information that it is intended to convey: a) the top third of the certificate identifies the decedent; b) the second third of the certificate relates the cause or causes of death. The international manual lists around 140 possible causes of death, including pneumonia, meningitis, myocardial infarction; c) the last third of the certificate is perhaps the most important for our interests. It is intended to tell us *how* the person died. It normally indicates one of four conceptual crypts into which each of us is eventually placed. I call this world-wide taxonomic scheme the NASH classification of death, standing for the four *modes* of death: natural, accidental, suicidal and homicidal. The main terms can be combined or modified: e.g., "Accident-Suicide, Undetermined" or "Probable Suicide."

It is evident that the *cause* of death does not automatically tell us the *mode* of death. "Asphyxiation due to drowning" or "barbituate overdose" does not automatically tell us whether the death was accidental or suicidal or homicidal. This NASH scheme tends to obscure rather than to clarify the nature of human death.

Much of this anachronistic classification can be traced to the 1600s, when the English crown was interested in assigning blame. Natural and accidental deaths were by definition acts of nature or of God. The survivors could only be pitied and the legitimate heirs would come into their rightful inheritances. On the other hand, the culprit must be identified and punished in homicidal and suicidal deaths. Suicide was *felo-de-se*, a felony against the self, and the crown took the dead man's goods. The coroner's judgment thus could affect the fortunes of a family. From the beginning, certification of the mode of death served quasi-legal functions with distinct monetary overtones.

This anachronistic omission of the part that a man plays in his own death ties us to seventeenth-century Cartesian thinking and keeps us from enjoying the insights of contemporary psychology and psychiatry. In order to put man back into his own dying—a time of life when he is very much alive—we shall need to call upon social and behavioral science.

It can be argued that most deaths, especially in the younger years, are unnatural. Perhaps the termination of life might properly be called natural only in cases of death in old age. Consider the following confusions: if an individual (who wishes to live) has his chest invaded by a lethal steering wheel, his death is called accidental; if he is invaded by a lethal virus, his death is called natural; if his skull is invaded by a bullet in civilian life, his death is called homicidal. A person who torments an animal into killing him is said to have died by accident, whereas one who torments a drunken companion into killing him is called a victim of homicide. An individual whose artery bursts in his brain is said to have died with a cerebral-vascular accident, whereas it might make more sense to call it a cerebral-vascular natural.

In light of these confusing circumstances, I have proposed that we supplement the NASH classification by focusing on the *intention* of each person *vis-à-vis* his own death, that all human deaths be divided among those that are a) intentioned, b) subintentioned or c) unintentioned.

INTENTIONED

In an intentioned death, the individual plays a direct and conscious role in effecting his own demise. Persons who die intentioned deaths can be divided into a number of subcategories:

1. *Death-seeker*. He has consciously verbalized to himself his wish for an ending to all conscious experience and he acts to achieve this end. The criterion for a death-seeker does not lie in his method—razor, barbiturate, carbon monoxide. It lies in the fact that *in his mind* the method will bring about cessation, and in the fact that he acts in such a manner that rescue is unlikely or impossible. An individual's orientation toward death shifts and changes. A person who was a death-seeker yesterday might take tender care of his life today. Most of the individuals who are death-seekers ("suicidal") are so for relatively brief periods; given appropriate surcease and sanctuary they will soon wish to live.

2. *Death-initiator*. He believes that he will die in the fairly near future or he believes that he is failing and—not wishing to accommodate himself to a less-effective and less-virile image of himself—does not wish to let death happen to him. Rather *he* wants to play the dominant role; he will do it for himself, at his own time and on his own terms. In investigations among persons in the terminal stages of disease, it has been found that some, with remarkable and totally unexpected energy and strength, take out their tubes and needles, climb over the bedrails, lift heavy windows and jump. When we look at the occupational history of such individuals we see that they have never been fired—they have always quit.

3. *Death-ignorer*. Some people who kill themselves believe that one can effect termination without cessation. But in our contemporary society even those who espouse a religious belief in a hereafter still put the label of "suicide" on a person who has shot himself to death. This is so probably because, whatever *really* happens after termination, the survivors are still left to mourn in the physical absence of the deceased. Thus this subcategory of death-ignorer or, perhaps better, death-transcender, contains those persons who, from their point of view, terminate themselves and continue to exist in some other manner.

    The concept of death-ignoring is necessary; otherwise we put ourselves in the position of making comparable a man who shoots himself in the head in the belief that he will meet his dead wife in heaven and a man who travels to another city with the expectation of being reunited with his spouse. We must consider that cessation is final as far as the human personality that we can know is concerned.

4. *Death-darer*. He bets his continuation (i.e., his life) on a relatively low probability of survival. Regardless of the outcome a person who plays Russian roulette—in which the chances of survival are only five out of six—is a death-darer, as is the uncoordinated man who attempts to walk the ledge of a tall building. The rule of thumb is, it is not what one does that matters but the background (of skill, prowess and evaluation of his own abilities) against which he does it.

UNINTENTIONED

At the other extreme an unintentioned death is any cessation in which the decedent plays no significant role in effecting his own demise. Here death is due entirely to trauma from without, or to simple biological failure from within. At the time of his cessation the individual is going about his own business (even though he may be hospitalized) with no conscious intention of hastening cessation and with no conscious drive to do so. What happens is that something occurs—a cerebral-vascular accident, a myocardial infarction, a neoplastic growth, a malfunction, an invasion—whether by bullet or by virus—that for him has lethal consequences. *It* happens to *him*.

Most traditional natural, accidental and homicidal deaths would be unintentioned, but no presently labeled suicidal deaths would be. Persons who die unintentioned deaths can be subcategorized as follows:

1. *Death-welcomer*. Although he plays no discernible (conscious or unconscious) role in hastening or facilitating his own cessation, he could honestly report an introspective position of welcoming an end to his life. Very old persons, especially after long, painful, debilitating illness, report that they would welcome the end.

2. *Death-accepter*. He has accepted the imminence of his cessation and is resigned to his fate. He maybe passive, philosophical, resigned, heroic or realistic, depending on the spirit in which this enormous acceptance is made.

3. *Death-postponer*. Most of the time most of us are death-postponers. Death-postponing is the habitual orientation of most human beings toward cessation. The death-postponer wishes that cessation would not occur in the foreseeable future; that it would not occur for as long as possible.

4. *Death-disdainer*. Some individuals, when they consciously contemplate cessation, are disdainful of death and feel that they are above involvement in this implied stopping of the vital processes. They are in a sense supercilious toward death. Most young children in our culture, aside from their fears about death, are probably death-disdainers—as well they might be.

5. *Death-fearer*. He fears death—and even topics *relating to death*—to the point of phobia. He fights the notion of cessation, seeing reified death as something to be feared and hated. His position may relate to his wishes for omnipotence and to his investment in his social and physical potency. Hypochondriacs are perhaps death-fearers. (A physically well death-fearer might, when he is physically ill, become a death-facilitator.)

   Imagine five older men on the same ward of a hospital, all dying of cancer, none playing an active role in his own cessation. Yet it is possible to distinguish different orientations toward death among them: one wishes not to die and is exerting his will to live (death-postponer); another is resigned to his cessation (death-accepter); the third will not believe that death can take him (death-disdainer); still another, although he takes no steps to hasten his end, embraces it (death-welcomer); and the fifth is frightened and forbids anyone to speak of death in his presence (death-fearer).

6. *Death-feigner*. It is of course possible to shout "Fire!" where there is no conflagration. It is also possible to yell or to murmur "Suicide!" when clearly there is no lethal intention. Calls like "Fire!," "Suicide!" or "Stop thief!" mobilize others. They are grab-words; they force society to act in certain ways. An individual who uses the semantic blanket of "Suicide!" in the absence of lethal

intent is a death-feigner. A death-feigner stimulates a self-directed movement toward cessation. He might ingest water from an iodine bottle or use a razor blade without lethal possibility or intent. He may seek some of the secondary gains that go with cessation-oriented behavior. These gains usually have to do with activating other persons—usually the "significant other" person in the neurotic dyadic relationship with the death-feigner.

SUBINTENTIONED

The most important death category—the one that I believe may be characteristic of a majority of deaths—is the *subintentioned* death, in which the decedent plays some covert or unconscious role in hastening his own demise. The evidence lies in a variety of behavior patterns that include poor judgment, imprudence, excessive risk-taking, neglect of self, disregard of medical regimen, abuse of alcohol, misuse of drugs—ways in which an individual can advance the date of his death by fostering the risk of his own dying.

Subintention is a somewhat mysterious concept, resting as it does on the powerful idea of unconscious motivation. It is "the subterranean miner that works in us all." The question is, as Herman Melville asked, ". . . can one tell whither leads his shaft by the ever shifting, muffled sound of his pick?"

Many deaths certified as natural have a subintentional quality about them. Many of us know of cases in which persons with diabetes, peptic ulcers, colitis, cirrhosis, Buerger's disease or pneumonia have, through psychologically laden commission, omission, disregard or neglect, hastened their own demise. In addition "voodoo deaths," inexplicable deaths in hospitals (especially in surgery), and some sudden declines in health can be considered subintentioned. There is a notion that the speed at which some malignancies grow may be related to deep inner psychological variables.

And if some natural deaths are subintentioned (and thus not entirely natural), many deaths certified as accident are even more so—and not entirely accidental. A run of inimical events in one person's life can hardly be thought to be purely accidental. Sometimes we see someone drive a car as though he were afraid that he might be late for his own accident; he may be hurling himself toward a subintentioned death. Many automobile fatalities are not quite accidents and may not comfortably be called suicides; they can be more meaningfully understood as subintentioned deaths.

Some suicides show aspects of the subintentioned death category. (This is especially true for many cases certified as probable suicides.) Indeed the entire concept of subintentioned death—which asserts the role of the unconscious in death—is similar in many ways to Karl Menninger's concepts of chronic suicide, focal suicide and organic suicide, except that Menninger's ideas have to do primarily with self-defeating ways of continuing to live, whereas the notion of subintentioned death is a way to stop the process of living. Cases of subintentioned death may in general be said to have permitted suicide.

Many fatal incidents certified as homicides might be better considered subintentioned deaths. It is obvious that in some close dyadic pairs (married couples, lovers, friends), the victim—like the chief mate of the *Town-Ho* in *Moby Dick*—''sought to run more than half way to meet his doom.'' To provoke another person to kill you is an indirect participation, at some level of personality functioning, in the manipulation of one's date of death.

The hypothesis that individuals may play unconsious roles in their own failures and act in ways that are inimical to their own welfare seems to be too well documented from both psychoanalytic and general clinical practice to be safely ignored. Often death is hastened by the individual's seeming carelessness, imprudence, foolhardiness, forgetfulness, amnesia, lack of judgment or another psychological mechanism. Included in the subintention category would be many patterns of mismanagement and brink-of-death living that result in death.

Subintentioned death involves the psychosomatics of death; that is, cases in which essentially psychological processes (fear, anxiety, derring-do, hate, etc.) seem to play some role in exacerbating the catabolic processes that bring on termination (and necessarily cessation). Several types make up the subintentioned death groups:

1. *Death-chancer.* If a death-darer has only five chances out of six of continuing, then a death-chancer's chances are significantly greater but still involve a realistic risk of dying. It should be pointed out that these categories are largely independent of method in that most methods (like razor blades or barbiturates) can legitimately be thought of as intentioned, subintentioned or unintentioned depending on the circumstances. Individuals who ''leave it up to chance,'' who ''gamble with death,'' who ''half-intend to do it,'' are subintentioned death-chancers.

2. *Death-hastener.* He unconsciously exacerbates a physiological disequilibrium so that his cessation (which would ordinarily be called a natural death) is expedited. This can be done either in terms of his life-style (the abuse of his body, usually through alcohol, drugs, exposure or malnutrition), or through the mismanagement or disregard of prescribed remedial procedures. Consider the diabetic who mismanages his diet or his insulin, the individual with cirrhosis who mismanages his alcoholic intake, the Buerger's-disease patient who mismanages his nicotine intake. Closely allied to the death-hastener is the death-facilitator who, while he is ill and his psychic energies are low, is somehow more than passively unresisting to cessation, and makes it easy for termination to occur. Some unexpected deaths in hospitals may be of this nature.

3. *Death-capitulator.* By virture of some strong emotion, usually his great fear of death itself, he plays a psychological role in effecting his termination. In a sense, he scares himself to death. This type of death includes voodoo deaths, the deaths reported among southwestern Indians and Mexicans in railroad-sponsored hospitals who thought that people went to hospitals to die, and other cases reported in psychiatric and medical literature.

4. *Death-experimenter.* A death-experimenter often lives on the brink of death. He consciously wishes neither interruption nor cessation, but—usually by excessive use of alcohol and/or drugs—he pursues a chronically altered, often befogged continuation. Death-experimenters seem to wish for a benumbed or drugged

consciousness. They will often experiment with their self-prescribed dosages (always increasing them), taking some chances of extending the benumbed conscious state into interruption (coma) and even (usually in a lackadaisical way) running some minimal but real risk of extending the interruption into cessation. This type of death is traditionally thought of as accidental.

It is important to distinguish between subintention and ambivalence. Ambivalence is perhaps the single most important psychodynamic concept for understanding death—or any of life's major psychological issues. Ambivalence represents at least two simultaneous movements within the mind of one person toward divergent, even opposite, goals. Examples of such contradictory activities would be loving and hating the same person, yearning for both autonomy and dependence, and, at rock bottom, moving toward both life and death. The concomitant movement toward each of these diverse goals is genuine in its own right. One can ingest pills, genuinely wishing to die, and at the same time entertain earnest fantasies of rescue. The paradigm of suicide is one of the deepest ambivalence; to cut one's throat and to cry for help—in the same breath.

On the other hand subintention does not emphasize the dual character of man's behavior so much as, in its own way, it emphasizes the unconscious aspects of man's being. Subintentioned acts, whether toward death or toward the expansion of life, are essentially movements toward outcomes that are not conscious goals. They are life's maneuvers that well up out of unconscious motivations and thus are more subtle in their appearance and more difficult to account. Is smoking suicidal? Drinking? Driving? Skiing? These questions cannot be answered yes or no. The answer is "It depends," and it may depend on a number of factors including the individual's orientations toward death and toward others in his life.

With some passionate emphasis Arnold Toynbee makes the point that death is essentially dyadic—a two-person event—and that as such the survivor's burden is the heavier. When he considers his own situation, he writes:

> I guess that if, one day, I am told by my doctor that I am going to die before my wife, I shall recieve the news not only with equanimity but with relief. This relief, if I do feel it, will be involuntary. I shall be ashamed of myself for feeling it, and my relief will, no doubt, be tempered by concern and sorrow for my wife's future after I have been taken from her. All the same, I do guess that, if I am informed that I am going to die before her, a shameful sense of relief will be one element in my reaction. This is, as I see it, the capital fact about the relation between living and dying. There are two parties to the suffering that death inflicts; and, in the apportionment of this suffering, the survivor takes the brunt.

In focusing on the importance of the dyadic relationship in death, Toynbee renders a great service to all who are concerned with death, particularly with suicide. The typical suicide is an intensely dyadic event. The crucial role of the "significant other" in prevention of suicide is one aspect of the new look in suicidology.

Although it is difficult to take a stance counter to Toynbee, I believe that in emphasizing the dyadic aspect of death he seems to leap from a sentimental attitude of burden-sharing in a love relationship—the noble husband's wish to save his beloved wife from the anguish of bereavement—to an unnecessarily romantic view of death itself. In cases of absolutely sudden and precipitous deaths, the total sum of dyadic pain is borne by the survivor (inasmuch as the victim cannot experience any of it). But in protracted dying the present pain and anguish involved in the frightening anticipation of being dead may very well be sharper for the dying person than the pain suffered then and afterward by the survivor. The algebra of death's suffering is complicated.

For all his wisdom I believe that Toynbee indulges in the romanticization of death. In my view the larger need is to deromanticize death and suicide.

Certainly one of the most remarkable characteristics of man's psychological life is the undiluted and enduring love affair that each of us has with his own consciousness. Trapped as he is within his own mind, man nurtures his conscious awareness, accepts it as the criterion for mediating reality, and entertains a faithful life-long dialogue with it—even (or especially) when he takes leave of his senses. Often man communicates with his mind as though it were a separate "other," whereas he is really communicating with himself. Indeed, the other to whom he talks is in large part what he defines himself to be. Death peremptorily decrees an abrupt, unwelcome and final adjournment and dissolution of what Henry Murray has aptly called "the Congress of the mind." Death—i.e., being—is total cessation, personal nothingness, individual annihilation. Should one traffic with one's greatest mortal enemy, rationalize its supposed noble and saving qualities and then romanticize it as an indispensable part of dyadic life?

One difficulty with death is that within himself each man is noble—indestructible and all-surviving. Being conscious is all one has. That is what one's life is. Consciousness defines the duration and the scope of life, and the scope can be rich or the scope can be arid, a partial death that can come long before one's cessation.

Our current attitudes toward death are unconscionably sentimental. The several notions—of "heroic death," "generativity" and "wise death" in mature old age—are culture-laden rationalizations, as though the cerebrator could ever be truly equanimous about the threat of his own naughtment or his annihilation.

Although there are undoubtedly special circumstances in which some individuals either welcome their own cessation or are essentially indifferent to it, for almost everyone the heightened probability of his own cessation constitutes the most dire threat possible. By and large the most distressing contemplation one can have is of his own cessation. Much of religion is tied to this specter—and perhaps all of man's concern with immortality. We must face the fact that completed dying (i.e., death or cessation) is the one characteristic act in which man is forced to engage.

In this context, the word *forced* has a special meaning. It implies that a characteristic that death shares with torture, rape, capital punishment, kidnapping, lobotomy and degradation ceremonies is the quality of impressment. The threat of being reduced to nothingness can be viewed reasonably only as the strongest and the most perfidious of forced punishments.

In all this I do not believe that I am echoing Dylan Thomas's "Do not go gentle into that good night. Rage, rage against the dying of the light." Rather I am saying that one should know that cessation is the curse to end all curses, and *then* one can, as he chooses, rage, fight, temporize, bargain, compromise, comply, acquiesce, surrender, welcome or even embrace death. But one should be aware of the dictum: Know thine enemy.

Death is not a tender retirement, a bright autumnal end "as a shock of corn to his season" of man's cycle. That notion, it seems to me, is of the same order of rationalization as romanticizing kidnapping, murder, impressment or rape.

Nor does it mollify the terror of death to discuss it in the honorific and beguiling terms of maturity, postnarcissistic love, ego-integrity or generativity, even though one can only be grateful to Erik Erikson for the almost perfectly persuasive way in which he has made a generative death sound ennobling and nearly worthwhile.

I wonder if it would not be better to understand generativity as reflecting pride and gratitude in one's progenitors and perhaps even greater pride and faith in one's progeny, without the necessity of deriving any pleasure from one's own finiteness and the prospect of one's demise. There is (or ought to be) a reasonable difference between experiencing justifiable pride in what one has been and is and has created, on the one hand, and, on the other hand, feeling an unwarranted equanimity when one reflects that he will soon no longer be. Maturity and ego integrity relate to the former; the latter is supported largely by the romantic, sentimental rationalization that one's cessation is a blessing. Such a rationalization is nothing less than psychologically willing what is biologically obligatory. It may be more mature to bemoan this fact and regret it.

All this means that death is a topic for the tough and the bitter—people like Melville, in "The Lightning-Rod Man": "Think of being a heap of charred offal, like a haltered horse burned in his stall; and all in one flash!" Or Camus, especially in Meursault's burst of antitheistic and antideath rage just before the end of *The Stranger*.

A look at another culture might throw some light on this problem. When I was in Japan a few years ago, it seemed to me that one of the most pervasive religio-cultural features of the country was the romantically tinged animism that infused the religious thinking. It was not a more primitive feeling, but rather a more personal and spirited feeling, especially about nature. For example the Japanese feelings about a cherry tree in its ephemerally beautiful bloom seemed totally different from the feelings that an average American would muster on looking at a blossoming apple tree. The Japanese closeness to nature, akin to deification, seems to lead to a special Japanese feeling toward death—which I would have to call romanticization.

When I addressed a group of Japanese university students, one youth asked me if I could give him any reason why he should not kill himself if he sincerely believed that he would then become one with nature. The very quality of this question illustrates this animizing and romanticizing of death. Further I recall a young engineer who sat beside me on the new Tokaido train and wrote out: "Cherry blossoms is blooming quickly and scattering at once. Better to come to fruition and die like the blossom." He added: "We have had many great men among our forefathers whose deeds remind us of the noble characteristics of cherry blossoms."

In this country, the romanticization of certain types of homicides is an especially troublesome part of our national heritage. Ther honorifics go to the man with the gun.

We have glamorized our rural bandits and our urban gangsters. The romanticized myth of the Western frontier, built around the image of the man with a gun, has set its homicidal stamp on our culture. The problem for television may not be the effects of violence but the effects of the romanticization of violence.

This romanticization of death goes to the beginnings of our national history. We depict our revolutionary heroes as Minutemen with rifles—as though it were primarily guns that had won the war. Perhaps more appropriate monuments at Lexington and Concord—we have even lost the meaning of the word "concord"—might have been statues of Paine and Jefferson seated, with pens. Unquestionably these representations would have implied quite different values and might have shaped our culture in a somewhat different direction. Our recent inability to amend our gun laws in the wake of a series of catastrophic assassinations has been a national disaster and a grisly international joke, highlighting our irrational tie to our own essentially anti-intellectual legends of romanticized homicide.

Romantic notions of death are obviously related to suicide. Individuals who are actively suicidal suffer—among their other burdens—from a temporary loss of the view of death-as-enemy. This is the paradox and the major logical fallacy of self-inflicted death. It capitulates to the decapitator.

Suicidal folk have lost sight of the foe: they sail with full lights in the hostile night. They are unvigilant and forgetful. They behave in strange, almost traitorous ways. They attempt to rationalize death's supposed lofty qualities and—what is most difficult to deal with—to romanticize death as the noblest part of dyadic love. Loyal-to-life people are inured against nefarious propaganda leading to defection. One should not traffic with the enemy. Suicidal individuals have been brainwashed—by their own thoughts.

How could the de-romanticization of death help suicidal persons? Would it be salutary or beneficial to embark on programs of deromanticizing death in our schools—with courses in "death education"—or in our public media? In the treatment of the acutely suicidal person what would be the effects of directing his mind to a view of death as an enemy? Would such a psychological regimen hasten the suicide, have no effect at all, or would it make a death-postponer of him? In my own mind, the nagging question persists: would not this type of effort, like practically every other earnest exhortation in this alienated age, itself be doomed to an untimely figurative death?

But perhaps even more important is the question: how would the de-romanticization of death reduce the number of those especially *evil* deaths of murder, violence, massacre and genocide? Here, paradoxically, I am a trifle more optimistic. If only we can recognize that our three crushing national problems—the black citizen, the war in Vietnam, and the threat of nuclear death—all contain the common element of dehumanizing others (and, concomitantly, brutalizing and dehumanizing ourselves), then acting out of the urgent need to reverse our present national death-oriented course, we might bring new dimensions to life. But in order to avert the death of our own institutions we shall, in addition to being the home of the brave and the land of the free, have to become the country of the humane.

KENNETH P. COHEN

Hospice: A Caring Community

Within the general orientation of the hospice programs, several different approaches are possible. Here, Cohen outlines models of hospice care for home, independent facility, or hospital. Because cure of the patient is no longer the objective, the attention shifts to treatment of symptoms that cause discomfort, and to psychological support for the patient and family.

To live without feeling or exciting sympathy, to be fortunate
without adding to the felicity of others, or afflicted without
tasting the balm of pity, is a state more gloomy than solitude: it
is not retreat, but exclusion from mankind.
                                        Samuel Johnson, *Rasselas*

Attend a workshop or meeting with hospice-interested people, and a sense of camaraderie pervades the setting. Not only are old friendships renewed, but the feeling of sharing, and an indescribable sensitivity brought about by dealing with death, ripple through the discussions both at the formal sessions and at the informal social gatherings. This sense of sharing is different and more intense than I have found at similar gatherings of hospital-interested people. there is also no comparable tone in meetings of those who do not provide personal services in their everyday lives. Barbara Hill, former executive director of Hospice of Marin, described this special hospice feeling beautifully at the Third National Hospice Symposium:

My belief is that a specific environment needs to be created to develop a hospice—that of the love relationship. I believe that in a truly accepting, undemanding love environment the source exists for growth of the individual. It matters not whether that love is the love of husband and wife, therapist and client, mother and child, or hospice staff member and hospice family—when that mutual love and trust develop, miracles happen.[1]

Source: Reprinted from *Hospice: Prescription for Terminal Care*, © 1979, Aspen Systems Corporation, Germanton, Md.

Plant contends that "hospices are gaining favor in the U.S. because they are a curious amalgam of reactions and responses." She claims that one reaction is against the cure-at-any-cost syndrome that pervades the acute-care hospital. Another is the rebellion against hospital regulations that tend to keep patients and families apart in times of crisis. A third reaction is against certain of society's attitudes about death that prevent the provision of the best care to the dying. The responses are all part of the slowly emerging movement toward death with dignity and the search for alternatives to institutionalization.[2]

All programs that care for the dying and their families are not necessarily hospice programs.[3] "A hospice is not a hospital and not a nursing home. The hospice is inspired by a different philosophy of care, relates to different goals, and provides different services to an entirely different population of cancer patients."[4] The hospice concept does not suggest a deficit in hospital care, but rather recognizes the fact that neither general, teaching, nor research hospitals are staffed for and oriented to providing care for terminally ill patients.[5]

HOSPICE MODELS

As noted earlier, a hospice is not necessarily an institution; a hospice is a program of care. It may be a home care program, a free-standing institution, a separate hospital department, or an interdisciplinary team that moves within a general hospital to wherever the patients may be located within the facility. It may offer outpatient services or day care; it may offer the home care in conjunction with the institutional settings, or it might combine variations of these models. A controversy is currently brewing over which of these models is the best for terminally ill patients. There is, however, no one "best" model.

Home Care and Institutional Hospice Services

Most people, given the choice, would prefer to die at home. Hence, home care hospice services seem to be most appropriate. Yet, a point may come in the home care regimen when the patient may have to be sent to an institutional hospice for a time to control new symptoms, provide the psychological boost of a fresh environment, or to provide relief and rest for the family members who must provide 24-hour-per-day aid to the patient.

The patient, then, will be transferred to the institutional hospice for a few days before being returned to the home and familiar surroundings so important to the terminally ill.

The dying have the right to a great many things that hospitals and nursing homes simply cannot provide. They need life around them, spiritual and emotional comfort and support of every sort. They need "unsanitary" things, like a favorite dog lying at the foot of the bed. They need their own clothes, their own pictures, music, food, surroundings that are familiar to them, people they know and love, people they can trust to care about them. Hospices can provide this in their inpatient units; and yet, for many individuals and their families, it is much better for it to happen at home.[6]

Free-Standing Versus Hospital-Based Hospices

At this writing, the National Cancer Institute has provided funding for three separate free-standing hospices. At this writing, only one is operative: Hillhaven Hospice in Tucson, Arizona. Under construction is Hospice, Inc. in New Haven, Connecticut, and to become operational by mid-to-late 1978 is Kaiser-Permanente Medical Care Progam in Los Angeles. Although British hospices are almost exclusively free-standing, it appears unlikely that United States hospices will emerge as free-standing facilities.

Several additional free-standing facilities will probably be built in the future, but growth of the movement will depend on expansion of the home care and hospital-based models. Home care-based hospices will grow because of the inherent cost-saving features, and hospital-based hospices will proliferate because of the excess hospital beds available throughout the country. Because of the excess hospital beds, capital construction funds are and will be extremely difficult to obtain. Lawrence Burke of the National Cancer Institute feels that "it would more than compromise and complicate the [hospice] program to have it initiated within a general hospital."[7] On the other hand, Balfour Mount of the Royal Victoria Hospital questions the economic feasibility of free-standing hospices. "Analysis of the economics of maintaining such institutions . . . suggests that society cannot afford to support an adequate number to meet the need."[8]

A major objection to the hospital-based hospice unit is the almost diametrically opposed philosophies of *acute* care and *palliative* care. Opponents reason that the terminally ill patients are torn apart by observing hospital patients who will be leaving the hospital in the matter of a few days well on the road to recovery. To be in a hospital and know that patients in other parts of the hospital will be *cured* of their illnesses s a tremendous psychological barrier to the effective care of the hospice patients. Then, too, the acute-care training of personnel has run counter to that needed for hospice care. Hospital personnel will frequently refer to the hospice unit as the "dead end," or they may make other disparaging remarks that only serve to antagonize the hospice personnel and that may result in counter productivity to the type of care to be provided to hospice patients.

The Mixed-Community Hospice

A 1950 study of cancer patients concluded that facilities for the care of terminal cancer patients should not be set up as specialized institutions operated solely for the care of *cancer* patients, a places where patients go to die from cancer. The report wisely proclaimed that, "specialization of this type is almost inhuman in the emotional trauma it produces for the patient and his family.''[9] British hospices do not care only for the terminally ill, nor do they concentrate only on problems associated with advanced cancer. For example, St. Joseph's Hospice in Hackney, London has always had a well-mixed community of patients, and it has a home care program in its geographical area for anyone dying of anything. It also has a unit for long-term rehabilitation and home support. St. Christopher's Hospice in Sydenham, London has a wing for frail elderly and has a number of longer-stay patients with various diagnoses in its wards.[10]

APPROPRIATE TREATMENT

The distinction between appropriate and inappropriate treatment of patients is a paramount concern of hospices. "This distincton means concentration on control of symptoms when definitive treatment for disease is no longer possible," writes Sylvia Lack. She adds that the best way to do this is with a centrally coordinated service of in-patient beds and a home care program under an autonomous hospice administration.[11] When a person's life is in its last few hours, that person needs a quiet place in which to die naturally. Most patients in a hospice die peacefully with no intravenous injections or gastric tubes, but if such treatment is appropriate, it is used.[12]

Patients come to hospices only when they have terminal illnesses that can no longer be treated or cured. The omission of further surgery or radiotherapy for these patients is the omission of extraordinary and optional means of prolonging the dying process. Thus, hospices do not practice dysthanasia; they practice JUCTO (justifiable use of conservative therapy only).[13]

> Formerly, when most people died at home, children grew up with a realistic understanding of death from which they are now shielded. Yet watching someone die in the loving and caring surrounding of a hospice surely does less emotional damage to a young child than watching even one evening of televison violence.[14]

Britain's 30-odd hospices are homelike places of care where terminally ill patients, with or without money, are given everything possible to allow them to die with dignity and to avoid unnecessary prolongation of life. The hospices are constantly developing new techniques to reduce pain, and doctors and nurses are devoting their entire careers to furthering this aim.[15]

ELEMENTS OF A HOSPICE PROGRAM

The most common indication for admission to hospices—in some 40 percent of cases—is the need to give respite to relatives. On the other hand, 20 percent of admissions are social isolates with no one able or willing to care for them. At the same time,

60 percent of admissions need help with better control of their pain. Thus, hospice patients represent a mix of social and clinical need.[16]

A hospice program, then, is not just a program that purports to care for the terminally ill. It is a program for meeting a wide range of physical, psychological, social and spiritual needs, a program of health care delivery consisting of ten clearly identifiable elements:

1. Service availablity to home care patients and inpatients on a 24-hour-a-day, seven-day-a-week, on-call basis with emphasis on availability of medical and nursing skills
2. Home care service in collaboration with inpatient facilities
3. Knowledge and expertise in the control of symptoms (physical, psychological, social, and spiritual)
4. The provision of care by an interdisciplinary team
5. Physician-directed services
6. Central administration and coordination of services
7. Use of volunteers as an integral part of the health care team
8. Acceptance to the program based on health needs, not ablity to pay
9. Treatment of the patient and family together as the unit of care
10. A bereavement follow-up service[17]

Not all existing hospice programs incorporate all ten of these elements. For example, some are entirely home care oriented, while others are exclusively institution based with no home care services; some have very limited bereavement follow-up service, while others have extensive bereavement service; many have services available on a 24-hour-a-day, seven-day-a-week basis; while some have more limited hours. Nevertheless, the ten elements represent the ideal to be achieved by any hospice program.

Home Care Plus Inpatient Services

The goal of hospice care is to help a patient continue life as usual—working, being with a family, doing what is especially significant before life comes to a close, and feeling a part of the ongoing life—not being different. Much of this type of care is fostered through the home care and outpatient programs. Hospices place primary emphasis on home care so that patients can maintain their life styles as long as possible, but they usually supplement the home care with their own inpatient unit, or they may have an arrangement with a local palliative-care hospital unit. The practical needs are to relieve families for a while, to provide 24-hour medical supervision when symptoms cannot be controlled at home, and to guarantee the professional care that is necessary during the final weeks of life. The overriding ideological and practical need, however, is continuity of care, for without a hospice-run inpatient unit, patients must enter hospitals or nursing homes and lose touch with the special symptom-control measures and medication regimens that typify hospice care.[18] The knowledge that a hospice bed is available in the inpatient facility often makes it possible for the patient to remain at home longer than either the family or the patient consider possible.

Emotional and Psychological Support

Emotional and psychological support is as essential an element of care as symptom control. Each patient is seen as part of a family unit, whose total well-being and lifestyle affect and are affected by care. Flexibility geared to the patient's mental and physical comfort characterizes the inpatient unit. Visiting hours are flexible (usually 24 hours per day), very young children and even pets are welcome at any time, meals are provided on demand, and wine and liquor are served in moderation. Patients also wear their own clothing and can bring favorite possessons, including furniture from home.[19]

In an article in the popular press, English hospice residents were described as being able to move about and enjoy days filled with a variety of activities, including art classes, pottery, crafts, bingo games, musical entertainment by volunteers, gardening, and automobile drives. All this while the patients were heavily dosed with pain-killing narcotics—yet most seemed alert.[20] For the patient with too much time to think, the systematic use of games of all kinds, under the supervision of the occupational therapist, is necessary.

In English hospices, even mealtime is a social event. Sherry or beer is always served before the meals. This stimulates the appetite and relaxes the patient as well as contributes to the nutritional state. Each course is then brought in separately and served to the patient in small portions. The nurse or volunteer takes the necessary care and time to make the patient feel wanted. This is unlike American hospitals, where large portions of food are placed on a tray in front of the patient, and personnel return in one-half to three-fourths of an hour to remove the usually uneaten meal.[21]

In an age of specialization and fragmentation, when a variety of medical specialists may be fascinated by the disease process and forget the patient, it falls to the nurse to reaffirm the personal identity and unique worth of the patient. However, care must be exercised that the staff address the patients as adults who understand. It is all too easy to talk down to patients, as though they were children or mentally deficient.[22] If this is done, the patient's emotional needs will not be met and all the good work of the hospice will be undone.

Little things are important, such things as washing a patient's hair, helping the patient to write a letter, moving the bed closer to the window to afford a better view of outdoor activities; these services can all be performed by either nursing personnel or volunteers. And of course physical touch is extremely important. Holding hands, caressing the face, stroking the hair—these are all forms of intimate communication, communication that does not depend on the spoken word. These continual personal reassurances to the dying patient speak of love, deep compassionate love between human beings.

The Interdisciplinary Team Approach

Fundamental to the hospice concept is the interdisciplinary team approach. No one person has all the answers to the problems of the dying patent and the family; such problems are multitudinous. The team is usually headed by a clinical physician. "The hospice program of care usually is directed by a physician for two reasons: first, symptom control, the focus of hospice care, is a medical concern, and second, a medical director is best able to generate understanding and support for the hospice concept among other physicians."[23]

It is the physician who gives general direction to members of the other disciplines—nurses, social workers, chaplains, physiotherapists, psychiatrists, dieticians, pharmacists, and volunteers. The composition of the interdisciplinary team will, of course, differ with each hospice.

> Clearly the roles of doctor, priest and nurse are not going to be in neat compartments, for at times they will be completely interchangeable. To be instantly responsive to the patient's needs, one requires nurses who can alter the dosage of drugs, recognize when to give a wide range of "when necessary" prescriptions, and insert a urinary catheter. One needs doctors who can also be spiritual advisers and clergymen who can competently impart a grave prognosis. It is the widening of the scope of one's work, closer to the traditional role of the old-time family doctor, which is the principal attraction in care of the dying.[24]

Because the physician, the psychiatrist, and the nurse have acquired the image of being too busy, the person whom the patient and family frequently confide in about their deepest concerns is the volunteer, who is seen as the one person who has time and understanding.[25] Volunteers are utilized both in inpatient and home care programs. There are no standards for numbers of volunteers who might be used in various programs, but for home care programs a ratio of 12 lay volunteers to each professional is suggested.[26]

The legal counselor can be an important part of the interdisciplinary team. An attorney can help with legal, financial, or estate-planning needs, drafting the documents necessary to guarantee that patients' dependents will be sensibly provided for. Patients will then at least have peace of mind knowing that their wishes will be honored and that their loved ones will be protected.[27]

When unpleasant symptoms are under control and the patient is able to return home from the hospice facility for a time, then a social worker can be the liaison between the two and can help to deal with the economic consequences of a disease that has destroyed a person's earning capacity. All financial worries should be resolved before the death.[28]

Some of the team members may experience the "burn-out" phenomenon, especially the nursing personnel. Dealing with death, becoming intensely involved emotionally with patients and their families day after day, can affect a care giver psychologically and emotionally. The emotional drain caused by several deaths occurring in a relatively short period of time can take its toll in pent-up emotions screaming to be released; therefore, some hospice facilities are providing "scream rooms" to provide this release. Jerry Coash, director of the Encino Hospital palliative care unit, explained that he copes with this problem by having the nurses who spend the majority of their time in the hospice unit occasionally rotated to other nursing units within the hospital, even though continuity suffers.[29]

The Family as Patient

To the hospice team, the "patient" is undeniably the patient and the family. The family, in the broad sense, includes not only the natural family (immediate and other relatives), but also the extended family (natural family plus friends, and even pets) and the adopted family (the care givers).[30] Figure 6-1 shows the relationship of the elements of care to the unit of care: the terminally ill patient and the family.

Naturally, some relatives will be part of the caring team, some will be patients along with the dying person, while others will alternate between the two roles. It may be that they will need to be put up in the facility overnight, if they are too distressed to return home alone, or if they want to be close at hand when death is imminent.[31]

Because they are also patients, relatives need to be cared for as well. For this reason, some hospices have a "relative's day off," when visiting of all but the most severely ill patients is discouraged. This releases the friend or relative who feels a duty to be visiting the loved one as much as possible and who consequently never gets out. Otherwise, visiting is unrestricted.[32]

The death of a person should leave the family with no feelings that they did not do enough. They should be directly involved in the patient's care. The team can teach the family various health care measures that will enable the patient to remain at home and, when inpatient care becomes necessary, should encourage the family to participate in that care too, by helping the nurses with feeding, turning, washing, and so on. Since this is their last offering, they want to be as close as possible to their loved one.[33]

Bereavement Services

Since grief begins at the moment when the patient's illness is diagnosed as terminal, relative should not be told of this condition and then left to their own devices. They should be invited to come back and talk over their distress and to ask questions.[34] "To support a family through grieving before and after bereavement demands understanding and tolerance from the care givers. Understanding implies a familiarity with the patterns and processes of normal grief, while tolerance implies a capacity to accept the variable forms the process may assume."[35]

Figure 6–1. The Hospice in Patient Care

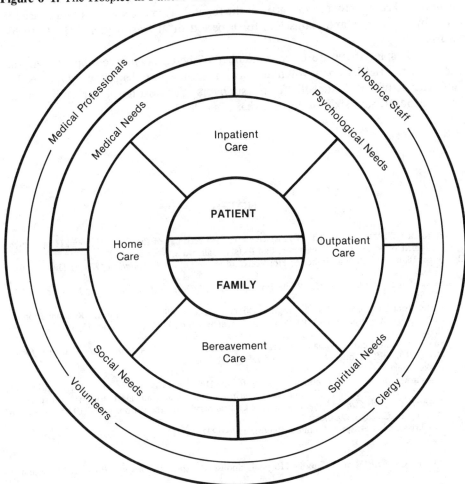

Source: "The Hospice Movement," Management Services Special Report, unpublished (Newport Beach, California: Advanced Health Systems, Inc., October 1977), p. 4. Reprinted by permission of Advanced Health Systems, Inc., 881 Dover Drive, Suite 20, Newport Beach, California 92663.

Bereavement follow-up is an essential part of hospice care. Follow-up can last for any length of time and take various forms, including home visits by team members who had treated the patient, phone calls, notes, or assisting a lonely spouse in finding a job. Such follow-up helps to support not only the family at a time when its members are particularly vulnerable to physical and psychological stress, but also the hospice team, which has also suffered a loss in the death of a patient.[36] William Lamers, in an interview describing the operation of Hospice of Marin, stated, "When our nurses and counselors have worked with a family and ultimately death occurs, each individual who worked with that family attends the funeral. Then we see that families are followed by our nurses and counselors for a period of at least a year after death has occurred."[37]

In a hospice there are often a number of bereaved people who are working through their grief by doing voluntary work for a few months following the death.[38] Thus, this activity is therapeutic for the survivors. Yet most hospices permit this only for a period of, say, six months to a year after death.

NOTES

1. Barbara Hill, "The 'How To' of Hospice Care," Proceedings of the Third National Hospice Symposium, Dominican College Campus, San Rafael, California, May 26-28, 1977, p. 18.
2. Janet Plant, "Finding a Home for Hospice Care in the U.S.," Hospitals, JAHA 51 (July 1, 1977): 53-62.
3. Sylvia Lack, "I Want To Die While I'm Still Alive," Death Education 1, no. 2 (Summer 1977): 165-76.
4. Letter from Lawrence D. Burke, Program Director for Rehabilitation Treatment, Rehabilitation and Continuing Care Branch (DCCR), National Cancer Institute, HEW, December 15, 1977.
5. Ibid.
6. Sandol Stoddard citing William Lamers, The Hospice Movement: A Better Way of Caring for the Dying (Briarcliff Manor, N.Y.: Stein and Day, 1978), p. 51.
7. Burke letter.
8. Balfour M. Mount, "The Problem of Caring for the Dying in a General Hospital: The Pallative Care Unit As a Possible Solution," Canadian Medical Association Journal 115 (July 17, 1976): 119-21.
9. Terminal Care for Cancer Patients (Chicago: Central Service for the Chronically Ill of the Institute of Medicine of Chicago, 1950), p. 15.
10. St. Christopher's Hospice, "Annual Report, 1976-1977," p. 12.
11. Lack, loc. cit.
12. Ibid.
13. D.G. McCarthy, "Should Catholic Hospitals Sponsor Hospices?" Hospital Progress 57 (December 1976): 61-5.
14. Ibid.
15. Richard Kolbe, "Inside the English Hospice," Hospitals 51 (July 1, 1977): 65-7.
16. E. Wilkes, "Terminal Care and the Special Nursing Unit," Nursing Times 71 (January 9, 1975): 57-9.
17. Sylvia Lack, "Philosophy and Organization of a Hospice Program," Unpublished paper, n.d.; "I Want To Die," loc. cit.
18. Plant, loc. cit.
19. Ibid.
20. Michael Satchell, "How to Enjoy Life—Up to the Last Moment," Parade, October 16, 1977.
21. M.A. Rose and Walter J. Pories, "Some Additional Notes on Hospice," Ohio State Medical Journal 73 (June 1977), 379-82.
22. Palliative Care Service: October 1976 Report (Montreal: Royal Victoria Hospital, McGill University, 1976), p. 75.
23. Plant, loc. cit.
24. Richard Lamerton, Care of the Dying (Westport, Connecticut: Technomic Publishing Co., 1976), p. 22.
25. Lack, "I Want to Die," loc. cit.
26. Burke letter.

27. Barton E. Bernstein, "Lawyer and Counselor As an Interdisciplinary Team: Interfacing for the Terminally Ill," *Death Education* 1 (Fall 1977): 277-91.
28. Lamerton, p. 21.
29. "Hospice Care—A New Concept for the Care of the Terminally Ill and Their Families," Workshop at UCLA Extension, Los Angeles, April 8-9, 1978.
30. Robert Woodson, "The Concept of Hospice Care in Terminal Disease," *Breast Cancer,* ed. J.M. Vaeth (Basel, Switzerland: Karger, 1976), pp. 161-79.
31. Lamerton, p. 20.
32. Ibid., p. 21.
33. Ibid., p. 40.
34. Lamerton, p. 125.
35. *Palliative Care Service,* p. 84.
36. Plant, loc. cit.
37. "Hospice," Interview with William Lamers, Jr., Medical Director, Hospice of Marin, *Thanatos,* March 1977, pp. 6-11.
38. Lamerton, p. 129.

ROBERT KASTENBAUM

Exit and Existence:
Alternative Scenarios

Hospice programs, once part of a visionary scenario, are now institutional realities. Robert Kastenbaum looks ahead in the following article sketching contrasting scenarios for the exit from existence. Noting that society has the power to develop scripts for the whole human life span, Kastenbaum explores the range of decisions available for expanding the quality of life during the latter part of the life span. Through a series of life-affirming decisions, society can make age a positive value.

HOW IT WILL BE FROM NOW ON: A SCENARIO

This projection is organized with reference to the way society has been answering the following question: what value is there in being an old, dying, or dead person?

It is useful to introduce one further concept: "the death system." This term refers to the functional network through which a society comes to terms with death, including people, places, objects, and symbols.[1] Some of these components are identified primarily, and permanently, by their role in the death system—for example, the funeral director, cemetery, death certificate; other components may be recruited into the system as the occasion demands. The death system performs several vital functions: predictions and warnings of the possibility of death and actions intended to prevent it; care of the dying or otherwise doomed person; physical disposition of the corpse; consolation and reintegration of survivors and the establishment of an orientation toward or relationship with the dead. Explanations and rationalizations of death are part of the system. Those actions which have the effect of bringing about death are as much a part of the system as the components of prediction and prevention. Certain aspects of the society's economic function and structure are, of course, part of the

352   Source: Selection from Robert Kastenbaum, "Exit and Existence: Society's Unwritten Script Paper for Old Age and Death," in David D. Van Tassel, ed., *Aging, Death and the Completion of Being*, © 1979, Case Western Reserve University. Published by University of Penn-

death system. How much money do you suppose changes hands in our society each year for death-related reasons? The answer to this question would include much if not all of the national defense budget; "life" insurance premiums, payments, and commissions; floral offerings; the pet-food industry; newspaper income from death notices; and so on.

These functions can be discerned in all societies; relative emphasis varies, however, from one society to another, or within the same society in different periods. The relative proportions of children, adults, and elderly adults at a given time will be a factor; but so will the prevailing system of religious beliefs and practices or a cycle of good or poor harvests.

The scenario for the future that suggests itself for our own society is based on the assumption that certain current trends will become dominant while other already entrenched attitudes and practices will continue. It is important to emphasize that this present-tense description represents one view of the way things *might* be. One approach to this scenario can be obtained by working backward from death itself.

1. There is no point in being dead. This view has now been made palpable by the systematic conversion of burial grounds to other, more utilitarian, purposes. Except for those relatively few cemeteries now designated as historical sites, the burial ground has virtually disappeared from the landscape. Again, with few exceptions, the recently deceased are not commemorated by conspicuous, space-wasting monuments. This practice had been losing much of its vitality for decades, anyway, as suggested by the increasing standardization of tombstone inscriptions. Other kinds of memorial practices have also been reduced to a minimum that a previous generation might not have thought possible. Traffic is no longer held up by the slow-moving cortege of limousines and mourners. Busy people no longer miss a day's work to stand in the wind or rain while a deceased colleague is lowered into the earth. Efficiency and common sense have at last prevailed. Our death system's gradually lessened interests in relating to or utilizing the dead, a phenomenon observed by a few in previous years, has moved from the mental-emotional sphere to the physical and official change of visible practices associated with disposal of the dead and with remembrance.[2] Naturally, services are available for those deviant and troubled individuals whose functioning is impaired by unresolved feelings about a dead person. According to the latest clinical and scientific reports, systematic desensitization to bereavement as a routine activity of the behavior modifiers has had reasonably consistent success.

2. There is little point in dying. In fact, as compared with the previous generation or two, there is relatively little "dying" per se. One reason for the diminished significance of dying, of course, has been the perfection of an integrated, computerized system for (1) determining a person's level of viability; (2) evaluating availability and cost of alternative treatment and maintenance procedures; and (3) resolving the problems of terminal care and body disposal. The United States Public Health Service operates the Super-Euthanasiac Computer, into which all relevant data are constantly programmed. When the computer detects and validates a critical configuration of disability, prognosis, and cost estimate, a quick and painless termination is accomplished—including selection of the appropriate body-disposal route. It is no wonder that the president of the American Medical Association has expressed unstinting

approval of this technique. The need to make life-and-death decisions that began to weigh so heavily upon medical personnel in the 1960s and 1970s has now been almost entirely eliminated. Moreover, the unacceptable expense of maintaining incurable and unproductive citizens has been sharply reduced (although it must be admitted that the cost of the new computer system has been considerably higher than anticipated). Some observers were surprised, however, when the Pope herself expressed strong approval. Few could quarrel, however, with her assertion that the new system would promote favorable reallocation of scarce resources for safeguarding the lives of those who still had a chance. The development of the Church's own Vaticaniac Computer Program to guide determinations of viability of Catholic patients based on applicable tenets of their religion no doubt had something to do with the acceptability of the system as a whole.

Another reason for the reduced significance of dying and of being a dying person is more psychosocial than technological. Dying retained some importance as long as there was any point at all in being dead. Now that the status of the dead has become so attenuated, little significance need be attributed to the preparatory phase. The "exit" phase of existence has become relatively unimportant and vestigial. It is not a critical part of the transition from one social status to another; there is little significance that dying can borrow from its destination. "I am not going to be anything to anybody when I am dead; therefore, as I approach dead-status through the process of dying, my value progressively diminishes." Much of the individual's social value is depleted, then, before the moment of death arrives.

3. There is no point in being old. This is in part a function of the reverse sequence we have been describing. Society has no use for the dead, and therefore little use for the dying. For many years, being old has meant a general reduction in social value for reasons not directly associated with death. However, with the shift in mortality peaks from early to late in the lifespan, and with other socioeconomic and attitudinal changes, a more specific association has also been strengthened between *advanced* age and death. Now when a person is recognized as "old," this status initiates a trajectory of dysvalue that moves inevitably through dying- and dead-status. "I am an old person, which means that before long I will be a dying person; therefore, as I approach dying-status through the aging process, my value progressively diminishes." Old, dying, and dead are stations of life still differentiated by our society, but collectively they represent an essentially trivial postscript to authentic existence as a person in society.

This situation was anticipated by the low priority which society gave for many years to the care of the aged. Moreover, the growing trend for the aged to die in an institutional setting, coupled with the usual way in which institutions responded to the dying and the dead, provided a firm model for progressive dysvaluation.[3] Aged residents were likely to observe that the dying were isolated, and the dead removed quickly. Implicit were the messages that "Nobody has died," and "Dying and being dead are nothing." These messages registered with the impact that "Nobody has been alive," and "I *will have been* nothing when *I become* nothing." So thoroughly were the aged dying and dead ejected from the scene that the fact that they had ever been alive (and perhaps valuable) seemed entirely inconsistent. With this sort of rehearsal for their own deaths, the institutionalized aged saw their present existence drained of value.

Today, the transitions from old to dying to dead are better managed. Much of the ambiguity has been eliminated, along with the accompanying tension and occasional guilt on the part of caregivers and family as well as the aged themselves. Only a few of the factors contributing to this change can be cited here.

One important development was the change in official recognition of the start of old age, from sixty-five to seventy.[4] Although gerontologists argued, with good evidence, that even seventy is "too young to be old" for many people today, a compromise at seventy prevailed. In retrospect, the identification of official old age with the biblical specification of "threescore and ten" seems to have proved fortuitous. People in their sixties now receive a full share of benefits and privileges. The slide of value-into-dysvalue throughout the seventh decade of life has been sharply reduced. Other factors in the change include the development of more flexible retirement plans, the cultivation of multiple careers, and the increased prominence of women in the work force.

Perhaps the single most important factor, however, has been the great success of the voluntary-termination plan. Once surrounded by prohibitions and negative emotions, suicide has become, under certain circumstances, an action with great positive value. This trend was anticipated some years ago. It was shown that the implicit preferences of most Americans regarding the "ideal" way to die included the following characteristics: (1) an identifiable and rational cause; (2) some element of control; (3) an acceptable physical setting; (4) occurrence at the right time; (5) little or no suffering or experiencing; (6) rapid onset; (7) consistency with the individual's distinctive or most valued style of life. It was predicted that all of these characteristics could most dependably be invoked by suicide.[5] The suicide would, of course, have to meet certain pragmatic and moral criteria, which were also discussed in some detail.

Apparently, two major factors in the success of the voluntary-termination plan were the decades-long subjection of the aged to low-priority status and the rapid diminution of the value of the dying and the dead in our death system. People simply incorporated these cultural orientations into their own attitude structures, and when they had themselves grown old, they began to act upon the implicit commands.

The well-achieved suicide (to use the old-fashioned expression) bestows upon the old person's exit a value that it can attain in no other way. Instead of fading into a prolonged phase of senescence and dysvalue, the man or woman on the brink of old age now can elect a self-termination mode that consolidates and validates his or her existence up to that point. A good citizen, having lived a good life, no longer faces the prospect of a retroactively spoiled identity because of unnecessary aging and dying.

AN ALTERNATIVE SCENARIO

It is possible to accept the background facts and trends that generated the above scenario and yet arrive at a different one. This requires the recognition of several other trends and options that have not yet been mentioned.

"The Road Doesn't End Here Anymore"

The county historical society almost lost in its campaign to preserve the street in its old form as a designated reminder of how things used to be. Little could be said in favor of the structures themselves. The aesthetic appeal was virtually nil, and somehow the "bad vibrations" seemed to cling to the walls. Yet enough people appreciated the moral and educational value of preserving the row of "nursing homes" and "funeral homes" to allow the historical society to keep this relic of the not-so-distant past before contemporary eyes.

Surprising, the street has proved to be a popular if sobering attraction. "So this was the end of the road," a visitor may say, shaking his head as though to clear away disbelief. "You have to wonder how people felt when they turned down this street. It must have been like leaving life behind, entering a kind of slaughterhouse district, but with most of the bleeding *inside*, in the heart. How could people let the road end that way?"

The street of nursing homes and funeral homes—peculiar remnants of the past—certainly is out of place now. Old age and death once were considered the end of the road, almost functionally equivalent in many people's minds. This inaccurate assumption no longer burdens society. Advances in scientific knowledge have contributed to the change: increasingly, it has been recognized that many of the so-called inevitable changes "caused" by the aging process can in fact be attributed more accurately to a variety of specific factors. Each new rank of chronologically old men and women reaches a particular age checkpoint in better health and with greater functional capacity than the preceding one. There was no single "breakthrough"; instead, health maintenance throughout the lifespan has steadily improved. The physical impairment and vulnerability to chronic disease that were fostered by sedentary, careless, and unmonitored life styles have been sharply reduced. Sixty-five-year-olds are more physically active today than many forty-year-olds of a few generations back. Good nutritional habits carefully cultivated in the early years of life are now paying good dividends in the later decades. Specific changes, such as the enrichment of beer with vitamins, have helped to preserve the functioning of memory and the overall integrity of personality among people who in the past might have suffered deterioration not much past midlife.

The overall change, however, has occurred in the minds both of the elders themselves and of the allied health professionals. Suffering, impairment, and disease are no longer considered especially "natural" in old age. More can be done to prevent problems and to correct or compensate for them when they do occur.

Gerontologists from a variety of disciplines have helped to clarify the distinction between growing old and becoming ill. A core of processes remains that could be characterized as "normal aging," although even this core is still subject to continuing review and experimentation.

In similar fashion, a clearer distinction has been recognized between growing old and "getting stale." As developmental psychologists finally enlarged their horizons to encompass the whole lifespan and to establish appropriate ways of assessing behavior and experience from infancy through old age, it became evident that individual patterns are at least as significant as age-related changes. There was no escaping the conclusion that some men and women have "staled out" by their forties or fifties—or even their twenties or thirties—while others show few, if any, of the stereotypical age changes after they have passed their seventieth, eightieth, or ninetieth birthday. Circumstantial evidence has long suggested the importance of individual patterns; now, abundant research supports this view in detail.

In both biomedical and psychosocial terms, then, the assumption of a close link between old age and deterioration—and therefore between old age and death—has been shown to be faulty. While it is still true that some chronologically old people are physically ill and impaired, and some very limited in their ability to experience and adapt to their environments (not necessarily the same persons in both cases) such difficulties and illnesses no longer *define* old age. In addition to the greater national commitment to the maintenance of physical health throughout life, there is now more encouragement of continuing personal growth. Recreation, for example, has become more re-creational for many people; education is now a lifelong process for a greater number; and self-development groups have survived the fad stage to become an effective and respected part of the cultural milieu. While, of course, some people continue to reach the end of the road early in life, this is no longer the expected pattern. Chronological age simply does not have much to do with the quality of one's life. As old age (in the once-traditional chronological sense of the term) has been liberated from its association with the end of health and mental vigor, so the association with dying and death has been reduced to more realistic dimensions. People still die old if they do not die young, but they are not surrounded by clouds of gloom and dysvalue while they still walk the earth.

Many other changes have contributed to the revised image and reality of old age. Reaching a particular age (and remember when that was as young as sixty-five!) once meant a virtually complete exit from the social scene. The individual stepped (or was pushed) across a single threshold and from that point on was little more than an occasional offstage voice. Now, of course, fewer of the exits are controlled by chronology. Mandatory retirement did not tremble and fall with an overwhelming crash after a fierce struggle; it just gradually passed away.

More flexible ideas of what constitutes a working life have made the single-career pattern just one among several. The framework of young adult to elderly retiree has altered just as the nine-to-five workday has given way to more flexible arrangements. Now, people move into and out of occupations in a variety of patterns, taking a year out here for re-education, six months there for community service, and so on. The availability of a large number of vigorous, skilled elders who are interested in part-time or temporary employment has proved extremely helpful to many industries and government agencies. The "average" person now may have, in effect, "retired" several times before reaching age sixty-five and yet, in another sense, not have retired at all. The ever-changing flow of workers of various ages and degrees of development of their capacities has made age-based mandatory retirement anachronistic—and eliminated one of the main symbols of exit from social participation.

The great improvement in the status of women has also been very important. The woman of today must have an informed sense of history in order to recognize that once her life might have been considered over when the last child had left the "nest," or when she became a widow (as often happened to women in earlier generations before the longevity of males improved). Today's woman, fully competent in the management of her life outside as well as inside the home, brings many skills, achievements, and interests to the later years of her life. She is seldom faced with a confusing and unfamiliar world of financial management, for example, or frustrated by other problems that someone else would have looked after in the past. She is resourceful and successful throughout her life and has no reason to be otherwise as she reaches any particular chronological-age mark.

Both men and women, of course, have found the toppling of assumptions and prohibitions regarding sexual intimacy in later life to be a truly liberating development. In the past, physical death seemed almost an afterthought for some people when they had already exited (in society's view) from the life of labor and the life of love. Now, better general health has contributed to the general maintenance of sexual tone in elders; but the change in attitudes has also been very important. The overall maturation of public opinion in relation to many aspects of human development shows some of its most favorable results in relation to old age and intimacy. There was a period in which the existence of only two "kinds" of women was generally acknowledged: "good women," and those who enjoyed sex. Then, as women achieved sociopolitical equality with men, sexual liberation followed, sometimes accompanied by new problems for some men. It took some time for many men to adjust to women who were at least their equals in all spheres, and there *were* some "casualties" along the way. Now, however, adults share sexual intimacy at all points of the life span.

In general, men and women, now able to function well physically, maintain and develop personality strengths, participate fully in the work and productivity of society according to their individual interests, and remain sexually active, seldom regard any chronological age as the end of the kind of lives they have made for themselves. Those who choose, or are forced, to leave a particular domain in which they have functioned successfully can open other doors to a rewarding life. The humanization and individualization of technology has provided many more possibilities for maintaining control after such functions as muscular strength, mobility, reaction time, and sensory acuity have been impaired. In other words, a person is not necessarily rendered powerless and isolated just because a particular physical function has become less dependable. This ability to compensate for age-related deficits has, in turn, greatly reduced passive yearning for death, as well as active suicide, among older adults.

In essence, society has come to realize that within its power is the ability to develop alternative "scripts" for the whole human lifespan. The *programmed impetus* given to each person as birthright may run its course around mid-life, if not before: the "job specifications" written into the genes have completed their schedules.[6] For many centuries there was no concerted effort on the part of society to augment this partial script for a human life; few people survived long enough to require it. Now, however, a variety of alternative paths exists for the second half of life, and the variety is constantly increasing. Development through old age is almost as enthusiastically demanded and expected—and applauded and enjoyed—as development through the childhood years.

Society places greater value on the *completed person*.[7] Although a child of ten may be, in one sense, all that he or she can be, true fulfillment of human possibilities is now seen as requiring a long life in which knowledge increases and is enriched over the years. The young are fresh and daring; middle-aged people (the term now applies to a much longer space of life) would please Aristotle with their balancing of the novel and the familiar, the necessary and the possible; elders integrate all the qualities of previous years with a cultivated sense of perspective.

The Exit From Existence

Being old has shifted to a positive value. Yet dying and death have not been banished from the human conditions, nor have they continued to operate secretly and to bizarre effect under the lugubrious apparatus of massive denial. Compared with the situation in the past, in fact, dying and death are much more out in the open today. This is due, in part, to the increased value placed upon *life* in old age. As a number of keen observers have remarked over the centuries, the person who has lived well and fully does appear more at ease with mortality.

But part of the new attitude is a result of a greater appreciation of dying, death, *and the dead* per se. When the old death system was functioning at its peak, the elderly progressed on a sort of assembly line from old age through dying to death and oblivion.[8] It is perhaps easier to understand this progression in reverse. For a time, honoring and memorializing the dead became a greatly attenuated process. Funeral processions, the use of cemetery space, and most forms of integrating the dead psychologically into the lives of individual survivors and the culture were under attack and erosion. In effect, the dead seemed to have no role in the symbolic life of society, with a few notable exceptions.

The nonutility of the dead was a phenomenon which then worked ahead in time. It made the dying person more of a threat, annoyance, or burden than a gathering place for social values and concern. There was no point in "being dead," hence little point in being a person who would soon be forgotten. This part of the process often was exemplified in congregate facilities for the care of the aged. The nonutility of the dying person worked forward in time to strip value from the old person. The elder would die, and the dead would blow away like the wind with its debris. Little wonder that many aging men and women, taking their cues from mandatory retirement, the death of a spouse, or some other major change in their lives, would disassociate from themselves just as society was pulling away from them.

Today, the aged have been liberated in both directions. In life, there is no longer an age-determined exitus from full participation and status. On the side of death, society has regained its sense of history and continuity. We no longer feel so lost, shift our feet, and avoid eye contact at leave-taking rituals. Death is not seen as a failure by the individual or the health professions. Thoughts and feelings toward the dead are accepted as a vital thread of continuity that symbolizes our existence as members of the human race rather than as solitary individuals. The neutral, objective-functional abandonment of the dead once in vogue has yielded to a more intuitive relationship, one that gives the present generation more in common with ancestors across the centuries than with those of just a few years ago. In caring about the dead and the dying, those who have barely started to approach their own elder years are already preparing the way for a personal sense of continued value throughout all the bright days and deep nights of life's seasons.

NOTES

1. R. Kastenbaum and R.B. Aisenberg, *The Psychology of Death* (New York: Springer Publishing Company, 1972); R. Kastenbaum, *Death, Society, and Human Experience* (St. Louis: C.V. Mosby Company, 1977).

2. Kastenbaum and Aisenberg, *Psychology of Death;* R. Blauner, "Death and Social Structure," *Psychiatry 29* (1966): 378-94; R. Kastenbaum, "Two-way Traffic on the River Styx" (Paper presented at the annual meeting of American Psychological Association, 1969); R. Fulton, private communication.

3. E.g.,R. Kastenbaum and S.E. Candy, "The 4% Fallacy: A Methodological and Empirical Critique of Use of Population Statistics in Gerontology," *Aging and Human Development 4* (1973): 15-22.

4. This was a futuristic proposition when presented at the conference; it is now becoming the law of the land.

5. R. Kastenbaum, "Suicide as the Preferred Way of Death," in *Progress in Suicidology*, ed. E.S. Schneidman (New York: Grune & Stratton, 1976), pp. 425-43.

6. R. Kastenbaum, "Theories of Human Aging—The Search for a Conceptual Framework," *Journal of Social Issues 21* (1965): 13-36.

7. R. Kastenbaum, "Time, Death, and Ritual in Old Age," in *The Study of Time,* ed. J.T. Fraser (New York, Heidelberg, Berlin: Springer-Verlag, 1975), 20-38.

8. R. Kastenbaum, *Death, Society, and Human Experience.*

Questions

1. Define the following terms. Those marked with an asterisk are terms the authors expect the reader to know already. It you are not familiar with them, consult a dictionary.

cessation
termination
interruption
continuation
altered continuation
intentioned death
unintentioned death
subintentioned death
romanticization
generativity
elective death
*a right
vitalistic error

euthanasia (active, passive, direct, indirect, voluntary, involuntary)
radical vitalism
dysthanasia
"mercy killing"
*morals
*ethics
*humanism
situation ethics
*truism
*pragmatic heresy
heroics
moral dying

2. Opponents of euthanasia often argue that an acceptance of elective death would ultimately result in a "cheapening of life." But Joseph Fletcher claims that "prolonging life beyond any personal or human state" is just as likely to end in a mockery of life. Write brief arguments for each side of the following debate resolution: That prolongation of life beyond natural limits undermines respect for life.

3. Shneidman infers conscious or unconscious motivation from the patterns of behavior that he presents as illustrations of orientations

361

toward death. Describe five cases of death where you might infer "subintention." List the criteria you would use in determining the appropriateness of your inference. Consider how you might test the hypothesis that someone was "rushing to his own funeral."

4. a. In "Suicide Note," Anne Sexton writes:
        But surely you know that everyone has a death,
        his own death
        waiting for him.
        So I will go now
        without old age or disease . . .
        Do you share her view? Why, or why not?
    b. To what extent do you think that the writings prior to an author's death reveal his motivation?

5. Much of the discussion of death in the poetry of Anne Sexton centers on the "tools" of death. Using the views outlined in Shneidman's paper, "The Enemy," develop an explanation for why suicides may discuss method more than decision.

6. Extrapolating the consequences of Kastenbaum's statement in the scenario: "Being old has shifted to a positive value," consider the practical consequences for advertising, education and social policy.

7. a. Shneidman condemns the romanticization of death for blurring the realization that death is "the enemy." What does he mean by the term *romanticization*? If death is viewed as "the enemy," can acceptance be possible? Explain.
    b. To what extent do you believe that our culture romanticizes death? Use examples from the media or literature.

8. a. The continuum of choices suggested by the range of papers in this chapter could extend to a consideration of altruism and martyrdom. List several examples of altruistic acts involving risk (e.g., the donation of an organ to a child, fighting a forest fire). How would you explain the difference between altruism and martyrdom? Are there contemporary martyrs? If so, give examples and state what benefits their martyrdom produced.
    b. What are the possible motivations for the acts you listed in 8a? Try to apply Shneidman's descriptive categories of orientations toward death to your examples. Would you describe the individuals in your examples as death-seeking? Why, or why not?

9. The selections in Chapter Five return the reader to the central question of Chapter One, What is an appropriate death? Or to put it another way, What is death with dignity? Identify both the implicit and the explicit conceptions of death that are expressed by the Van Dusens, Fletcher,

Anne Sexton and Shneidman. Compare and contrast their views. Describe the role of "choice" in each view.

10. a. List the factors that should be taken into account in choosing palliative care over acute care in the case of a terminal illness. Whose decision is it?

    b. In what ways should public policy recognize hospice concepts? What factors should be taken into account in determining the appropriate proportion of public funds for palliative care?

11. Argue the proposition that: Since refusing heroics is, in a sense, a shortening of one's life and is widely accepted as a valid option, shortening one's life by other means should also be an acceptable option.

12. Have your own ideas concerning the role of personal decision in death been influenced since the opening discussions in Chapter One? In what ways?

Projects for Further Study

1. In recent years many communities have developed "hot lines," and "suicide prevention centers," to meet the crisis of suicide or attempted suicide. The movement has greatly increased our understanding of the demographics and the dynamics of suicide, thereby improving our chances of preventing suicide.

    a. Research the dynamics of suicide, differentiating between the long-term personality and adjustment of the suicide victim and the precipitating events which most commonly precede a suicide attempt. The Los Angeles Suicide Prevention Center has developed a procedure for rating the "lethality" of a suicide threat as a means of evaluating the immediate, self-destructive potential of a suicide threat. From your own research construct a description of a high lethality suicide attempter, a low lethality attempter. Include in your profile personality factors, existing sources of psycho-social support, and the immediate motivation for the suicide attempt. Lethality scales and crisis intervention are covered extensively in the collection of papers contained in *The Cry for Help*, edited by Farberow and Shneidman.

    b. Community "hot lines" deal with many personal crises besides suicide and they are often staffed by student volunteers working under professional supervision. Suicide prevention centers, on the other hand, are specialized efforts to deal with self-destructive behaviors and, consequently, are staffed by a higher proportion of health care professionals to lay volunteers. Visit a suicide prevention center or "hot line" in your area to research the training that lay volunteers receive, the concrete steps they are trained to take, the point at which a referral to a professional is made, and the steps that the professional is likely to take.

2. Death has proven a most abundant theme in literature where the tensions between the rights of the individual and the rights of society can be sensitively searched. Identify categories for the study of literary presentations of death—e.g., death in the war novel, death and disease, death and self-definition and death in poetry—then select one work to study individually. Read the work carefully and then develop a critique of the presentation of death in that work. Include in your report responses to the following.

a. Why did you select this particular work?

b. How was death portrayed in the work? (Who died? Why? With what effect on the other characters?)

c. To what extent was the presentation of death realistic? Clinical?

d. What attitudes does the author convey about death?

e. What symbols of mortality are used in the work?

f. In what ways did individual choice or decision affect the death?

g. What are your reactions to the presentation of death in the work?

After all students have completed their individual reports, the class can divide into groups on the basis of the categories they previously decided to study. In the small groups, each student can report on the work he read, then the group members can work together to identify features in the presentation of death that are common to the specific category. The bibliographic references that follow may serve as a beginning.

DEATH IN THE WAR NOVEL

Catton, Bruce. *A Stillness at Appomatox*. New York: Doubleday & Co., Inc., 1954.

Crane, Stephen. *The Red Badge of Courage*. New York: Grosset & Dunlap, 1952.

Deighton, Len. *Bomber*. New York: Signet, 1971.

Remarque, E. *All Quiet on the Western Front*. Boston: Little Brown & Co., 1958.

DEATH AND DISEASE

Alsop, S. *Stay of Execution*. New York: J.B. Lippincott & Co., 1973.

Craven, Margaret. *I Heard The Owl Call My Name*. New York: Doubleday Books, 1973.

Lund, D. *Eric*. New York: J.B. Lippincott & Co., 1974.

Solzhenitsyn, A. *Cancer Ward*. New York: Farrar, Straus & Giroux Inc., 1969.

DEATH AND SELF-DEFINITION

de Beauvoir, Simone. *A Very Easy Death*. New York: Warner Books Inc., 1973.

Fuentes, Carlos. *The Death of Artemio Cruz*. New York: Farrar, Straus & Giroux Inc., 1964.

Plath, S. *The Bell Jar*. New York: Harper & Row Inc., 1971.

Shaw, Bernard. *Saint Joan*. New York: Penguin, 1951.

DEATH IN POETRY

Plath, Sylvia. *Ariel*. New York: Harper & Row, 1966.

Sexton, Anne. *The Death Notebooks*. Boston: Houghton Mifflin, 1974.

Tennyson, Alfred, Lord. *In Memoriam*. W.W. Norton & Co., Inc., 1974.

3. To explore society's attitude to aging, collect samples (pictures or tape recordings) of advertisements portraying people over sixty-five years of age. Observe your materials carefully for indicators of the subject's degree of engrossment in society, physical condition and advertised need. You might want to make a comparison with similar materials portraying younger adults. Speculate on how each subject would allocate his time on a daily basis, and what other people he would see frequently.

Structured Exercises

Before beginning these exercises, please read "Note to the Instructor" on page xiii.

1. The bureaucracy of death throws a harsh light on death's aftermath. The objective details of death that are required for the official forms which accompany the disposition of the body offer a sharp contrast to what Shneidman has described as the "romanticization of death." In order to focus on the *facts* of death, have the students conduct the following fantasy exercise: Assume that you have died in some chosen manner at some future time. Now, take fifteen minutes to visualize the circumstances of "your death" and complete the Certificate of Death found in the Appendix at the end of this book.

    After each member of the class has finished, break up into groups of four to discuss the results of the exercise. Answer the following questions.
    a. How did you die? When? Where?
    b. What was the mode of death? The cause of death?
    c. Was there an autopsy? The cause of death?
    d. How might others assess the "intentionality" of your death? On what would they base their assessment?
    e. What effect has this exercise had on you? How has it affected your attitude toward the physical facts of death?

2. As the medical choices in extending life have increased, the general public has become more aware of the choices that must be made. Have the students review the Harvard Criteria in Appendix A-2. The last several years have seen the growing interest in documents such as the "Living Will" reproduced in Appendix B-3 (although at the present time they have no legal status). A California statute provides for a legally binding "Directive to Physicians" (see Appendix A-3). Such proposals respond to the individual's fear of being forced to endure unnecessary prolongation of life, and his desire for a voice in medical

367

decision-making, but the full implications of a particular proposal may go unnoticed until it is applied to specific situations.

Three illustrative cases are given below. Working as a class, discuss each case using the proposed criteria for brain death in Appendix A-2 to ground the discussion. Refer to the directive given in Appendix A-3 and answer the questions following each example. Compare and contrast the three cases, considering the relative suitability of the Directive to each.

At the end of your discussion list any changes you would propose to the directive or the safeguards you would write into a "Right to Die" law.

Case 1

As a result of a drug overdose, a 16-year-old boy has remained in a deep coma for six months. His physician judges the coma to be irreversible but cannot state that recovery at a distant time in the future is impossible. In the meanwhile, the boy is unable to breathe without mechanical aid from a respirator, although there is evidence of residual sub-cortical functioning. The boy's parents are reluctant to let their son go, but continued financial burdens threaten the stability of the home.

1. Does continued maintenance on a respirator meet the criterion for a "life-sustaining procedure" as given in the proposal (see Appendix A-3)?
2. If you were the parents, would you want the boy to be maintained on the respirator? For how long?
3. A teenager is unlikely to consider signing a document like a living will and is legally too young to sign a directive such as the one given in Appendix A-3. If the boy had indicated in previous discussions with his parents that he would not have wanted to be maintained indefinitely on a respirator, what action would you recommend?

Case 2

Mr. V., age 48, is suffering from a malignant brain tumor and is in a semi-comatose state. He has been referred by the family physician to the tumor ward of a Veteran's Administration hospital for terminal care. The VA oncologist suggests to Mrs. V. that a new drug might have some positive effects: an "extraordinary" treatment but one without painful side effects. Mrs. V. gives permission for treatment and subsequently Mr. V. recovers sufficiently to live comfortably for another twelve months.

1. From the description, do you consider that the drug represented a "life-sustaining procedure" as defined in the proposal?
2. If you were Mrs. V., what would you have decided, regardless of

whether Mr. V. had signed such a directive?

3. If Mr. V. had signed the directive six months earlier, in his current semi-comatose condition would there be a way to allow his receiving the treatment?

Case 3

A 68-year-old grandmother with terminal bone cancer is being maintained on heavy doses of pain-relieving drugs. Since the cancer has not spread to vital organs, she faces an indeterminate period of intense pain before death occurs, most likely from a complication of the cancer such as pneumonia. In the course of her long illness she has reached the limit of her physiological tolerance to narcotics; increasing the dosage to alleviate her pain is likely to result in a fatal overdose. She has indicated unwillingness to sign the directive. Her husband is urging the physician to act to prevent further suffering, yet the doctor realizes the serious risk to the patient in administering higher doses of drugs.

1. As an observer what do you feel the doctor should do? Would your response differ if you were the husband? The patient?
2. How do you believe the final decision should be made?
3. Had the woman signed the directive, what options, if any, would the doctor have?

3. The study of death and dying forces a reexamination of personal goals and values. In Chapter One, the exercise, Coat of Arms, asked you to identify some of your values. The concluding exercise in this chapter is meant to help the student assess his or her resources for realizing those values.

Take ten to fifteen minutes working quickly to list as many answers as you can for each of the following questions. Share your responses with other members of the class. As you discuss your responses, you may wish to add to your list.

a. When do I feel fully alive? What things, events, activities, etc., make me feel that life is really worth living, that it's great to be me and to be alive?
b. What do I do well? What have I to contribute to the life of others? Over what skills do I have mastery? What do I do well for my own growth and well-being?
c. Given my current situation and given my aspirations, what do I need to learn to do?
d. What wishes should I be turning into plans? Are there any dreams I've discarded as "unrealistic" that I should start dreaming again?
e. What underdeveloped or misused resources do I have? (Resources might be material things or talents or friends, etc.)
f. What should I start doing *now*?
g. What should I stop doing *now*?

For Further Reading

The following books provide in-depth coverage of topics introduced in this chapter.

Alvarez, A. *The Savage God: A Study of Suicide.* New York: Random House, 1972.

Carse, J.P. and Dallery, A.B. *Death and Society: A Book of Readings and Sources.* New York: Harcourt Brace Jovanovich, 1977.

Cutler, D.R., ed. *Updating Life and Death.* Boston: Beacon Press, 1969.

Farberow, N.L., and Shneidman, E.S., eds. *The Cry for Help.* New York: McGraw-Hill, 1961.

Gorovitz, S., Jameton, A.L., Macklin, R., O'Connor, J.M., Perrin, E.V., St. Clair, B.P., and Sherwin, S., eds. *Moral Problems in Medicine.* Englewood Cliffs, N.J.: Prentice-Hall, 1976.

Korein, J., ed. *Brain Death: Interrelated Medical and Social Issues.* New York: New York Academy of Sciences, 1978.

Maguire, D.C. *Death by Choice.* New York: Doubleday and Company, 1974.

Marshall, V.W. *Last Chapters: A Sociology of Aging and Dying.* Belmont: Wadsworth, 1980.

Menninger, K. *Man Against Himself.* New York: Harcourt Brace and World, 1966.

Perlin, S., ed. *A Handbook for The Study of Suicide.* New York: Oxford University Press, 1975.

Epilogue

ROBERT BECKER

Portrait of Jen: Memories from the Children's Cancer Ward

To reflect your own understanding of death and dying at this point, read the selection through twice; first for your personal reactions, and then to identify as many concepts and behaviors as you recognize from your study of the readings in this text.

A nurse on the floor ushered us to a room and handed me a small, open-backed gown for Jen to wear.

"Leave my clothes on," the child insisted. "I want my shirt on. Don't take my shoes off." Jen was terrified. It was our seventh visit to Children's Hospital in three weeks, visits which invariably began in the outpatient clinic on the first floor with a technician pricking her finger for a blood sample, followed by a doctor's probings and palpations. The more recent trips, like this one, often turned into a two- or three-day stay in the hospital, much to Jen's growing dismay.

Ten months earlier, when Jennifer was 20 months old, her mother and I noticed a lump on her side after lifting her from the tub one Sunday night. She had been lethargic for a couple of weeks before that, but the pediatrician said she was probably anemic and prescribed iron pills. After the swelling appeared, though, we took her to Alexandria Hospital where they operated and discovered neuroblastoma, the most common form of solid-tumor cancer that strikes infants and toddlers.

In the months that followed, we had taken her to a private oncologist for chemotherapy every other week, and to the radiologist every day for the first two months. We were lucky. The combination of drugs and radiation had worked and produced what the doctors said was "complete remission," which simply meant there was no trace of the disease. It was not to be confused with a "cure."

Source: *Los Angeles Times*, November 10, 1974. © The Washington Post.

373

Still, we had begun to allow ourselves the luxury of believing she just might be cured anyway, when suddenly the lethargy, the failing appetite, the constant crying from the discomfort—and the tumor—all reappeared. A relapse.

Realizing there was little he could do, the oncologist, a rather large man with an air of determined detachment, arranged for Jen's admission to the fourth floor of Children's Hospital—the children's cancer ward.

But before Jen's first appointment at Children's, this bitter, abrupt change started me on the last stretch of a psychic marathon, a race known to countless families of the cancer-stricken—The Miracle Chase. I am talking now of hope and fear. Sunrise, sunset, the dread remains, the hope remains. I placed phone calls all around the country to leading hospitals and clinics. Was there any new treatment, any drug that looked hopeful? Desperate for help, I found none. Most likely, there was none then to be found. There still isn't.

The fourth floor at Children's brims with activity, at least during the day. Youngsters on short, spindly legs waddle along the length of the hallway like small penguins. Assorted toys, mostly the bulky wooden types found in pediatricians' waiting rooms, litter the hall at odd intervals, abandoned by youngsters whose interests have been diverted or who have been taken elsewhere for treatment.

At her insistence, I carried Jen up and down the long hallway pointing out other youngsters in their beds and trying to coax her with, "Look how that little boy is resting in his bed; wouldn't you like to take a little rest, too?"

"No, I want you to carry me," she shot back.

As a concession to get her to stay in bed, my wife Carolyn and I spent most of the day reading Jen's favorite books to her over and over. Periodically, someone would come in either to prick her finger, take her temperature or check the intravenous fluid tube that had been inserted once we got her settled down. By late afternoon, Jen finally fell asleep and a nurse offered to stay with her while we went downstairs to get something to eat. But we did so reluctantly, knowing Jen was never receptive to strangers in the first place and fearful of losing any time with her in the second.

When we returned about a half-hour later, there was Jen in the woman's arms, feebly smiling up at her. The whole scene went through us like a knife. Jen wanted so much to be near someone. She was so frightened at being alone that, surprisingly, she found comfort in this kindly stranger and actually asked the nurse to hold her. Happily, the nurse had the good sense and kindness of heart to pick her up, I.V. and all, and rock her—a gesture we would never forget.

That night Carolyn and I slept in shifts, watching over Jen when she woke to throw up bile. She didn't really have the strength to do anything more than simply turn her head. So we had to watch her carefully and occasionally slide a small stainless steel bowl beside her mouth to avoid soiling the bedsheets.

During the night, a thought kept recurring to me. It was something one of the doctors had said some nine or ten months ago, back in Alexandria Hospital. I had asked him why it was that Jen didn't seem to complain very much about her discomfort and pain. He said, "Children are often the easiest patients to treat simply because small youngsters in these circumstances, those with severe and sometimes painful illnesses like Jennifer's, don't know enough about life to complain. For them, this is what life is all about: they haven't yet experienced enough to know that life is not all pain. This is part of life and they just accept it.''

The next morning, I sat on the edge of the bed and started to read a new book I had picked up, Gay Talese's *The Kingdom and the Power*, while Carolyn slipped downstairs for a quick breakfast and Jen slept. I read only enough that morning to learn that *New York Times* reporter Tom Wicker's 106-paragraph on-the-spot report of the assassination of John F. Kennedy would be saved "by hundreds, perhaps thousands of readers'' and that students and historians would be reading it again and again a half-century later. I wondered if 50 years from now anyone would give a damn that Jen died of cancer or even that she had lived at all.

But my thoughts were interrupted by our doctor who came into the room at that point to examine Jen. She was awake now and lay quietly as he breathed on his stethoscope and briskly rubbed it on his jacket to warm it before he touched her chest with it. For the first time, I thought I noticed some irregularity in her breathing as he bent over her; he stared at the wall as he listened.

"There's something in her lungs,'' he said. He wanted to put her in an oxygen tent. While the oxygen equipment was brought in, he wanted to have her X-rayed to see what that "something'' was.

I wasn't prepared for all this. "Now wait a minute,'' I said. "She's really pretty uncomfortable. I don't see what an X-ray is going to accomplish.''

The doctor tried to reassure me he only wanted to take a look to see if anything was obstructing her breathing.

This was all a little too sudden for me, but I reluctantly agreed.

Jen was difficult for them to handle in the X-ray department. They asked me to sit her up, turn her on her side and hold her head. Jen didn't want any part of this. "Daddy, my tummy hurts,'' she cried.

I was getting angry and impatient with the technicians. "Look, I'm sorry, but she can't sit up. You're not going to get her to sit up. Try something else. Let's get this over with.''

I felt my eyes start to burn as I spoke now and I fought to hold back the tears. "She's dying,'' I said feebly. It was 10:30 a.m.

When we returned to the room, the oxygen tent was in place, draped over the top of the bed. An oxygen bottle was installed at the head of the bed.

To try to make Jen happy and comfortable, I read her a book, "Raggedy Ann and Fido.'' She paid close attention to the story, watching the pictures intently as I read. Midway through the story, she said, "Daddy, you hold me.'' That request has haunted me ever since she said it. I was terribly torn. There wan't anything I wanted to do more than to pick her up. But I hesitated. I thought about the I.V. and the oxygen tent. It was supposedly doing her some good. So I didn't pick her up. Like a damn fool I went on with the story, trying to divert her attention.

She watched me read and looked at the pictures again as I held the book up for her. She even mumbled, "Uh-huh,'' or "Uh-uh,'' to questions I'd ask her about the story. Or I'd leave out key words in sentences and she'd fill them in.

I again noticed her starting to have trouble breathing. I reached under the tent and tried to elevate and arch her back and maybe turn her on her side to face Carolyn. I cranked the bed up a bit, hoping that by raising her head slightly, it might ease her breathing. Nothing helped.

"I'm going to get the doctor to make sure there's nothing wrong with her," I said to Carolyn on my way out.

I saw our doctor talking to nurses halfway down the hall, near the nurses' station. "Hey, Doc," I called. "Come here quick." He turned and started for me at a quick trot and followed me into the room. "Doc, she's not breathing right. What's going on?"

He examined her with his stethoscope but I couldn't detect any show of concern on his face. I don't remember exactly what he said, but I think he must have known what was happening.

Carolyn was standing right behind me and I began to talk to Jen. I held her right arm, the one with the I.V. still plugged into it, and stroked her forehead.

I kept telling her, "Daddy's going to make you feel better, baby. Everything's going to be all right." I thought perhaps she was getting upset or excited: her breathing became even more irregular. Then her attention turned away from me. She had been looking at me, but now she looked straight ahead. Her breaths began getting shorter and closer together, like gasping.

I still wasn't quite fully aware of how serious things were at this point. Somewhere along the line, the doctors had told us that we would be told when Jen entered the terminal phase.

I looked across the bed at the doctor. He wasn't doing anything. Just standing there looking at her. I looked back down at Jen and she was struggling for breath now.

Excited now, I shouted, "Hey! Hey, man! Doc!" I was waving my arms at him, directing him to the door. "Go get something. Go, man. Right now!"

He started for the door, then he stopped and started to say, "Well, Mr. Becker . . ." and then started to leave again.

Before he got past the foot of the bed, though, I motioned him back. I knew there was nothing he could do and I wanted him to stay there. I guess I was half hoping there might be some last-minute thing he could do. Maybe, too, I expected some help from him, for me.

There was a sound in Jen's throat. I felt Carolyn's fingers grasp my shoulders. Small flecks of saliva seeped through her teeth, and she gritted her teeth. Her gaze was still fixed ahead.

That tore me. "This is it," I thought. "Holy good God, man, this is it!" I could feel everything slipping away.

I began to plead, "No, no, Jen. Don't. No, no, Jen. . . ." I looked up at the doctor. "Doc, what's happening?" He had a deadpan look on his face. A nurse must have heard the commotion because I thought I heard the door shut.

Carolyn was vigorously patting my shoulders, trying to calm me down. She was saying something, but I didn't hear her.

I felt the sting in my eyes. "No, Jen. Don't. Don't go, Jen. Stay with me now. Don't go." And then her eyes rolled back. There was silence for a couple of seconds.

Then a sudden tensing of her features, almost like shivering from a chill. Then she relaxed. In that split second, I looked up and asked the doctor what time it was.

"Eleven twenty-five," he replied.

"I want to remember that."

For a few minutes, it was totally quiet in the room. None of us said a word. We all just looked at Jen.

Inside, a monologue was going on, telling all the other parts about what had just happened.

"Man, this really happened," the voice said. "She's gone. That's the end of the line." Then it all began to cave in, all at once.

Carolyn was crying now, and I was coming unglued. I started talking to Jen again, quietly, almost whispering. "Jen, Jen. Come on, Jen. Jen . . ." Her lips were only slightly parted. Her eyes were half open. They were different, though. Not like the eyes of people who are alive. There was no contraction of the pupils. There was absolutely nothing.

"This is my child," I kept thinking. "How the hell does this happen? It's unbelievable something like this could really happen."

The thought of death had never completely registered in my mind; the finality of it, I mean. It's something the mind blocks out on its own. We had become accustomed to dealing with life on a minute-to-minute basis, almost totally without regard to what had passed or what lay ahead. But now, suddenly in the past few moments, all was very different and it all came rushing in on us, crushing us, that it has happened. This is it.

The doctor had left the room unnoticed by either of us until we finally stood up. Carolyn held my arm with both hands and helped me to stay calm long enough to say a prayer at the foot of the bed.

We left to call the family while the nurses unplugged the I.V. and tried to make Jen look comfortable. Everyone reacted predictably, crying at first, then trying to comfort us and finally saying they'd all come down together the next day.

After the calls we went back to the room. The nurses were still there.

"Say, look," I said to their somber faces. "I'm really sorry about coming unglued. I guess I really wasn't quite prepared."

"Oh, please don't apologize, Mr. Becker," said one nurse. "You have to do whatever you feel." She was right.

We stayed with Jen for the next three hours. Strangely, it seemed just like minutes. Neither of us was tense any longer. We were comfortable with Jen now. We were no longer anxious about the tumor spreading or causing pain and discomfort. She didn't murmur or cry out or turn from side to side hoping to avoid the nagging pain. She just rested comfortably now.

Shortly after 3 p.m., we left the hospital. I looked up at the fourth floor window of Jen's room.

"I'm leaving her up there," I thought. "We're leaving her behind." And it was very strange for me, suddenly, going somewhere without Jen. I looked over at Carolyn and knew from the tears that she sensed the same loneliness. I imagined what

Jen would feel being left like this. Even before she got sick, we rarely went out without her. She had a great fear of being separated from Carolyn.

When we got home, Carolyn went into our room to lie down while I went to Jen's room. I began to hear Carolyn crying softly, the sound muffled by the pillow. I hung my head over Jen's crib and let it all out, sobbing. Carolyn heard me and came in to comfort me. It was odd. Neither of us wanted the other to grieve. It hurt each of us to see the other cry.

Sun and moon. Time goes. Four years have passed since Jen died. The sorrow sears less. But an intense need to keep her memory alive remains. I dread that one day she might fade from memory and the incidents of her life and death drift into haziness. Recollections have already become clouded with the subsequent births of Krista, now three, and Kathleen, just turned three months. Krista, it seems, is an extension of Jen. The two are virtually indistinguishable in photographs. She delights in the same games we played with Jen so long ago, though Krista is a good deal more aggressive and certainly more bold about life than Jen.

And, as I watch Krista and her sister grow and pass through the stages of maturity Jen had before them I'm constantly reminded of a clipping someone handed me shortly after Jen died. I never found where it came from, but it was by a Richard J. Needham writing about relationships between parents and their children.

He said: "My favorite philosopher, George Santayana, had many distinguished friends, among them the Marchesa Iris Origo. When her little boy died, he wrote to her: 'We have no claim to any of our possessions. We have no claim to exist; and as we have to die in the end, so we must resign ourselves to die piecemeal, which really happens when we lose somebody or something that was closely intertwined with our existence.'

"This would seem a wise attitude to take toward children. They are not possessions, we have no claim on them, they owe us nothing. They are lent to us, you might say, and are taken away by death or, more commonly, by the natural process of growing up."

Appendices

Appendix A:
Additional Materials for
Structured Exercises

1. KIDNEY MACHINE PSYCHOLOGICAL REPORTS SHEET*

Re: Patients for Kidney Machine
From: Hospital Psychological Staff

In routine preadmission interviews the following patients were examined and evaluated as per the following data:

Re: Alfred—He is presently distraught about his physical condition and reports that it interferes with his work. Seems very committed to his work and appears to be legitimately on the verge of an important cancer discovery. It was hard for the staff to get him to talk about his work in terms that they could understand.

Family relations seem strained and have been for some time because of his commitment to his work. The staff feels that he is a first-rate scientist and scholar who has contributed much and could contribute more to medical research. But they also believe him to be a mentally disturbed individual who, in time, will probably need psychiatric help.

Re: Bill—He is a well-oriented Negro, who does not appear to be swayed by the blandishments of black extremist groups. He is strongly devoted to his family and appears to be an excellent husband and father.

Bill's capacity for growth in his chosen occupation, however, seems limited. His high school record was poor, although he had no record of delinquency and was always regarded by his teachers as a student who tried hard. Therefore, he will probably not succeed with his business plans and will remain employed at a fixed rate permanently.

*Editors Note: The Kidney Machine Psychological Reports Sheet is to be used in conjunction with the Structured Exercise number one in Chapter One.

His wife is trained as a legal secretary. Her prognosis for employment is good, although Bill has discouraged her from seeking work because of mutual agreement to have her be a full-time mother. Bill seems unaware of the serious implications of his illness.

Re: Cora—One of the staff members evaluating Cora described her as a *professional Jew*. She is president of the local Hadassah organization and seems able to talk about nothing but her religion and her children. Although her recently found interest in interior decorating may be a sign of change, it was not clear to the staff whether this interest was real or only generated artificially when she heard of the interview requirement.

She seems resigned to her illness and likely death. Her husband works long hours, is in good health, and enjoys the respect and love of his children. Cora's mother, who also lives with the family, handles most of the child care.

Re: David—Typical of young student activists, David is a bright—almost straight "A"—student who enjoys the respect of most of his teachers and friends. But he appears confused about his future and demonstrates a penchant for jeopardizing it by involving himself in various student "causes." Indeed, his college's dean of student affairs regards him as an individual who will "demonstrate for anything."

He is bitter, almost paranoid, about his illness. His father has invested a good deal of money, time, and emotion in him and has always hoped that David would become a lawyer. His relations with his father are presently strained, however, and he seems only mildly concerned about his two sisters, although they still think highly of him. His future father-in-law, who is a highly successful businessman, expects him to enter the family enterprise upon college graduation.

Re: Edna—She is a self-contained, inner-directed woman and a model of the "career girl." It was clear to the staff that her natural aggressiveness and combative tendencies militated against any sort of marital attachment, and it is not impossible that she has lesbian tendencies.

Her employers regard her as indispensable. Her work record is superb, and her activities in church and charitable groups have been very effective. She is well regarded by all who know her, although she seems to have few, if any, close friends. She appears resigned to her death. In fact, she indicated that she would prefer to have someone other than herself go on the machine. Her offer did not seem in the least insincere.

selection from
Refinements In Criteria
for the Determination of Death

---

2. REPORT ON CRITERIA: DEFINITION OF BRAIN DEATH

APPRAISING A SPECIFIC PROPOSAL

The most prominent proposal of new criteria and procedures for determining, in the difficult cases, that death has occurred has been offered in a Report of the Ad Hoc Committee of the Harvard Medical School to Examine the Definition of Brain Death.[1] The following criteria were presented, and described in some detail: (1) unreceptivity and unresponsivity to externally applied stimuli and inner need; (2) no spontaneous muscular movements or spontaneous respiration; (3) no elicitable brain reflexes; and (4) flat electroencephalogram. (The complete description of these criteria as given in the Harvard report is presented in the box on the following page.) In addition, the report suggests that the above findings again be verified on a repeat testing at least 24 hours later, and that the existence of hypothermia and CNS depressants be excluded. It is also recommended that, if the criteria are fulfilled, the patient be declared dead before any effort is made to disconnect a respirator. (The reasoning given for this recommendation was that this procedure would "provide a greater degree of legal protection to those involved. Otherwise," the report continues, "the physicians would be turning off a respirator on a person who is, under the present strict, technical application of the law, still alive.")

383

CRITERIA FOR THE DETERMINATION OF DEATH
(AD HOC COMMITTEE, HARVARD MEDICAL SCHOOL)

1. *Unreceptivity and Unresponsivity.*—There is a total unawareness to externally applied stimuli and inner need and complete unresponsiveness—our definition of irreversible coma. Even the most intensely painful stimuli evoke no vocal or other response, not even a groan, withdrawal of a limb, or quickening of respiration.

2. *No Movements or Breathing.*—Observations covering a period of at least one hour by physicians is adequate to satisfy the criteria of no spontaneous muscular movements or spontaneous respiration or response to stimuli such as pain, touch, sound, or light. After the patient is on a mechanical respirator, the total absence of spontaneous breathing may be established by turning off the respirator for three minutes and observing whether there is any effort on the part of the subject to breathe spontaneously. (The respirator may be turned off for this time provided that at the start of the trial period the patient's carbon dioxide tension is within the normal range, and provided also that the patient had been breathing room air for at least 10 minutes prior to the trial.)

3. *No Reflexes.*—Irreversible coma with abolition of central nervous system activity is evidenced in part by the absence of elicitable reflexes. The pupil will be fixed and dilated and will not respond to a direct source of bright light. Since the establishment of a fixed, dilated pupil is clear-cut in clinical practice, there should be no uncertainty as to its presence. Ocular movement (to head turning and to irrigation of the ears with ice water) and blinking are absent. There is no evidence of postural activity (decerebrate or other). Swallowing, yawning, vocalization are in abeyance. Corneal and pharyngeal reflexes are absent.

As a rule the stretch of tendon reflexes cannot be elicited; i.e. tapping the tendons of the biceps, triceps and pronator muscles, quadriceps and gastrocnemius muscles with the reflex hammer elicits no contraction of the respective muscles. Plantar or noxious stimulation gives no response.

4. *Flat Electroencephalogram.*—Of great confirmatory value is the flat or isoelectric EEG. We must assume that the electrodes have been properly applied, that the apparatus is functioning normally, and that the personnel in charge is competent. We consider it prudent to have one channel of the apparatus used for an electrocardiogram. This channel will monitor the ECG so that, if it appears in the electroencephalographic leads because of high resistance, it can be readily identified. It also establishes the presence of the active heart in the absence of EEG. We recommend that another channel be used for a noncephalic lead. This will pick up space-borne or vibration-borne artifacts and identify them. The simplest form of such a monitoring noncephalic electrode has two leads over the dorsum of the hand, preferably the right hand, so the ECG will be minimal or absent. Since one of the requirements of this state is that there be no muscle activity, these two dorsal hand electrodes will not be bothered by muscle artifact. The apparatus should be run at standard gains 10μv/mm. 50μv/mm. Also it should be isoelectric at double this standard gain which is 5μv/mm or 25μv/5 mm. At least ten full minutes of recording are desirable, but twice that would be better.

It is also suggested that the gains at some point be opened to their full amplitude for a brief period (5 to 100 seconds) to see what is going on. Usually in an intensive care unit artifacts will dominate the picture, but these are readily identifiable. There shall be no electroencephalographic response to noise or to pinch.

All of the above tests shall be repeated at least 24 hours later with no change.

The validity of such data as indications of irreversible cerebral damage depends on the exclusion of two conditions: hypothermia (temperature below 90 F [32.2 C]) or center nervous system depressants, such as barbiturates.

The criteria of the Harvard Committee Report meet the formal characteristics of "good" criteria, as outlined in this communication. The criteria are clear and distinct, the tests easily performed and interpreted by an ordinary physician, and the results of the tests generally unambiguous. Some question has been raised about the ease of obtaining an adequate electroencephalographic assessment, but the report does not consider the electroencephalographic examination mandatory. It holds that the EEG provides only confirmatory data for what is, in fact, a clinical diagnosis. Recognizing that electroencephalographic monitoring may be unavailable, the report states "when available it should be utilized."

On the score of comprehensiveness, the tests go beyond an assessment of higher brain function to include a measure of various lower brain-stem (vegetative) functions, and go beyond an assessment just of brain activity by including the vital function of spontaneous respiration. It is true that the circulatory system is not explicitly evaluated. However, because of the close link between circulation and respiration, a heartbeat in a patient on a mechanical respirator (i.e., in a patient who has permanently lost his spontaneous capacity to breathe) should not be regarded as a sign of continued life. The continued beating of the heart in such cases may be regarded as an "artifact," as sustained only by continued artificial respiration.

The new criteria are meant to be necessary for only that small percentage of cases where there is irreversible coma with permanent brain damage, and where the traditional signs of death are obscured because of the intervention of resuscitation machinery. The proposal is meant to complement, not to replace, the traditional criteria of determining death. Where the latter can be clearly established, they are still determinative.

The Harvard Committee Report does not explicitly require that the physician declare the patient dead when the criteria are fulfilled; because it was a novel and exploratory proposal, it was more concerned to permit, rather than to oblige him to do so. However, once the criteria are accepted as valid by the medical profession and the community, nothing in the report would oppose making the declaration of death mandatory on fulfillment of the criteria. Thus, the alternative criteria and the traditional criteria could be—and should be—used identically in determining the physician's actions.

Experience to date in the use of these criteria and procedures for determining death suggests them to be reasonable and appropriate. Support for their validity has come from post-mortem studies of 128 individuals who fulfilled the Harvard criteria. On autopsy, the brains of all 128 subjects were found to be obviously destroyed (E. Richardson, unpublished results). The electroencephalographic criterion has received an independent evaluation. The largest single study,[2] done with 2,642 comatose patients with isoelectric (i.e., flat) EEGs of 24-hours' duration, revealed that not one patient recovered (excepting three who had received anesthetic doses of CNS depressants, and who were, therefore, outside the class of patients covered by the report). Although further evidence is desirable and is now being accumulated (in studies by the American EEG Society and by the National Institute of Neurological Diseases and Stroke, among others), the criteria seem well suited to the detection of whether the patient has indeed died.

We are not prepared to comment on the precise technical aspects of each of the criteria and procedures. Medical groups, and especially neurologists and neurosurgeons, may have some corrections and refinements to offer. Nevertheless, we can see no medical, logical, or moral objection to the criteria as set forth in the Harvard Committee Report. The criteria and procedures seem to provide the needed guidelines for the physicians. If adopted, they will greatly diminish the present perplexity about the status of some "patients," and will thus put an end to needless, useless, costly, time-consuming, and upsetting ministration on the part of physicians and relatives.

NOTES

1. "A Definition of Irreversible Coma: Report of the Ad Hoc Committee of the Harvard Medical School to Examine the Definition of Brain Death," *JAMA* 205: (1968): 337-340.
2. D. Silverman, R. Masland, M. Saunders, et al., "Irreversible Coma Associated with Electrocerebral Silence," *Neurology* 20 (1970): 525-533.

3. A PROPOSAL FOR RIGHT TO DIE LEGISLATION: DIRECTIVE TO PHYSICIANS

The Directive to Physicians and list of definitions reprinted below appear in the "Natural Death Act" passed in California in September, 1976. The bill authorizes the withholding or withdrawal of life-sustaining procedures from adults who have a terminal condition and who have executed such a directive.

DIRECTIVE TO PHYSICIAN

Directive made this _____day of _____ (month, year).

   I _____, being of sound mind, willfully, and voluntarily make known my desire that my life shall not be artificially prolonged under the circumstances set forth below, do hereby declare:

1 If at any time I should have an incurable injury, disease, or illness certified to be a terminal condition by two physicians, and where the application of life-sustaining procedures would serve only to artificially prolong the moment of my death and where my physician determines that my death is imminent whether or not life-sustaining procedures are utilized, I direct that such procedures be withheld or withdrawn and that I be permitted to die naturally.

2 In the absence of my ability to give directions regarding the use of such life-sustaining procedures, it is my intention that this directive shall be honored by my family and physician(s) as the final expression of my legal right to refuse medical or surgical treatment and accept the consequences from such refusal.

3 If I have been diagnosed as pregnant and that diagnosis is known to my physician, this directive shall have no force or effect during the course of my pregnancy.

4 I have been diagnosed and notified at least 14 days ago as having a terminal condition by _____, M.D. whose address is _____, and whose telephone number is _____. I understand that if I have not filled in the physician's name and address, it shall be presumed that I did not have a terminal condition when I made out this directive.

5 This directive shall have no force or effect five years from the date filled in above.

6 I understand the full import of this directive and I am emotionally and mentally competent to make this directive.

                                       Signed _____

City, County and State of Residence _____

The declarant has been personally known to me and I believe him or her to be of sound mind.

                                     Witness _____

List of Definitions

a. "Attending physician" means the physician selected by, or assigned to, the patient who has primary responsibility for the treatment and care of the patient.

b. "Directive" means a written document voluntarily executed by the declarant in accordance with the requirements of Section 7188. The directive, or a copy of the directive, shall be made part of the patient's medical records.

c. "Life-sustaining procedure" means any medical procedure or intervention which utilizes mechanical or other artificial means to sustain, restore, or supplant a vital function, which, when applied to a qualified patient, would serve only to artificially prolong the moment of death and where, in the judgment of the attending physician, death is imminent whether or not such procedures are utilized. "Life-sustaining procedure" shall not include the administration of medication or the performance of any medical procedure deemed necessary to alleviate pain.

d. "Physician" means a physician and surgeon licensed by the Board of Medical Quality Assurance or the Board of Osteopathic Examiners.

e. "Qualified patient" means a patient diagnosed and certified in writing to be afflicted with a terminal condition by two physicians, one of whom shall be the attending physician, who have personally examined the patient.

f. "Terminal condition" means an incurable condition caused by injury, disease, or illness, which, regardless of the application of life-sustaining procedures, would, within reasonable medical judgment, produce death, and where the application of life-sustaining procedures serves only to postpone the moment of death of the patient.

Appendix B:
Social Facts of Death

---

1. DEATH RATES IN THE UNITED STATES FOR
THE 20 LEADING CAUSES OF DEATH, BY COLOR AND SEX, 1977

Cause of Death	Total population	white		all other	
		male	female	male	female
All Causes	**878.1**	**998.2**	**783.3**	**967.1**	**672.5**
Diseases of heart	332.3	392.4	301.8	273.3	216.4
Malignant neoplasms	178.7	202.5	164.5	183.2	121.2
Cerebrovascular diseases	84.1	73.2	96.5	75.2	79.2
Accidents (other than motor vehicle)	24.8	32.7	15.7	45.4	16.8
Influenza and pneumonia	23.7	25.9	22.0	28.6	16.2
Motor vehicle accidents	22.9	34.1	12.7	33.8	9.8
Diabetes mellitus	15.2	12.7	16.5	14.6	23.1
Symptoms and ill-defined conditions	14.9	14.9	10.2	35.9	24.8
Cirrhosis of liver	14.3	18.3	9.1	24.9	12.9
Arteriosclerosis	13.3	11.7	16.7	6.9	7.4
Suicide	13.3	21.4	7.3	11.4	3.5
Other diseases of arteries, arterioles, and capillaries	12.2	15.8	10.0	8.7	7.3
Certain causes in early infancy	10.8	10.3	7.0	29.3	21.2
Bronchitis, emphysema, and asthma	10.3	16.5	6.1	7.4	2.8
Homicide	9.2	8.7	2.9	53.6	12.0
Congenital anomalies	6.0	6.4	5.1	8.5	7.1
Nephritis and nephrosis	3.9	3.8	2.9	8.2	7.5
Septicemia	3.3	3.2	2.7	6.2	0.5
Peptic ulcer	2.7	3.5	2.3	2.6	1.4
Hypertension	2.6	2.4	2.5	4.0	3.8

Source: Compiled from data in National Center for Health Statistics, "Advance Report: Final Mortality Statistics, 1977," *Monthly Vital Statistics Report*, Vol. 28, No. 1 Supplement (May 11, 1979), pp. 28-29, Table 9.

2. SPECIFIC DEATH RATES FOR SELECTED CAUSES IN THE DEATH REGISTRATION STATES, 1900, 1920, 1940, 1960, and 1970

Cause of death	Number of deaths per 100,000 population				
	1900	1920	1940	1960	1970
Pneumonia and influenza	202.2	207.3	70.3	37.3	30.5
Tuberculosis of the respiratory system	174.5	99.8	42.2	5.6	2.1
Diarrhea, enteritis, and ulceration of the intestines	142.7	53.7	10.3	5.2	1.1
Diseases of the heart	137.4	159.6	292.5	369.0	360.3
Intracranial lesions of vascular origin	106.9	93.0	90.9	108.0	101.7
Nephritis	88.6	88.8	81.5	7.6	3.9
Congenital malformations, etc.	74.6	84.4	49.2	12.2	8.1
Other accidents	72.3	60.7	47.4	31.0	28.0
Cancer and other malignant tumors	64.0	83.4	120.3	149.2	162.0
Senility	50.2	14.2	7.7	11.4	14.1
Bronchitis	45.2	13.2	3.0	2.5	3.2
Diphtheria	40.3	15.3	1.1	0.0	0.0
Typhoid and paratyphoid fever	31.3	7.6	1.1	0.0	0.0
Puerperal causes (females only)	26.9	38.6	13.5	0.9	0.9
Tuberculosis (other forms)	19.9	13.4	3.7	0.5	0.6
Measles	13.3	8.8	0.5	0.2	0.0
Cirrhosis of the liver	12.5	7.1	8.6	11.3	15.8
Whooping cough	12.2	12.5	2.2	0.1	0.0
Dysentery	12.0	4.0	1.9	0.2	0.0
Syphilis	12.0	16.5	14.4	1.6	0.2
Hernia and intestinal obstruction	11.9	10.5	9.0	5.1	3.6
Diabetes mellitus	11.0	16.1	26.6	16.7	18.5
Suicide	10.2	10.2	14.4	10.6	11.1
Scarlet fever	9.6	4.6	0.5	0.0	0.0
Appendicitis	8.8	13.2	9.9	1.0	0.7
Malaria	6.2	3.4	1.1	0.0	0.0
Alcoholism	5.3	1.0	1.9	1.2	2.3
Diseases of the prostate (males only)	3.3	8.2	13.3	2.5	2.1
Ulcer of stomach or duodenum	2.7	3.6	6.8	6.4	4.1
Homicide	1.2	6.8	6.2	4.7	7.6
Pellagra	0.0	2.5	1.6	0.0	0.0
Cerebrospinal meningitis	—	1.6	0.5	1.1	0.9
Motor vehicle accidents	—	10.3	26.2	21.3	26.2

Source: Compiled from data in Forrest E. Linder and Robert D. Grove, *Vital Statistics Rates in the United States, 1900-1940* (1943), pp. 253-273; Robert D. Grove and Alice M. Hetzel, *Vital Statistics Rates in the United States, 1940-1960* (1968), pp. 595-603; National Center for Health Statistics, *Vital Statistics of the United States, 1966*, Vol. II, *Mortality*, Part A, Section 1 (1968), pp. 53-86, Table 22; and "Annual Summary for the United States, 1970," *Monthly Vital Statistics Report*, Vol. 19, No. 13 (September 21, 1971), p. 18, Table 7.

Source: T. Lynn Smith and Paul E. Zopf, Jr., *Demography: Principles and Methods*, 2nd Ed. Port Washington, N.Y.: Alfred Publishing Co., Inc., 1976. Pp. 433, 453.

3. LIFE EXPECTANCY BY SEX AND RACE, 1930-2050

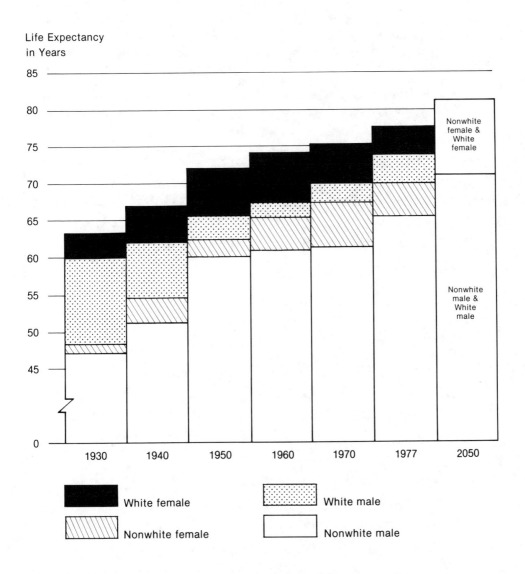

4. CERTIFICATE OF DEATH

It is easy to lose sight of the physical facts of death, particularly in the interim between the moment of clinical death and final rites. Yet a complex bureaucracy exists to deal with the many stark details of closing out a civil existence; the following forms chart the passage from dying person to physical remains. Although they are official records from one state, they can be considered representative documents for other regions; the information reported tends to be standardized to facilitate nationwide collection of health statistics.

CERTIFICATE OF DEATH
STATE OF CALIFORNIA

STATE FILE NUMBER | LOCAL REGISTRATION DISTRICT AND CERTIFICATE NUMBER

DECEDENT PERSONAL DATA

1A. NAME OF DECEDENT—FIRST | 1B. MIDDLE | 1C. LAST | 2A. DATE OF DEATH (MONTH, DAY, YEAR) | 2B. HOUR

3. SEX | 4. RACE | 5. ETHNICITY | 6. DATE OF BIRTH | 7. AGE | IF UNDER 1 YEAR: MONTHS / DAYS | IF UNDER 24 HOURS: HOURS / MINUTES | YEARS

8. BIRTHPLACE OF DECEDENT (STATE OR FOREIGN COUNTRY) | 9. NAME AND BIRTHPLACE OF FATHER | 10. BIRTH NAME AND BIRTHPLACE OF MOTHER

11. CITIZEN OF WHAT COUNTRY | 12. SOCIAL SECURITY NUMBER | 13. MARITAL STATUS | 14. NAME OF SURVIVING SPOUSE (IF WIFE, ENTER BIRTH NAME)

15. PRIMARY OCCUPATION | 16. NUMBER OF YEARS THIS OCCUPATION | 17. EMPLOYER (IF SELF-EMPLOYED, SO STATE) | 18. KIND OF INDUSTRY OR BUSINESS

USUAL RESIDENCE

19A. USUAL RESIDENCE—STREET ADDRESS (STREET AND NUMBER OR LOCATION) | 19B. | 19C. CITY OR TOWN

19D. COUNTY | 19E. STATE | 20. NAME AND ADDRESS OF INFORMANT—RELATIONSHIP

PLACE OF DEATH

21A. PLACE OF DEATH | 21B. COUNTY

21C. STREET ADDRESS (STREET AND NUMBER OR LOCATION) | 21D. CITY OR TOWN

CAUSE OF DEATH

22. DEATH WAS CAUSED BY: IMMEDIATE CAUSE (ENTER ONLY ONE CAUSE PER LINE FOR A, B, AND C) | (A) | APPROXIMATE INTERVAL BETWEEN ONSET AND DEATH | 24. WAS DEATH REPORTED TO CORONER?

CONDITIONS, IF ANY, WHICH GAVE RISE TO THE IMMEDIATE CAUSE, STATING THE UNDERLYING CAUSE LAST | DUE TO, OR AS A CONSEQUENCE OF (B) | 25. WAS BIOPSY PERFORMED?

DUE TO, OR AS A CONSEQUENCE OF (C) | 26. WAS AUTOPSY PERFORMED?

23. OTHER CONDITIONS CONTRIBUTING BUT NOT RELATED TO THE IMMEDIATE CAUSE OF DEATH | 27. WAS OPERATION PERFORMED FOR ANY CONDITION IN ITEMS 22 OR 23? TYPE OF OPERATION / DATE

PHYSICIAN'S CERTIFICATION

28A. I CERTIFY THAT DEATH OCCURRED AT THE HOUR, DATE AND PLACE STATED FROM THE CAUSES STATED. I ATTENDED DECEDENT SINCE (ENTER MO. DA. YR.) / I LAST SAW DECEDENT ALIVE (ENTER MO. DA. YR.) | 28B. PHYSICIAN—SIGNATURE AND DEGREE OR TITLE | 28C. DATE SIGNED | 28D. PHYSICIAN'S LICENSE NUMBER

28E. TYPE PHYSICIAN'S NAME AND ADDRESS

INJURY INFORMATION

29. SPECIFY ACCIDENT, SUICIDE, ETC. | 30. PLACE OF INJURY | 31. INJURY AT WORK | 32A. DATE OF INJURY—MONTH, DAY, YEAR | 32B. HOUR

33. LOCATION (STREET AND NUMBER OR LOCATION AND CITY OR TOWN) | 34. DESCRIBE HOW INJURY OCCURRED (EVENTS WHICH RESULTED IN INJURY)

CORONER'S USE ONLY

35A. I CERTIFY THAT DEATH OCCURRED AT THE HOUR, DATE AND PLACE STATED FROM THE CAUSES STATED. AS REQUIRED BY LAW I HAVE HELD AN (INQUEST-INVESTIGATION) | 35B. CORONER—SIGNATURE AND DEGREE OR TITLE | 35C. DATE SIGNED

36. DISPOSITION | 37. DATE—MONTH, DAY, YEAR | 38. NAME AND ADDRESS OF CEMETERY OR CREMATORY | 39. EMBALMER'S LICENSE NUMBER AND SIGNATURE

40. NAME OF FUNERAL DIRECTOR (OR PERSON ACTING AS SUCH) | 41. LOCAL REGISTRAR—SIGNATURE | 42. DATE ACCEPTED BY LOCAL REGISTRAR

STATE REGISTRAR

A. | B. | C. | D. | E. | F.

5. AUTHORITY FOR AUTOPSY

AUTHORITY FOR AUTOPSY

Date _____ Hour _____ .M

The undersigned hereby authorize the above named hospital to permit its Pathologist, and/or such doctors and assistants as he may desire, to perform an autopsy and complete post-mortem examination upon the body

of _____, deceased, including the taking of tissues for special study and microscopic examination, for the purpose of determining the exact cause of death.

Witnesses: Signed _____

_____   Relationship _____

_____   Signed _____

                               Relationship _____

6. AUTHORITY FOR RELEASE OF REMAINS

I hereby authorize Community Hospital to release
the remains of _____

to _____
                Undertaker   Address

_____ 19 ___   _____
                                    Relationship

                                    _____
                                    Witness:

UNDERTAKER'S RECEIPT

Received from Community Hospital

the remains of _____

_____ 19 ___   _____
                                            Undertaker

_____   _____
Witness: Community Hospital   Address

                                    _____
                                            Phone

7.   A GIFT OF LIFE; UNIFORM DONOR CARD

TO MY FAMILY AND PHYSICIAN

It is my wish that upon my death, my body, or any part of it, be used for the benefit of mankind.

I, therefore, execute the following Deed of Gift, under the Anatomical Gift Act, and I request that in the making of any decision relating to my death, my intentions as expressed herein shall govern.

I am of sound mind and 18 years or more of age. I hereby make this anatomical gift to take effect upon my death. The marks in the appropriate places and words filled into the blanks below indicate my desires.

I give: my body _____; any needed organs or parts _____; the following organs or parts _____

I give these to the following person or institution: the physician in attendance

at my death _____; the hospital in which I die _____; the following named

physician, hospital, storage bank or other medical institution _____

the following individual for treatment _____

for any purpose authorized by law _____; transplantation _____;

therapy _____; research _____; medical education _____.

Dated _____   _____
                                                                             signature of donor

Signed by Donor in presence of   _____
following who signs as witnesses   address of donor

_____   _____
                witness   witness

UNIFORM DONOR CARD

_____   _____
Name of Donor   Date of Birth

In the hope that I may help others, I hereby make this anatomical gift, if medically acceptable, to take effect upon my death. The words and marks below indicate my desires. I give:
(a) ____ any needed organs or parts (b) ____ only the following organs or

Specify: _____

_____   _____
Signature of Donor   Date & Place Signed

_____   _____
Witness   Witness

This is a legal document under the Uniform Anatomical Gift Act.

8. A LIVING WILL

TO MY FAMILY, MY PHYSICIAN, MY CLERGYMAN, MY LAWYER—

If the time comes when I can no longer take part in decisions for my own future, let this statement stand as the testament of my wishes:

If there is no reasonable expectation of my recovery from physical or mental disability, I, _____

request that I be allowed to die and not be kept alive by artificial means or heroic measures. Death is as much a reality as birth, growth, maturity and old age—it is the one certainty. I do not fear death as much as I fear the indignity of deterioration, dependence and hopeless pain. I ask that drugs be mercifully administered to me for terminal suffering even if they hasten the moment of death.

This request is made after careful consideration. Although this document is not legally binding, you who care for me will, I hope, feel morally bound to follow its mandate. I recognize that it places a heavy burden of responsibility upon you, and it is with the intention of sharing that responsibility and of mitigating any feelings of guilt that this statement is made.

Date _____   Signed _____

Witnessed by:

_____

_____

Source: Reprinted with permission of the Concern For Dying, 250 West 57th Street, New York, N.Y., 10019.

Appendix C:
Additional Teaching Resources

1. TOPICAL SUGGESTIONS FOR CURRICULAR PLANNING ON DEATH AND DYING

The list below could be used in several ways:
1. Suggesting additional topics for adapting classroom presentations to audiences with specialized interests
2. Assigning topics for brief research reports
3. Compiling published sources or annotated bibliographies
4. Suggesting topics for term papers

abortion
accidental death
accident-proneness
aggression and violence
assassination
autopsies

bullfighting
burial rites

causes of aging
cemeteries
chemical and biological warfare
class and cultural differences
  in life expectancy
courage and death
cryonics

death and mysticism
death customs
death fantasies
death of a culture
death of God
death of the soldier
different cultural approaches
donation of body parts
dynamics of prayer and
  supplication

embalming
epitaphs and eulogies
ethics and medical
  experimentation
euphemisms for death

397

facing surgery
factors in life expectancy
fear of death

genocide
geriatric wards

Holocaust experience
human sacrifice

images of death
infanticide
infant mortality
isolation and alienation

last words of the dying
legal rights of the dying and
   dead
life review
LSD therapy with dying

martyrdom
mass hysteria
myths of death, rebirth and
   resurrection

natural disasters

out-of-the-body experience

perception of time
personality factors in facing
   death
population and ecological
   control
post-mortem changes
poverty and death
psychopathologies of
   aging

racial segregation of the
   dying and dead
reincarnation
resistance to torture by war
   prisoners

samurai
science fiction/time
   machines
"sudden death" syndrome
survival in extreme
   environments
symbols for death

uncertainty of dying
use of sedatives

voodooism, magical rites,
   occultism

2. MULTI-MEDIA REFERENCES FOR DEATH AND DYING

Chapter One

Confrontations of Death—Film, color, 35 min. Oregon Division of Continuing Education Film Library, P.O. Box 1491, Portland, Oregon 97201. Seminar participants discover their personal feelings about their own death through listening to music, viewing slides on death, and writing their own eulogies.

Day of the Dead—Film, color, 15 minutes. Pyramid Films, 2801 Colorado Street, Santa Monica, California 90406. Mexico's Festival for the Day of the Dead, in a film produced by Charles and Ray Eames.

Dead Man—Film, no sound, 3 minutes. Highly Specialized Promotions, 391 Atlantic Ave., Brooklyn, New York, 11217. Stark portrayal of the naked, dead body of an old man.

Death—Family of Man Series, Film, color, 45 minutes. Time-Life Films, 100 Eisenhower Drive, Paramus, New Jersey 07652. Contrasting attitudes toward death in various cultures of the world.

Chapter Two

Death—Film, black and white, 43 minutes. Filmmakers Library, 133 E. 58th St., Suite 703A, New York, New York 10022. Depicts the isolation of the dying in a hospital setting. Presents 52-year-old cancer patient portraying problems of meaningful communication with family, friends and hospital staff.

Dying—Film, color, 91 minutes, WGBH/Distribution, 125 Western Avenue, Boston, Massachusetts 02134. Cinema verite portrayal of incidents in the dying of three cancer patients and the responses of their families. Contrasts different styles of dying in non-judgmental fashion.

Ikiru—Film, black and white, 140 minutes. Macmillan Films, Inc., 34 MacQuesten, South, Mt. Vernon, New York 10550. Japanese with English subtitles. Depicts existential crisis of a widower in middle age whose terminal diagnosis results in personal growth.

Joan Robinson: One Woman's Story—Videocassette, color, 165 minutes. Time-Life Video, Time & Life Building, New York, New York 10020. An intimate and powerful record of a woman, her husband, physician, and friends, as they face the anguish of her terminal illness. Explores issues of pain management, and family relationships.

Leinbach-Eisdorfer Series—Videotape, six programs. Instructional Media Services Booking, DG-10, University of Washington, Seattle, Washington 98195. Interviews with the patient, his family and those who attended to his physical and spiritual needs. Interviews with the patient - 25 minutes. The role of the physician - 41 minutes, pain management - 37 minutes, religion and the clergy - 35 minutes, the grieving process, part I - 25 minutes, and the grieving process, part II - 45 minutes.

Until I Die—Film, color, 30 minutes. Audio Visual Department, American Journal of Nursing Company, 555 W. 57th St., New York, New York 10019. Kübler-Ross explains her work with the terminally ill.

Why Me?—Film, color, 10 minutes. Pyramid Films, Box 1048, Santa Monica, California, 90406. Animated film humorously portraying the reactions of a man who learns that he only has five minutes left to live. With conciseness and levity the film portrays the full range of responses described by Kübler-Ross.

Chapter Three

The Crisis of Loss—Film, color, 30 minutes. American Journal of Nursing Co., 555 W. 57th St., New York, New York, 10019. Loss and mourning are examined within the framework of crisis theory. Examples support the importance of the perception of control and responsibility in coping with loss.

Death, Grief, and Bereavement—Audiocassettes. Charles Press Publ. Inc., Bowie, Maryland 20715. Series of 24 programs by various authorities on death.

Journey's End—Film, color, 28 minutes. USC Division of Cinema, Film Distribution Section, University Park, Los Angeles, California 90007. Portrays the difficulties in adjusting to widowhood. Dramatizes the value of making wills and funeral arrangements before the need occurs.

Chapter Four

All the Way Home—Film, black and white, 103 minutes. Films Inc. 5625 Hollywood Boulevard, California 90068. The effects of a man's death on a six-year old boy. The mother's initial withdrawal into grief and the family's inability to deal with the boy's need to understand. Based on James Agee's novel, *A Death in the Family*.

Children's Conceptions of Death—Videocassette, color, 29 minutes. American Journal of Nursing Co., 555 W. 57th St., New York, New York, 10019. Depicts children's attitudes toward and understandings of death at different stages of development.

The Dead Bird—Film, color, 13 minutes. Bureau of Audio-Visual Instruction, P.O. Box 2093, Madison, Wisconsin 53701. Four children discover a dead bird and prepare a burial for it.

Last Rites: A Boy's Reaction to Death—Film, color, 30 minutes. Filmaker's Library, 133 E. 58th St., Suite 703A, New York, New York, 10022. A young boy attempts through fantasy to bring his dead mother back. A stranger's support helps him to accept the reality of her loss.

Winning Battles: Children with cancer—Film, color, 8 minutes. Filmakers Library, 133 E. 58th St., Suite 703A, New York, New York, 10022. Presentation of a pilot program at Stanford University Children's Hospital, where the family is actively involved in the child's treatment. Death is discussed openly while at the same time hope for the future is maintained.

Chapter Five

As Long as There is Life—Film, color, 40 minutes. Hospice Institute, Suite 900,111 Eighth Ave., New York, New York, 10011. Cinema verite's portrait of a young family facing the death of the mother from cancer with the support of the Hospice Home Care Team.

But Jack Was A Good Driver—Film, 12 minutes, color. C R M Educational Films, 1104 Camino del Mar, Del Mar, California 92014. As the friends of a teenager killed in an automobile crash leave his funeral, they come to the realization that his death was probably a suicide.

Everybody Rides the Carousel: The Later Years—Film, color, 9 minutes. Pyramid Films, Box 1048, Santa Monica, California, 90406. Based on Erikson's view of the final stage of life, contrasts two couples who live their final years in vastly different ways.

Gravity Is My Enemy—Film, color, 30 minutes. Churchill Films, 662 N. Robertson Boulevard, Los Angeles, California 90069. Portrait of a young artist, paralyzed from the neck down, and the relationship of his work to his life.

The Last of Life: A Positive Look at Aging. Filmmaker's Library, 133 E. 58th St., Suite 703A, New York, New York 10022. Informative survey of the biology of aging and the emotional aspects of later life. Develops the view that life should be added to years, not years to life.

The Right to Die—Film, color, 56 minutes. Macmillan Films, Inc., 34 MacQuesten Parkway, South, Mount Vernon, New York 10050. Involves the conflicts as to whether one has the right to end his own life and whether technology should be withheld to enable a patient to die with dignity.

Will to Die—Right to Live—Film, color, 18 minutes. American Journal of Nursing Co., 555 W. 57th St., New York, New York, 10019. Views death from the point of view of theology, law and medicine and presents both positive and negative views on euthanasia.